An Illustrated Encyclopaedia

WONDERS
of
ANIMAL LIFE

also available by the same editor

An Illustrated World Gazetteer

Peoples of all Nations

Their Life Today and Story of Their Past

In 14 Volumes

Volume One
Abyssinia **to** Azerbaijan
Volume Two
Belgium **to** British Empire in America
Volume Three
British Empire in Asia **to** Canada
Volume Four
Ceylon **to** Dahomey
Volume Five
Danzig **to** England
Volume Six
Esthonia **to** France
Volume Seven
Georgia **to** Iceland
Volume Eight
India **to** Italy
Volume Nine
Japan **to** Mexico
Volume Ten
Monaco **to** Oman
Volume Eleven
Palestine **to** Rumania
Volume Twelve
Russia **to** Sin-kiang
Volume Thirteen
South Africa **to** The Ukraine
Volume Fourteen
The United States **to** Wales
with General Index

About the Editor

Sir John Alexander Hammerton (1871-1949) was an English statesman and author, best-known for his editorship of popular encyclopaedias published in the first half of the 20th century, such as the 10-volume New Book of Knowledge.

From 1914 to 1919, Hammerton was joint editor with HW Wilson of the periodical "The Great War: The Standard History of the All-Europe Conflict", published by the Amalgamated Press. It was lavishly illustrated with photographs and with realistic drawings which were sometimes hardly distinguishable from photographs.

He was also a contemporary and friend of Arthur Mee, about whom he wrote a biography.

An Illustrated Encyclopaedia

WONDERS
of
ANIMAL LIFE

by Famous Writers on Natural History

Volume Two

Edited by

J.A. Hammerton

Over Three Thousand Illustrations from Photographs and Thirty-three Colour Plates

LOGOS PRESS, NEW DELHI

ISBN -13: 978-81-7268-175-3 (Set)
ISBN -10: 81-7268-175-5 (Set)

ISBN -13: 978-81-7268-176-0 (Vol. I)
ISBN -13: 978-81-7268-177-7 (Vol. II)
ISBN -13: 978-81-7268-178-4 (Vol. III)
ISBN -13: 978-81-7268-179-1 (Vol. IV)
ISBN -13: 978-81-7268-180-7 (Vol. V)
ISBN -13: 978-81-7268-181-4 (Vol. VI)
ISBN -13: 978-81-7268-182-1 (Vol. VII)
ISBN -13: 978-81-7268-183-8 (Vol. VIII)

ISBN -10: 81-7268-176-3 (Vol. I)
ISBN -10: 81-7268-177-1 (Vol. II)
ISBN -10: 81-7268-178-X (Vol. III)
ISBN -10: 81-7268-179-8 (Vol. IV)
ISBN -10: 81-7268-180-1 (Vol. V)
ISBN -10: 81-7268-181-X (Vol. VI)
ISBN -10: 81-7268-182-8 (Vol. VII)
ISBN -10: 81-7268-183-6 (Vol. VIII)

Edition : 2008

Printed & Published by

LOGOS PRESS

Building No. 4788-90, Street No. 23, Ansari Road, Darya Ganj, New Delhi-110 002 (India)
Phone : 23272187

Foreword

Here is not a 'natural history' in the accepted meaning of that description. There exist many and excellent natural histories and more than fifteen years ago the present editor was associated with the publication of one which, in its authoritative letter-press and profuse illustration, had wide acceptance. But it is undeniable that the general reader finds large and exhaustive treatises on animal life, encumbered with Latin names, somewhat hard reading, however fine their illustrations, if they are arranged on the approved scientific divisions—order, family, genus, species—into which naturalists split up animated nature. A proper natural history, however, must follow this method of treatment if it is to form the basis of a scientific knowledge of the subject.

Does the ordinary reader desire such knowledge? Does he require it?

The answer to both questions is a negative: emphatic in the first and modified in the second case. No matter how slightly youth is drawn to the conventional study of zoology, not even the forbidding scientific approach to natural history can rob it of its inherent fascination.

A boundless curiosity about the infinite diversity of creatures that share the life of the globe with him is a deep and abiding and a most natural trait in man. The stories of a Adam naming the beasts, and of the animals, two by two, going into the ark are ancient evidence of man's interest in his fellow-creatures of the so-called lower orders. A study of the life-histories of many animals and birds, fishes and reptiles, or of the astounding social systems of certain insects, is calculated to limit man's pride in himself as the incarnation of the highest intelligence or the finest physical product of the animal world. Especially is it likely to extend his sympathy to all lowly things that are living out their little days with him upon this planet. It lies at the root of humanitarianism. Interest in animal life is never an idle curiosity, and it may prove more absorbing than any other interest that could be named.

Not, then, to add a new natural history to a list already adequate, but to meet this universal and most healthy interest in the astonishing realities and the mysterious ways of the animal kingdom is the purpose of WONDERS OF ANIMAL LIFE. Its title adequately suggests its scope: to enquire into and to illustrate all that is of uncommon interest in the life of the animal kingdom.

While the reader will find in our pages a constantly changing panorama of animal life, with no more apparent order than the naturalist finds in the Brazilian jungle, he can hardly fail to be interested and he is certain to be instructed, for though the only method that is observed throughout our chapters is a rough alternation of interest, now in mammals, next in reptiles, then in birds, fishes, insects, each chapter of this work is written either by one of the leading specialists on his subject or—where expert knowledge is less needed than vividness of descriptive style—by a popular author.

A glance at the list of contributors, their scientific and literary credentials, and the subjects allotted to them in our scheme, will indicate to the reader that though WONDERS OF ANIMAL LIFE is designedly popular in its appeal, it is not the less authoritative in being more entertaining than the conventional sort of natural history.

Never before has there been brought together so representative and so varied a collection of photographic documents covering the whole range of animated nature. In the last decade, and particularly within the latter part of it, naturalists have acquired an immense amount of new knowledge, and marked progress has been made in recording the wild life of the world by means of direct photography.

The exploits of the camera experts employed by the organizers of some of the great 'nature and adventure' films—'Simba' is a fine example—that have fascinated millions throughout the world in these years have produced so rich a body of material for illustrating such a work as this that editorially we are in a more favoured position than any of our predecessors in the same field and we hope the reader will agree with us in thinking that we have taken advantage of that fortunate circumstance for his entertainment and instruction.

J.A. HAMMERTON

Publisher's Note

We are happy to present the illustrated encyclopaedia—Wonders of Animal Life—to the learned readers. As its title suggests, it attempts to enquire into the astonishing realities and the mysterious ways of life of the animal kingdom—mammals, reptiles, birds, fishes and insects.

Presented in eight volumes, each chapter of this work is written either by one of the leading specialists on the subject or—where expert knowledge is less needed than vividness of descriptive style—by a popular author. The text is enriched with a representative and varied collection of photographic documents covering the whole range of animated nature. Our other notable illustrated encyclopaedias include *The Living Animals of the World* (4 volumes), *The Wonders of the World* (4 volumes), *Peoples of All Nations* (14 volumes), and *The Earth and Its Inhabitants* (8 volumes).

TABLE OF CONTENTS

Volume One

List of Colour Plates

Volume Two

List of Colour Plates

Volume Three

List of Colour Plates

Volume Four

List of Colour Plates

Volume Five

List of Colour Plates

Volume Six

List of Colour Plates

Volume Seven

List of Colour Plates

Volume Eight

List of Colour Plates

An Illustrated Encyclopaedia

Wonders of Animal Life

by Famous Writers on Natural History

Volume Two

Aitken, Ltd

INDIAN ELEPHANTS IN THEIR ELEMENT: A BOISTEROUS BATHING PARTY

All elephants are fond of the water, but the Indian elephant is the best of them all as a swimmer. It is at home in the deepest water, and is very fond of staying for hours in a river with the body entirely below the surface and just the head and trunk appearing. This fondness for bathing is just as keen in the captive as in the wild animal, and a captive elephant, to be happy, must have a swimming pool in its cage. While the African elephant seems to be more or less indifferent to extreme heat, the Indian species likes plenty of shade, and no doubt it is the desire for cool surroundings that has led to its habit of prolonged immersion and its strength and skill in swimming.

Chapter XXIII

The Great Elephant & its Little Relation

By G. M. Vevers

Superintendent of the London Zoological Society's Gardens

It is curious that the greatest of all land animals, weighing several tons, and sometimes standing nearly twelve feet at the shoulder, should have as its nearest relative a little creature no bigger than a common rabbit; yet zoologists, after studying the anatomy of the elephant and comparing it with that of the rock rabbit, or coney of Africa, are agreed that this is most certainly the case.

In outward appearance it would be hard to find two animals so extremely dissimilar, for, in addition to the disparity in size, there is no single external feature which gives a clue to the relationship, and it is only by a careful comparison of the skeletal structure of the feet that kinship between these two creatures can be established. This kinship dates back to the Secondary Epoch in geological time, when the primitive stock of mammals seems to have started to divide up into the more or less distinct groups which we recognize to-day. In those days the elephant did not exist as we know it, nor had its then living ancestor developed anything worthy of the name of trunk. From fossil remains we suppose it to have been a rather clumsy animal, somewhat tapir-like in appearance and size, with only the barest suggestion of a proboscis. It is at this point that we get the first evidence of the relationship. This creature which is known to scientists as the Moeritherium was descended from the same line of ancestors as were the progenitors of the rock rabbit.

Next in the ancestry of the elephant came a beast called Palaeomastodon, which was the first of all the elephants to own the beginnings of a trunk. From the Palaeomastodon palaeontologists have traced a perfect succession of links in the chain of evolution of the elephant family down to the recently extinct mastodon mammoth and the elephants of to-day. In the earlier members of the group, the lower incisor teeth were almost as markedly developed as the upper incisors, which have become the tusks of the modern elephant, but after attaining an almost grotesque state of over-development in a creature known as Tetrabelodon, which flourished in Early Pliocene times, the lower incisors faded away, and in the more recent and existing forms of elephants have become non-existent. As the lower incisors gradually disappeared, the snout and upper incisors remained, developed in size and so became the trunk and tusks of the animal as we know it to-day.

From time to time during recent years, there have appeared in the daily press lurid accounts of four-tusked elephants of gigantic size which still lurk in the jungles of darkest Africa, but these stories come under the heading of "travellers' tales," for it is certain that, apart from malformed specimens, a few of which are known to exist, no four-tusker has ever walked the earth since the far days of Tetrabelodon. While in the course of evolution the elephant has increased in bulk, the coney appears to have decreased in almost the same proportions, for it had as one of its ancestors Megalohyrax, which was a contemporary of and about the same size as the Moeritherium.

Both groups originated in Africa, but whereas the elephant (as fossil remains show) wandered over the greater part of the earth, secure in its massive strength, the coney family hardly strayed from home and no remains of it have been discovered further afield than Greece. Here perhaps is a case in which the psychology of the individual has been to some extent a factor in the trend of evolution. Different habits became evolved, and on the one hand we have a story of increasing size and strength, culminating in the Mastodon, while on the other we have an animal of furtive, cringing habit, ever decreasing in courage and size till it reached its present state.

The hairy Mammoth which is found preserved in the frozen wastes of Siberia is the most recently extinct member of the elephant family. It is very closely allied to the Indian elephant, the main difference being the shape of the tusks which have a spiral curve, and the long, brown, woolly coat, which served to keep this lumbering creature warm during the bitterly cold period which preceded the last Glacial Epoch. So well preserved are the remains of these frozen giants that sometimes their flesh is found to be quite edible if eaten directly after it has been thawed. It is not, however, for the flesh that these semi-fossilised creatures are unearthed, but for the ivory of their gigantic tusks, of which many thousands of tons have found their way into the market during the past fifty years.

The elephants of to-day may be broadly divided into two races, the African (*Loxodon africanus*) and the Indian (*Elephas maximus*), although in both Africa and Asia there are local races showing slight variations in form and in Africa there is a pigmy race which has recently been described as a separate species (*Loxodon pumilio*). In Burma and Siam the occurrence of so-called White Elephants is not an uncommon event. Some sixty authentic cases of these have been recorded in historic times. They are albino forms of the true elephant, and, as a rule, are of a dirty pink colour, with mottled pigment here and there on the body. The iris of the eye in most cases is white, and in the dark the retinal reflection is pink. A living male White Elephant from Burma was shown during the summer of 1926 at the Zoological Gardens in London; it was about eight years old and little more than half-grown. This specimen was remarkably free from pigment, and was probably the most perfect specimen of a "White Elephant" ever captured. Albino elephants are held to be sacred in Burma, and

Bonnaire

HOW HANNIBAL FERRIED THE 'EARTH-SHAKING BEAST" ACROSS THE RHONE AGAINST THE ROMANS

At the time of the Second Punic War (218-201 B.C.) between Carthage and Rome, the elephant seems to have been common in Africa as far north as the Mediterranean hinterland, though now it has retired to the remote central regions of the continent. Thus the Carthaginians had an apparently formidable new " arm " to favour their warfare. In fact, these enterprising people used elephants in much the same way as the " tank " has been used in modern warfare. A howdah filled with armed men was strapped on the animal's back, but the main effect was undoubtedly a moral one. Hannibal, a military genius, invaded Italy by crossing the Pyrenees, the Rhone, and the Alps, but the hardship of the last barrier took great toll of his elephants.

Zoological Society's Bulletin

ANCESTOR OF THE ELEPHANTS, THE MAMMOTH, DISINTERRED IN SIBERIA

Like the other mammals, the elephant, as we now know it in its different species, has descended through the ages from strangely different ancestors. The most recently extinct of these forbears is the mammoth. This creature, which was smaller than the average Indian or African elephant, was covered with long hair, just as infant elephants are now. Its remains are dug up in Siberia where the ground is frozen for some feet below the surface. In some cases the flesh of these carcases has been found fit to eat, even after such ages of cold storage.

in Siam if one is caught it is at once sent to the royal stables to have a king for master.

Besides the disparity in the size of the ear, which is the most noticeable point of difference between the African and Asiatic forms, the ear of the former being much larger than that of the latter, there are several other very obvious characteristics in which the two races differ. In general outline when viewed in profile the two species are totally dissimilar. The forehead of the Indian elephant is flat and raised into two large bosses and the highest point of the body is always in the centre of the back, whereas in the African animal the head is domed and slopes gradually into the back, which attains its highest point between the shoulders. The trunks of the two animals also show points of difference, that of the Indian elephant being smooth and tapering when compared with the trunk of the African, which is markedly corrugated throughout its length. At the extremity of the trunk in the African species the two finger-like processes which are used in grasping small objects are almost equal in size, whereas in the Indian, the anterior process only is present. The latter also has one more toe nail on the hind foot, the African only having three. The tusks of the African elephant attain a very much greater length and weight than those of the Indian. The longest known tusk is one in the American Museum of Natural History, and measures eleven feet five inches along the outside curve. It weighs 293 pounds. The longest tusk from an Indian elephant measures nearly two feet less, and its weight is not recorded. In the female of the African species, the tusks are usually well developed, but those of the female Indian elephant are small and sometimes scarcely protrude beyond the mouth. The molar teeth of the two races also differ in structure, the puckering of the enamel and the ridges or plates of the teeth being very much more numerous and compressed in the Indian than in the African race, in which the teeth show a more primitive design.

In size the Indian elephant is decidedly smaller than its African relative, the record Indian measuring ten feet six inches, while the tallest African, a giant from Zuga near Lake Albert, stood no less than eleven feet six and a half inches at the shoulder. It was a "one-tusker" shot by Major P. H. G. Powell-Cotton and is now in his private museum at Birchington. "Jumbo," the famous African elephant which lived at the Zoo during the middle of last century, and was subsequently sold to Barnum

DOCILITY OF THE GREATEST OF THE BEASTS WHEN KINDLY AND INTELLIGENTLY TRAINED

Wild, the elephant does not appear to behave with much of the sagacity with which elephants in general are credited. But in the hands of man and after long training, a mature elephant seems to develop a sense of reasoning and, besides, soon becomes docile and full of intelligence. The same elephant which raises one of its great legs for a child to touch can be trained to help in the capture of its own kind. The right-hand photograph shows an elephant of the Zoo at its daily task of carrying people about the grounds. It sweetens its labours with the aid of an inquiring trunk thrust in among the crowd from which various tit-bits are to be obtained, so experience has taught this great beast.

Realistic Travels

TWO ROYAL ELEPHANTS FIGHTING IN THE PALACE GROUNDS

From time immemorial the elephant has been domesticated in India, and the rulers of the native states have always taken a pride in their royal stables. Our photograph shows two of the elephants belonging to the Gaekwar of Baroda set on to fight each other. Each animal is chained by one leg and a mahout or driver seated on the neck of the beast controls the proceedings. Elephant prices are much the same as motor-car prices, varying from £100 to £1,000, but animals under twenty years old are not valuable.

and Bailey's Travelling Menagerie in America, measured ten feet seven inches at the shoulder, and weighed over six tons. The mammoth was a smaller beast than either of the above, seldom exceeding nine feet in height, but there once existed in India an elephant, the fossil remains of which show it to have exceeded sixteen feet at the shoulder. This animal which is known as the Narbada elephant, was probably the largest proboscidean which has ever existed in the world.

In Malta, Cyprus, and other islands of the Mediterranean, remains have been found of several species of Pigmy elephants, none of which could have been much larger than a St. Bernard dog. Like the present Pigmy species, these appear to have been closely related to the African elephant as we know it to-day, and no doubt their small size can be attributed to their insular habitations. The existing Pigmy African species differs from its larger relative in having a very much smaller ear in comparison with the rest of its body. The extremity of the trunk also resembles the Indian rather than the African species in having the anterior finger-like process larger than the posterior. It probably never exceeds six feet in height. It inhabits the hinterland of the Congo, and is very rarely seen. Up to the present only three live specimens of this strange stunted type have been brought into Britain.

In habits the two races differ to quite a large extent. The Indian elephant is essentially a jungle-dwelling animal and is exceptionally intolerant to the rays of the sun, whereas its African cousin spends a great deal of time in more or less open country, and is apparently unaffected by extremes of heat. Similarly, in nature, the food of the two races differs considerably, that of the African elephant being composed of coarser materials than that of the Indian species ; the former feeds chiefly on branches of trees, bark and saplings, whereas the latter prefers more succulent substances such as bamboos, plantains, and figs. This marked difference in diet corresponds to the difference in the structure of the molar teeth which has already been alluded to. In drinking, the water is sucked up into the trunk, which is then turned into the open mouth and emptied. Rice and other grains are treated in the same way, being blown into the mouth. Although it is generally supposed that the young suckle by means of the trunk, they actually suckle directly by the mouth

YOUTHFUL BEHAVIOUR UNDER THE STIMULUS OF THIRST AND ANGER

When the animal drinks it sucks water up its trunk and then squirts the trunk-full into its mouth. In the lower photograph we see the use of this strangely-prolonged nose, for without it this elephant could not, even when kneeling, have obtained a drink from this pond. Above is a young elephant at the Berlin Zoological Gardens which are particularly fine. It was irritated by a dog—small dogs seem especially to frighten and annoy elephants—and stuck out its tail and trunk in indignation at not being able to reach the nuisance.

F. W. Bond

Chandos Studios

LORD OF THE JUNGLE DOES MENIAL SERVICE FOR ITS MASTERS

It is in the teak yards that the intelligence and strength of the elephant, developed and directed by man, are seen at their highest pitch. The animals are trained not only to carry the great balks of timber, but to arrange them carefully in stacks. The lower photograph shows an elephant at work drawing a teak log in the Southern Shan States of Burma. Above we see how the beast moves logs without the aid of harness—a unique performance among draught animals. The tusks play an important part in lifting

Wiele

HERD OF ASIATIC ELEPHANTS IN THE FASTNESS OF A SIAMESE FOREST

What are called Indian elephants are by no means confined to India, but are found in Burma and in Siam. While there are some local individualities, the Asiatic elephants are all of a distinct type as opposed to the African. The most striking points of difference between the types belonging to the two continents are the size of the ears, which in the Asiatic elephant are comparatively small; and in the shape. The Asiatic elephant has a flat forehead raised into two large bosses, and the centre of the back is always the highest point of the body. This marvellous photograph shows how a herd looks in the natural surroundings of a forest in Siam. The animals are sheltering from the heat and hot sunshine is suggested by the contrasts of light and shade.

F. W. Bond

LITTLE CREATURE THAT IS THE ELEPHANT'S NEAREST RELATIVE

This little animal, no larger than a rabbit, is nevertheless descended from the same remote ancestors as the mighty elephant and provides us with an example of the extremes to which evolution can lead. Its name is the hyrax and there are some twenty species including the Cape hyrax, the tree hyrax which makes a very entertaining pet, and the Syrian hyrax which is mentioned in the Old Testament as the "coney." This last is the only member of the family found outside the continent of Africa.

The period of gestation varies from eighteen to twenty-two months, and the young, which are born singly, are covered with woolly hair resembling the coat of the Mammoth.

Both species are fast movers over a short distance, and a speed of fifteen miles per hour is not uncommonly kept up for a quarter of a mile or so, but whereas the African can keep up a speed of ten miles an hour for several hours on end, the Indian, being shorter on the leg and more cumbersome, cannot maintain a speed of more than six or seven miles an hour. Generally speaking, the African elephant is the more active and powerful animal of the two and is the more ferocious and ready to charge when attacked or disturbed. The African charges with the trunk raised above the head, while the Indian coils up its trunk tightly and tramples its victims to death with the forefeet. Of the senses, that of scent is most highly developed in the African species, neither sight nor hearing being very acute in either race. Although both are fond of bathing, the Indian excels as a swimmer, and is quite at home in the deepest water, sometimes swimming for hours at a time with the body entirely submerged, and only the head and trunk appearing above the surface.

Mighty mountains of muscle and bone as they are, elephants are peculiarly lacking in powers of resistance to shock and disease. Many have been known to lie down and die of a broken heart when given too great a burden to carry, and they succumb to anthrax in a very few hours after the bacillus of that dread disease has found an entry into the bloodstream; in Burma alone this disease accounts for the death of several thousands of these animals every year. Indeed elephants seem to be particularly susceptible to anthrax.

From very ancient Assyrian and Egyptian records it is certain that in early historic times the Indian elephant had a much wider range than it has to-day, reaching as far westwards as Mesopotamia. Similarly, in the days of the Carthaginians, the African race extended to the shores of the Mediterranean, whereas now it is limited almost entirely to the central or equatorial belt of Africa.

In India, Burma and Siam, elephants have been domesticated from time immemorial, being used for hunting, hauling timber, and as beasts of burden generally. It follows, therefore, that in these countries good working elephants can command a high price, and £800 to £1,000 is not infrequently given for a fully-grown, well-trained "tusker." Working females are not worth so much, and immature animals under twenty years of age may be bought for about £100.

The young are not often born in captivity, and when a new "worker" is wanted it is usual to catch a fully-grown one out of a wild herd and put him through a course of training. In the wild state the

E.N.A.

WILD AFRICAN ELEPHANTS AS THE CAMERA DISCOVERED THEM BY DAY AND BY NIGHT

Steady hands and nerves are needed in the taking of such a photograph as this one of an old cow elephant (left) preparing to charge the photographer. Notice the enormous ears, outspread in anger, which are one of the characteristics of the African as distinct from the Asiatic elephant. Despite its bulk a charging elephant leaves one little leisure for avoiding it, and it can maintain a running speed of about fifteen miles an hour for four or five hundred yards. The African elephant slackens to about ten miles an hour for greater distances, but can keep up this average for several hours, whereas the Asiatic can only last a distance at little more than half this speed. The right-hand photograph shows a bull elephant of Tanganyika, and was taken at night.

Underwood

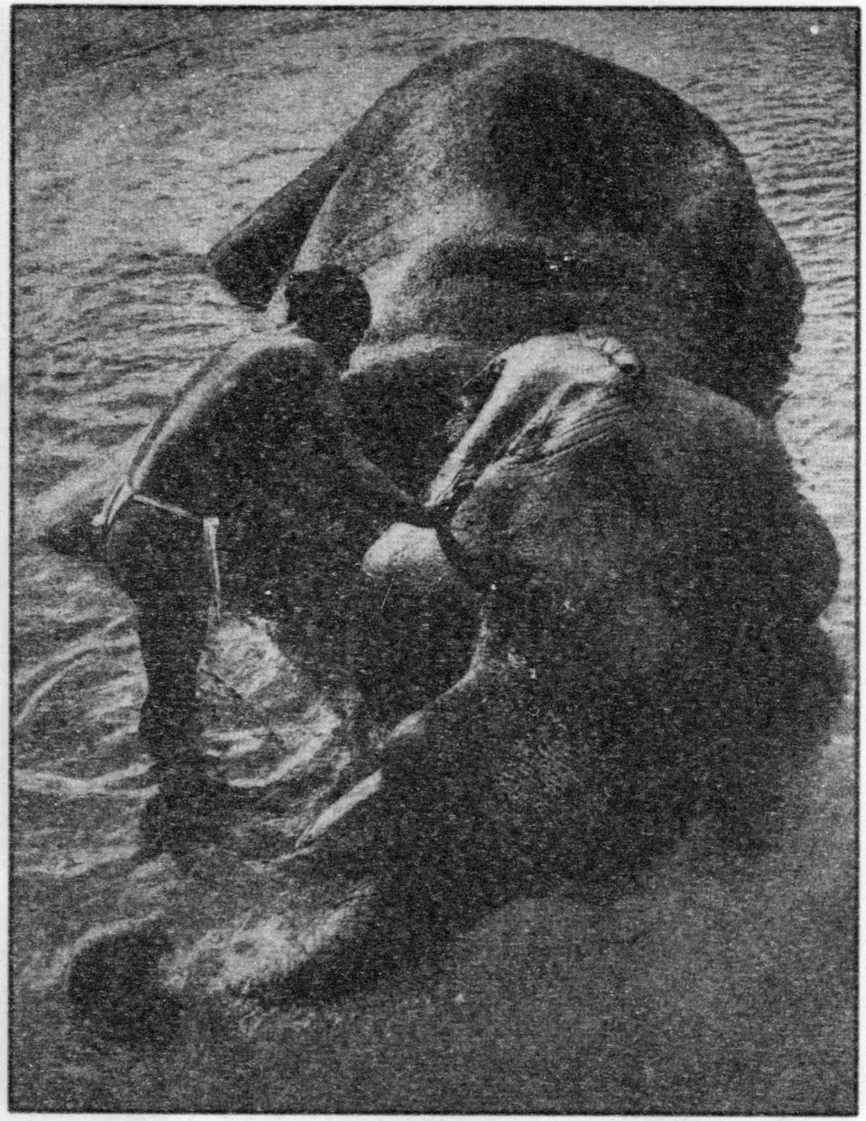

Photopress

WHAT MAN CAN DO WITH THE GREATEST BEAST THAT WALKS THE EARTH

By many ingenious methods man has learned to capture and tame the elephant in Asia. In Africa, there has never been the training of elephants on anything like the same scale, although it is now being shown that the latter species is far from being as intractable as used to be generally supposed. Our left hand photograph shows a man riding an elephant near Kandy, in Ceylon, while on the right an attendant is seen washing his enormous charge as it lies, cool and happy, in a river. Those in charge of elephants become very attached to them and the animals, which have very good memories, are well able to repay kindness just as they very seldom forget to return evil for evil.

E.N.A.

ELEPHANTS OF SIAM AND KENYA IN THEIR WILD HOMES

Like cattle, elephants have a great fondness for standing close together, and when a traveller through the jungle comes upon such a group the sight is an impressive one. In the lower view we have a glimpse of the wilds of Siam with a part of a herd cooling itself in the water. A very different scene is depicted in the upper photograph where we are shown the wild uplands of Kenya and a solitary elephant proceeding on his lordly way. The African elephant used to exist in vast herds, but the ivory hunters have reduced the numbers sadly.

ROYAL ELEPHANT CAPARISONED IN SILVER AND GOLD

Realistic Travels

Upon their elephants the native princes of India have always lavished all the wealth of Oriental ornament. This is the state elephant of the Maharaja of Patiala as it appears when the prince has to attend at some state occasion. Not only has it magnificent trappings—a howdah of gold and silver, rich embroidery and splendid trinkets—but its trunk and its great ears are brightly painted, too, when this leviathan of the land goes forth among its master's people upon occasions of pomp and princely circumstance.

Indian elephant is by no means an intelligent creature, but under the influence of man he becomes docile and obedient, and to some extent is able to develop the power of reasoning.

It is a popular supposition that the African elephant is not so docile or intelligent as its Indian relation, but this idea has arisen probably because in Africa from early historic times until quite recently no attempt was made to capture and train elephants on the same scale as it is done in India. There is, however, substantial evidence to show that the African elephant was used in battle and as a beast of burden by the Ptolemies in Egypt and by Hannibal in the Punic Wars: in fact, many ancient coins and medals have been found upon which are stamped elephants of undoubted African origin with riders on the head.

More recent evidence of the tractability of the African species may be found in the records of the Zoological Society of London, and of the elephant training school at Api, in the Belgian Congo, where systematic training of elephants has been going on for the past 25 years. The famous African elephant, "Jumbo," who came to this country when quite a youngster in 1865 and grew to maturity in the Zoo, until he was sold to America 17 years later at the age of 26, was in the habit of carrying scores of children for rides on his back every fine day during the summer months, and another African elephant, a female whose name has been forgotten, gave proof of her docility in the same way.

At Api, in the Congo, there were in 1928 fifty elephants in training, 19 of which had completed the course and were working animals. The training is done by local natives who learnt their business from seven Indian mahouts imported in 1920 as instructors. Half-grown wild elephants are chosen for training, which is carried on for ten years before the animal is strong enough for regular work. Attempts to shorten the period of training in the past have always ended in the death of the animal. At present the costs of running the school at Api are being met by the King of the Belgians out of his private purse.

From the days of the great Persian King Cyrus down to comparatively recent times, the elephant has been an important factor in warfare. The Romans met elephants in battle in 280 B.C., when they were used by Pyrrhus of Epirus, but they did not become really familiar with their use until the Second Punic War, when Hannibal invaded Italy from the north, bringing his troops and elephants over the Alps by way of the St. Gothard Pass. It is related by the Greek historian, Polybius, that many hundreds of these animals perished while crossing the mountains, and by the time the army had reached the Arno, in Central Italy, the only elephant to survive was the one that Hannibal himself rode.

It was left to Scipio Africanus to discover how to counter these new "engines of war," and at the Battle of Zama he ordered his archers to shoot their arrows at the trunk, which is the most sensitive part of the animal. The result was that the elephants became panic-stricken with pain and turning round, charged through the ranks of their own unfortunate infantry and trampled them to death.

The age to which elephants may live, in common with that of many other large animals, has always been a subject of much speculation. It was formerly thought that they could live for many centuries. In India the natives believe they live to any age up to 150 years; on the other hand Government statistics show that the life of a working elephant in captivity is seldom more than twenty years after purchase. Twenty-five years' duration in a menagerie or zoological collection is considered good. Metchnikoff, an accepted authority on longevity, states that the elephant, in proportion to its size, has not a high potential longevity, and that one hundred years is the probable age limit and thirty years a good average.

To return to the poor little relative of these colossal creatures which have played and are still playing an important part in the history of the world, would seem in some ways to pass from the sublime to the ridiculous, and yet the little coney or "dassie," as it is called in South Africa, is interesting in that by comparison with the elephant it provides an example of the extremes to which evolution may go. In external appearance, form and colour, the coney is not unlike a common rabbit with a somewhat rat-like head. There is no tail, but a small tubercle takes the place of this appendage and it does not hop like a rabbit but walks or runs, using its legs separately. The forelegs are shorter than the hindlegs, giving the animal the appearance of being low in front. This is accentuated by a bushy collar of hair round the throat. It has four toes on the front feet and three behind, each supplied with hoof-like nails except the inner toes on the hind feet, which are long and are used as "toilet digits."

The coney has no canine teeth, but it has two incisors in the top jaw and four in the lower, which resemble those of a rodent. The molar teeth, of which there are eight in the upper jaw and seven in the lower, resemble those of a rhinoceros in both form and number.

These little animals generally live in the hollows and caves of rocks on the hillsides and down on the seashore just above high-water mark. They are extremely timid and shy in the wild state, although in captivity they become tame, and some species even become aggressive to strangers. They are entirely vegetable feeders, and their flesh tastes like rabbit. Being exceedingly agile and quick in their movements, they are very rarely caught alive, but there is one species, the Tree Hyrax from Nigeria, which makes an ideal house-pet and is much sought after by animal dealers.

In all, about twenty species have been described, the commonest being the Cape Rock Rabbit (*Procavia capensis*). The only species found outside Africa is the Syrian Hyrax (*Procavia syriacus*), or coney of the Bible, which the writer of Proverbs describes as being a feeble creature having its dwelling among the rocks.

Chapter XXIV

The Mystery of The Puma

By Hamilton Fyfe

How or when the fear of man, which is instinctive in almost all wild animals, became an instinct we do not know. We do know that no other living creature is so generally mistrusted. Occasionally we hear of animals which have never before been in the presence of human beings showing curiosity rather than alarm at sight of them. It is very rare indeed to find a wild animal which seems to regard man as a friend, not an enemy. That is the chief of several reasons why the puma is so interesting and attractive a beast.

The largest after the jaguar of the American cat tribes, it is found—or, rather, it was found until populations grew thick—in all parts of the two Americas. In Brazil it was called cougar, and that name is used quite as much as puma, which is Peruvian. In North America it was known also as "painter," a contraction from panther.

It is not very large, from six to nine feet long, including some three feet of tail. Its colour is tawny on back and sides, whitish underneath, with a dark line along the backbone and a brown tip to the tail. Its ears are black, its upper lip white, its nostrils flesh-coloured instead of black. Once pumas were spotted; this is made clear by the cubs, which carry spots for six months, then lose them, as their ancestors lost them long ago.

The food which the puma prefers to any other is horse-flesh, but since the wild horse of the pampas has been almost exterminated by him he has to be content with sheep or cattle (he would rather have sheep), with deer, grouse, rabbits, or even rats and mice.

In the valley of the Orinoco and in that of the Amazon, pumas prey on monkeys, pursuing them in the trees with astonishing agility. They can leap from the ground on to boughs twenty feet above them; and they are just as fine performers at long jumping tor on the flat their jumps sometimes measure nearly forty feet.

In the Adirondack Mountains, U.S.A., they have been known to eat porcupines and snails. Here they would devour part of a kill and leave it to be finished another day. This they could do safely in a cold climate, but in the Argentine they seem to know that meat goes bad very quickly, so they never return after they have had their first meal off an animal killed.

Their method of attack is ingenious. They leap on a horse's back. One paw grasps its chest; the other paw seizes the head and, with a quick wrench, dislocates the neck.

North American observers describe the puma as a coward, yet they say that when he is wounded he rushes fiercely on his assailants, and they tell how any dog that ventures too near "receives such an energetic cuff from the puma's paw that he rarely solicits another." Those who have studied the species in South America deny that it can be called cowardly, but draw a sharp distinction between its behaviour to other animals and to men. That it will not attack or even in some circumstances defend itself from the human race, they admit; but this is not cowardice, they say. It is due to some unexplained influence which the human race seems to have upon it.

This influence is strong enough to make the puma, which will fly at the jaguar—a much larger beast than itself—run from man, and even sit unresisting and trembling while man deals it a death-blow.

Nor is that the most surprising manifestation of the instinct which has caused the natives of South America to call the puma *amigo del*

PUMA ON THE WATCH
After the jaguar this is the largest of the cat family in the New World, and it is found both in North and South America. In the former it is called painter or panther, and in Brazil the cougar. It is a handsome, fine-looking creature, as this photograph shows.

Neville Kingston

THE PUMA YAWNS

The photographer has taken the opportunity of a yawn to show us the magnificent array of teeth with which the puma is equipped. But the animal uses its powerful paws rather than its teeth for defence and for killing its prey.

cristiano, the friend of the Christian. It has actually been known to volunteer its services as a protector of man. W. H. Hudson heard and believed this story. A hunter of ostriches on the pampas fell from his horse, breaking his leg. He lay all night in the open, defended from a jaguar by a puma, which kept the fiercer creature off and saved the hunter's life.

Humboldt called the affections and antipathies of animals mysterious. Many naturalists say they are not more mysterious, however, than those of men and women. Yet no one who has studied the puma has ventured to suggest any explanation of its attitude towards human beings. That remains a mystery, and one of the most puzzling in nature.

It is too much to say, as W. H. Hudson said in his Naturalist in La Plata, that the puma "never makes an unprovoked attack on a human being." There is evidence to prove that on the North American continent unprovoked attacks have been made. For example, in the state of Washington, U.S.A., some schoolboys saw, as they went home from school, what they took to be a yellow dog in some bushes. They did not molest it. Suddenly it sprang on them, seized a little fellow of six, and ran off into the bushes with him. An elder boy, not more than twelve, bravely followed. With an empty bottle he hammered the animal's head to such good effect that it released the small boy and bolted.

It has been surmised that the puma was in a playful mood, and did not mean to hurt or devour the child. Pumas are often described as being like kittens in their behaviour. When they are caught young and brought up as pets, they never tire of games. In captivity they are cheerful and affectionate, seldom giving any cause for alarm. Edmund Kean, the English actor, kept one as a pet ; it used to follow him about. He was accustomed to exhibit it to friends in his drawing-room. There seems, indeed, to be some instinctive tie between human beings and pumas, as there is between us and cats.

In a record of travel in Central America (J. W. B. Whetham, 1877) the story is told of a mahogany cutter walking through a forest and feeling something soft press against his legs. "On looking down he saw a cougar, which, with tail erect and purring like a cat, twisted itself in and out of his legs and glided round him, turning up its fierce eyes as if with laughter." Unfortunately, the man was so terrified that he struck at the creature with his axe and it made off.

Possibly the puma which seized the little American boy had friendly intentions. That could hardly be the explanation, however, of the attack made by a puma on a Swedish settler in British Columbia. This man was clearing a site for his house when the animal leapt on him and fixed its teeth in his arm. With a yell of pain, he kicked it in the stomach and it let go. Then ensued one of the most enthralling fights between man and beast that have ever had the fortune to be recorded.

THE puma began the second round by springing at the Swede's throat. He guarded with his left and landed his right heavily on its ribs. It went back to its corner, breathing hard.

Third round. The puma sprang again and seized the man's left hand. With his right he pommelled and with his feet he kicked. It was at last forced to release its hold.

Fourth round. The puma sprang this time on to the Swede's breast, knocking him against a tree. He recovered himself and kicked it once more, inflicting severe punishment.

Fifth round. As the puma came at him, the Swede saw his spade on the ground. He managed to pick it up and successfully kept his antagonist at bay.

Sixth round. The puma leaped and got a hold on the man's leg, but now he was armed. He raised the spade and drove it through the animal's skull.

Both these instances of unprovoked attack on human beings happened in North America. Hudson drew his information entirely from South America. There is some difference between the pumas of the two continents and it may be that in the southern, or at any rate in the portion of it in and about the Argentine, they are as uniformly well-disposed towards man as Hudson imagined.

Mystery of the Puma

The puma of North America is certainly not so ill disposed to dogs as his relation in the centre and the south. He does not like them, but their mere presence does not provoke him to fury. Even when the South American puma is tamed, this fierce antipathy persists. One that had been for years in a menagerie was being taken about among visitors on a lead. Suddenly they saw it stop, fix an intent gaze on something, bristle up its hair and roll its eyes. Then it broke away from its keeper and bounded in among the crowd. They scattered in terror, but the animal took no notice of them. It had spied a dog; that was the whole cause of its excitement.

The South American puma will even disregard blows from a man when its attention is taken up by dogs. A Scottish sheep farmer in Patagonia told Hudson how he and some of his dogs came upon a puma. The dogs were afraid to attack it. The man struck at it with a stick. It dodged his blows, keeping its eyes on the dogs all the time. He lost his temper, hit out wildly, broke his stick on the ground. He was now defenceless and expected the puma to spring and tear, but it ran past him and rushed after the dogs. His partner came up then and shot it.

Europeans do not hesitate to kill pumas, but there is a strong feeling against it among South Americans. This goes back a very long way. In a History of Lower California it is related that the missionaries who went to that country towards 1700 found it overrun by pumas. It was impossible to keep cattle or poultry. The deer were almost exterminated. The Indians could only eat flesh when they saw vultures hovering over a puma's kill; they hurried to the spot and feasted on the remains. They would not for anything kill a puma. They were convinced that if they did they would themselves be struck dead.

The missionaries strove vainly against this superstition until there was sent out a man of stiff character and great bodily strength. He determined to show the Indians that there was no need to be afraid of the consequences of killing a puma. He went into the woods and brought one down with a large stone.

Neville Kingston

ONLY WILD ANIMAL THAT IS FRIENDLY TO MAN

The puma seems to be an engaging beast in many ways. It has long been known in South America as "the Christian's friend," although there have been plenty of Christians who have cursed its cattle and sheep-killing habits. But when confronted by man it usually seems to behave like a large and friendly cat. A wild puma will purr in the presence of man and even rub itself against his legs. But apart from this it has the pleasing habit of playing for hours by itself in the midst of the desert at hide-and-seek or at chasing butterflies.

Then he slung it across his mule and took it to show the Indians. They were very much alarmed; they looked to see him drop dead at any moment. But he remained alive and well and after this the puma was treated like any other wild animal. One cannot help wishing that the missionary had been inspired by the example of Saint Francis of Assisi and that the friendship between beast and man could somehow have been kept up.

THAT there must be foundation for the story seems certain from the reluctance to kill pumas which is still to be noticed in parts of South America. Even those who are not natives of the country are affected by it. Thus a gaucho, or cowboy, who was English by birth told Hudson that he had only once killed a puma and was filled with remorse whenever he thought about it.

"It sat with its back against a stone and did not move even when the noose of the lasso was thrown over it. When I went forward with my knife unsheathed, it made no attempt to get away. It seemed to know what was coming. It began to tremble, tears ran from its eyes, it whined in the most pitiful way. After I had killed it, I felt that I had committed a murder."

That this puma was not exceptional in its manner of meeting death at human hands is proved by the statement in the Natural History of Chile, by Claudio Gay, that "when attacked by man its energy and daring at once forsake it, and it becomes a weak, inoffensive animal, and, trembling and uttering piteous moans, it seems to implore compassion from a generous enemy."

The screams of the puma which old writers described as piercing and terrible existed, it is fairly certain, in their imagination only, or in the imaginations of those from whom they got their "facts." Darwin said pumas rarely yelled; the rare occasions were in the breeding season.

Unhappily, civilised man has seldom been a "generous enemy" to the puma. If fear did not urge its slaughter, if the desire to show skill did not impel hunters to lasso or shoot it, mere unreasoning hostility to all wild creatures or even spite has often been the motive for its destruction. Hudson heard a story in the Argentine which illustrated this and proved that pumas did sometimes hit back.

A cowboy who had failed rather ignominiously to justify his reputation as a jaguar-slayer was riding home angrily when he saw a puma come out of the long grass a little way ahead of him and sit down in his path. Here was a chance to wreak his fury and revenge, to release the savage rage that burdened his heart. He dropped from his horse, tied its forefeet together in a hobble, then drew his long knife and rushed at the puma. It did not run away. It waited for him to strike, then dodged the blow with lightning quickness, and lifting a paw tore the flesh from one side of the cowboy's face. Then, after looking at him for a little, it scampered away.

The man recovered, but was disfigured for life. But he could never forget his appalling punishment for the harm he had intended to an inoffensive beast.

W. S. Berridge

YOUNG PUMA AND THE SPOTS IT WILL LOSE WHEN ADULT

During its youth the puma is covered with black spots, but when it comes to riper years these markings disappear and the fur on its back becomes a very handsome cinnamon colour, while the chest is white. The tail, also, is very handsome, being long and beautifully rounded. And so, not only will this become a pleasant-mannered, but also a very handsome creature. In the meantime, it is as pretty to look at and as amusing to watch as any kitten and it keeps its playful habits all its life

W. S. Berridge

HOW MOTHER PUMA LIFTS AND CARRIES HER YOUNG

In the lower photograph we see a puma cub, three weeks old, being carried by its mother, while the upper photograph shows how the cub is picked up. No kitten ever played more wholeheartedly or more amusingly than a puma cub. But later on it can take life seriously, as various animals know. In forest regions of Brazil it takes to the trees and hunts monkeys with extraordinary agility, and it can leap twenty feet from the ground to a branch, a truly wonderful performance for any animal.

H. Bastin

SWARM THAT HAS NEWLY DESERTED ITS OLD HOME TO FOUND A NEW ONE

From early spring onwards, queen and workers are busy producing a populous and thriving colony. The drones are hatched, and the hive is full to overflowing with from 30,000 to 90 000 inhabitants. It is apparently decided in some way that the surplus population must emigrate. The queen of proved fruitfulness will go with the adventurers, leaving a number of developing queens in the cells. Suddenly, as at a prearranged signal, half the inhabitants rush out of the hive and gather in a cluster, hanging by their hooked feet about their queen.

Chapter XXV

The Wonderful Commonwealth of the Bee

By Rev. Tickner Edwardes

Author of "The Lore of the Honey Bee"

THERE have been more fictions, born in past ages and still popularly accredited, about the life of the honey bee than of any other living creature in the world. And yet, now that the mysteries of hive life have been, and are still being, honestly and painstakingly explored by competent observers, the truth stands out as far more wonderful than any of the extravagant fancies put forth by the self-styled savants in bee-craft extending over literally thousands of years.

It was always known—the most rudimentary intelligence could scarcely overlook the fact—that the life of a bee-hive was carried on under some sort of intelligently directed government. Any one could see that the busy throng of bees incessantly leaving and returning to the hive throughout a summer's day were actuated by a common motive. It was also obvious that a system of division of labour was in force among them. Some bees, the greater part apparently, went to the fields to suck the sweet juices from the flowers, and to gather pollen, bringing both home for the use of the hive, the pollen being carried very conspicuously in little highly coloured lumps attached to the thighs. Other bees would leave the flowers alone, passing straight over the most alluring pastures to the little stream or pool beyond, where they would eagerly fill up with water and return at once with it to the bee city.

But a large number of bees seemed not to leave the hive at all, even in the brightest hours of summer sunshine. These busied themselves with the internal work of the hive, crowding together between the combs, or ranging themselves in open rows just outside the entrance to the hive, with their heads towards it, rapidly vibrating their wings. Others were evidently performing the duties of guards or sentinels to the stronghold. These bees congregated about the entrance carefully scrutinising all incomers, and occasionally pouncing upon some intruding stranger and stoutly driving her away.

Then it was seen that the bees inhabiting the hive were of two different sizes—small bees who did all the fetching and carrying, and were about early and late; and larger bees who emerged from the hive only towards noon of the day, and seemed to do nothing but fly about with a great noise and get in the way of the busy ones. The limit of exact knowledge was reached when the presence in the hive of a single large bee was recognized; and this bee, never observed abroad in the ordinary way, was of course imagined to be the ruler or king of the whole colony, the rest of the hive inhabitants being his subjects, male or female according to their size.

To these meagre facts were added from time to time throughout the ages numberless inventions by the so-called bee-masters, who, seeing that the ancient hives were absolutely sealed books to the keenest human eye, and thus nothing could either be proved or disproved, had no compunction in letting their fancy run riot for the entertainment of the credulous. The modern bee-hive, however, with its combs built within movable frames rendering every corner of the hive readily explorable, has swept away this cloud of false witnesses, yet in doing so has only served to render the wonderful communal life of the honey bee more wonderful still.

The first truth which one must grasp in any attempt to gain an accurate view of hive life, is that it contains no sort of central directing principle resembling a monarchy, absolute or otherwise. It is pure Socialism, and that brought to what seems the finest point of perfection. The single large bee which the ancients observed to exist in every normal hive is, as every child knows to-day, no king but simply the mother bee of the colony, the single fertile female bee who is the parent of all the other inhabitants of the hive. We call her the Queen Bee. That is a pretty idea, but nothing more. In fact, it is a complete misnomer. The mother bee takes no part in the direction of hive affairs, nor has she either capacity or equipment for the task. She exists in the hive for one purpose only—the production of eggs.

To the worker bees alone belong not only the entire government of the commonwealth, but the duty of carrying out the various works and initiating

H. Bastin

WONDER WORKER OF THE HIVE

Efficiency, and efficiency only, seems to be the characteristic of the bee The photograph shows a "worker," and no machine was ever made to equal it in versatility; while, as a living creature, it has even eliminated sex so that nothing shall interrupt the work for which it is born.

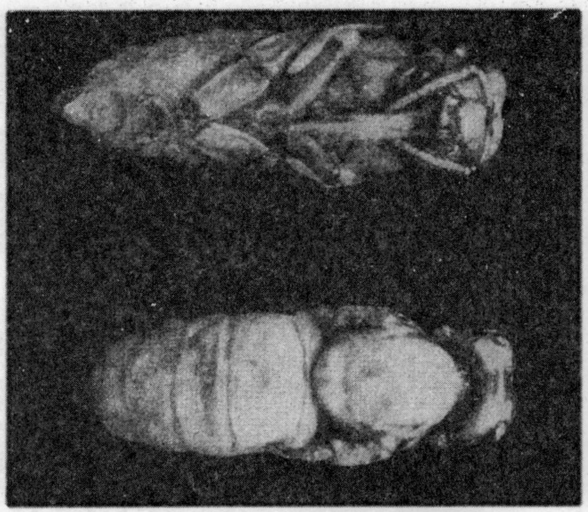

Pupa, upper and under sides

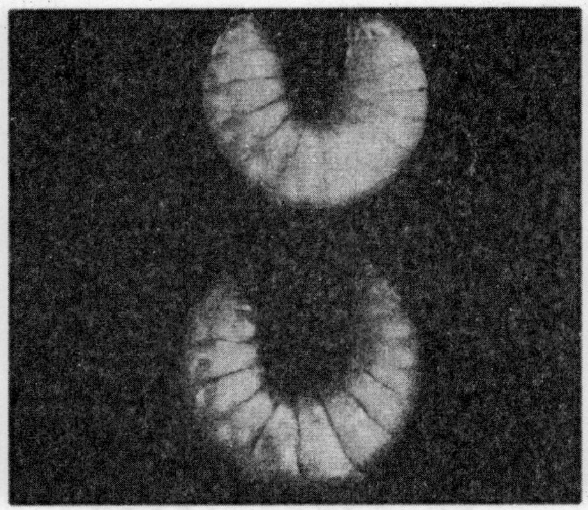

Early larval stages

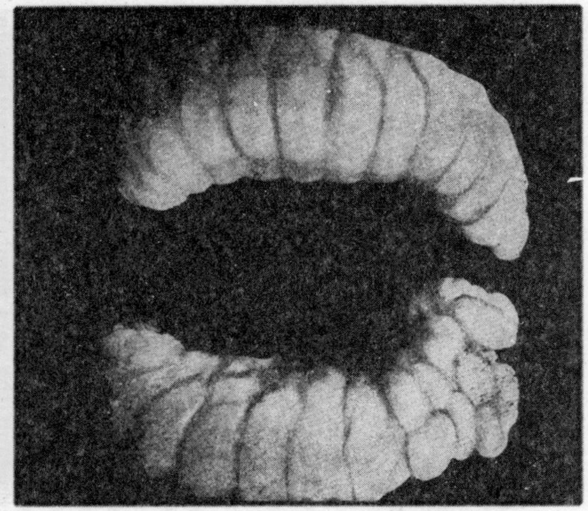

Larva changing to pupa

Queen

Worker

Drone

QUEEN, WORKER, AND DRONE BEES, AND THEIR STAGES OF LIFE

With the laying of an egg in a cell begins the life of every bee—worker, drone, or queen. In the case of the worker the egg hatches in three or four days into a small white grub and is then fed on a kind of bee-milk. On the fifth day the grub spins a silk cocoon and begins its pupa stage. Certain individuals told off for the work then come and seal up the mouth of the cell with a cover which, however, lets in air. Sixteen days later the grub has turned into a worker bee and begins to know its way out, sometimes assisted by the nurse bees. The process is the same for the drone save that it takes twenty-five days. The queen is fed on special food called royal jelly, and the egg from which she comes is housed in a special cell. These photographs are by H. Bastin.

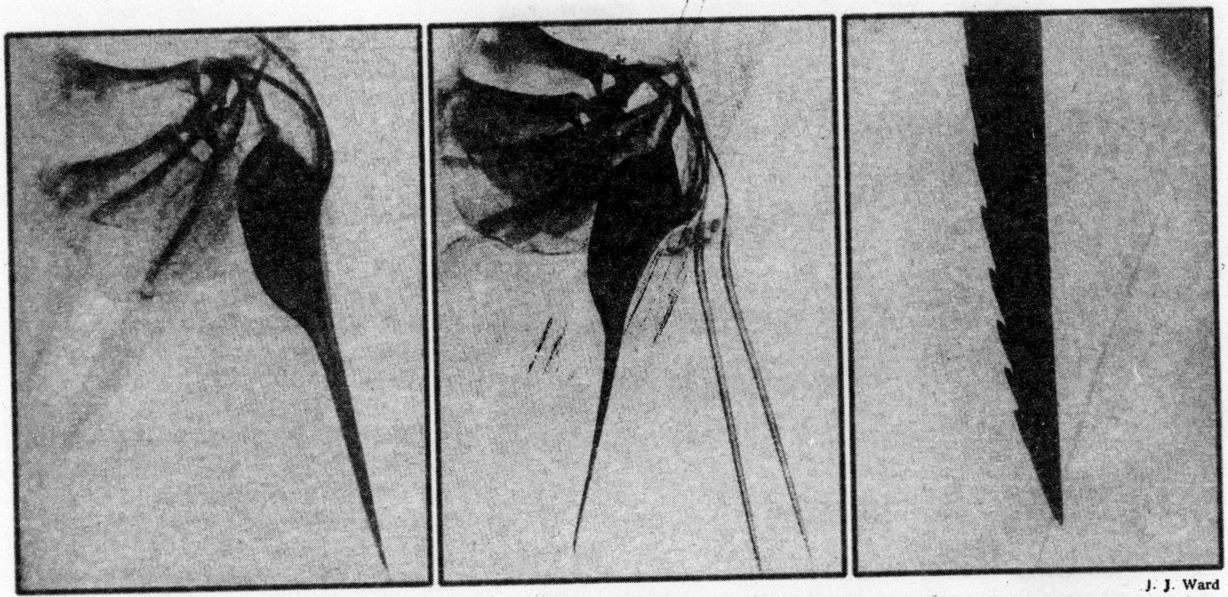

J. J. Ward

CASE OF POISON DARTS WHICH IS THE BEE'S STING

What is called the bee's sting is actually a sheath, or quiver (left), in which are two intensely sharp darts (centre). The sheath is barbed (right) like a savage's spear, and when driven through, say, the human skin, is held in place by the barbs. Then the darts drive up and down like pistons making a deeper and deeper puncture while formic acid is pumped from the poison-bag. All this takes place in a second or so. The bee, given time, can extricate the whole apparatus, but if brushed off is liable to be disembowelled.

every operation that arises in the crowded, complicated existence of the community. The worker bees build the bee city, producing from their own bodies the material necessary for its construction. The ancients believed that wax was gathered from the flowers. The fact is that wax is generated in certain glands situated in the underpart of the abdomen of the worker bees. When comb has to be built, a number of bees congregate in a dense cluster in the upper part of the hive, and there hang in a state of quiescence while the wax forms within them. At first the substance produced is very unlike beeswax, as we know it. It looks more like little transparent plates of mica, these protruding from beneath the horny scales of the abdomen, and often falling to the floor of the hive, where, if numerous enough, they show in a pale glistening drift. When comb-building the bee takes these plates out of their receptacles and chews them up, mingling an acid saliva with them the while until a soft, opaque plastic mass is formed. This is then moulded into the comb.

To the worker bees falls also the entire task of caring for and feeding the young larvae which hatch from the eggs laid by the queen. They produce from their bodies a white, dense liquid—veritable bee milk—and every larva in every comb cell must receive its due proportion of this food until it reaches full growth, when the worker bees seal it up in the cell. It then spins itself a silken cocoon and changes into a pupa, to emerge in due course as a perfect bee.

Other duties undertaken by the workers are the cleansing and scavenging of the hive, the establishment of a constant current of pure air through the hive by ranging themselves at the entrance and fanning their wings, mounting guard at the city gates to keep out strangers or robbers, and brewing the honey from the nectar brought in by the foraging bees. All these duties fall to the lot of the worker bees during the first fortnight of their lives, when they remain almost constantly at home. After that, the young worker gives up indoor duty and takes to the labour of the open fields. The duration of life of the worker bees may be anything from about seven weeks in summer time to as much as five or six months in the inactive close season. Mother bees have been known to persist for three or four years. The drones or male bees are produced in the late spring, live a merry, irresponsible life throughout the summer, their sole duty being to engage the young queens on their mating flight, and at summer's end meet with a violent death, the entire drone population of a hive being then killed off.

It has been said that the single mother bee in the hive is the parent of the whole colony, and here we are brought into touch with what is perhaps the most extraordinary fact in the whole wonderful bee economy. The mother bee seems to be endowed with the power of laying eggs which produce either drone or worker bees at will. In the active season she occupies nearly all her time in wandering over the combs and depositing in each vacant cell an egg. The drones, or male bees, are raised in slightly larger cells than the worker bees. The queen visits the two sizes of cells indiscriminately in the course of her busy day. But the bees ultimately emerging from the larger cells are invariably males, and those born in the small cells invariably turn out to be workers. The observer is left apparently with no other alternative but to believe that the mother bee can deposit either a male or worker egg at choice. To get light on this mystery, we must here examine

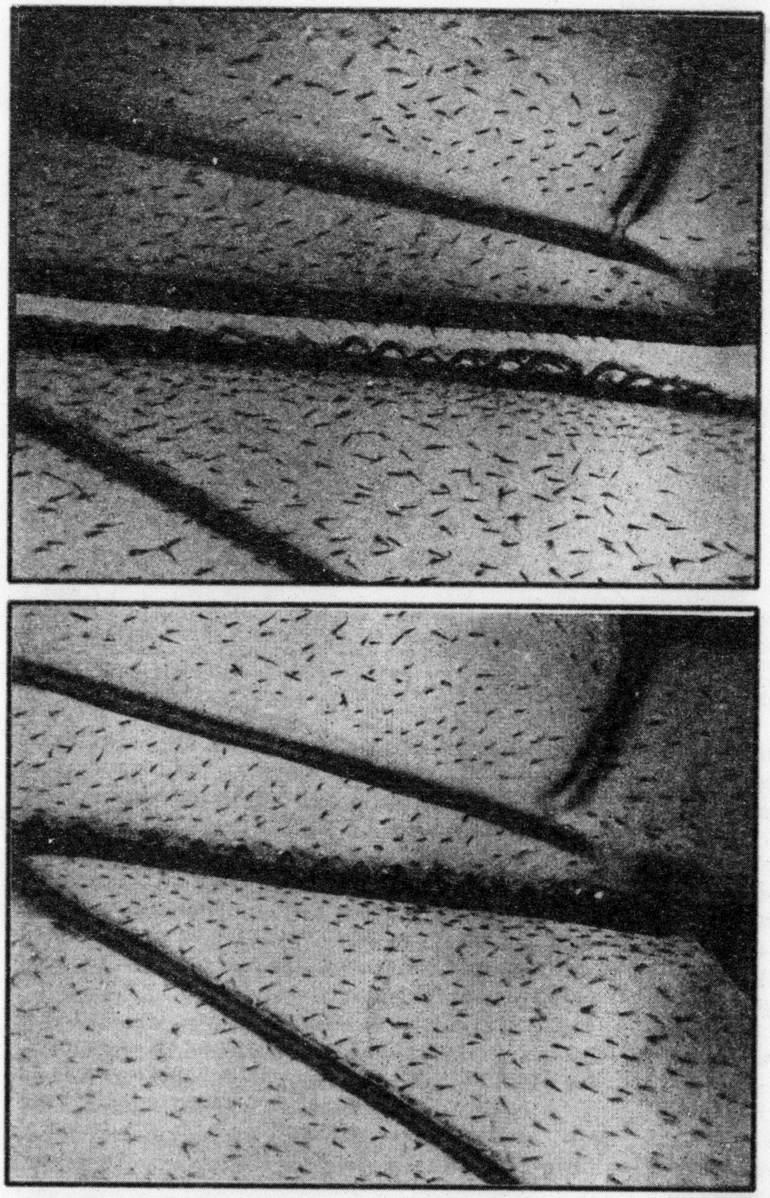

J. J. Ward

WONDERFUL WING MECHANISM FOR FOLDING AND FLYING

The bee must fold its wings within the limits of its own body measurement when entering cells. Therefore the wings must be divided for work and united for flight. The lower photograph shows the wing hooks on the posterior wings in operation, and the upper the wing hooks disengaged for the position when folded

the life-history of the mother bee and of the workers in conjunction. The fact is they are of one and the same sex, the fertile queen, however, being a fully developed female, while the little workers are females with their reproductive organs so undeveloped as to leave them practically neuters. Yet each results from identically the same egg. Extraordinary as this fact seems, the explanation is in part quite simple. The difference between the bodily equipment of the mother bee and that of the little sexless worker depends entirely upon treatment and environment while in the larval stage. The worker larva is raised in a small cell, and is supplied with a bare minimum of bee milk during its period of growth. The queen is raised in a cell many times larger, and is throughout supplied with an unlimited quantity of this predigested food of a specially rich kind. The queen larva literally lives up to the neck in this food, called by bee-keepers "royal jelly," for the whole of this first stage in her life.

But the result of this treatment is not only larger size and full development of the reproductive organs in the queen. Many other differences are brought about. If the queen were merely a bigger and better-equipped worker bee, the thing would be understandable. But this is not so. Queen and worker differ in many other important particulars than in degree. The shape of the body is different, the worker's being short and blunt, while that of the queen is longer, tapering to a fairly sharp point. The queen's sidelong jaws are notched, while the worker's jaws are smooth-edged. The queen's tongue is shorter than the worker's tongue. The queen possesses not the slightest trace of wax-generating organs, nor has she any pollen-carrying baskets on her thighs. She is generally of a strikingly different colour from the worker bee. Her sting is curved, and longer than the worker's, while the worker bee's sting is straight. Above all, the queen's mental equipment is vastly inferior to that of the little sex-atrophied worker bee. Shortly after her emergence from her royal cell, she makes one flight abroad for the purpose of her fertilisation by the drone; but thereafter, except when she goes off with a swarm, she spends her life entirely within the hive. She is fed by the worker bees, groomed by them, led by them over the combs on her interminable egg-laying rounds. She is, in fact, nothing but a living seed-barrow. That function she fulfils so completely that, during the height of the summer season, she will lay as many as 3,000 eggs a day and even more, giving out in 24 hours a weight of eggs equal to more than twice the weight of her whole body.

THE mother bee has indeed one strong mental attribute, and this forms one of the most striking dissimilarities between her and the worker bees. A queen bee is always ready for mortal combat with one of her own rank. It is always a duel to the death if two queens meet. On the other hand, the worker bees of a hive live and work together in perfect harmony.

It is hard to believe that all these differences between mother bee and workers are entirely due to super-feeding and unlimited room wherein to grow.

But that the two originate from eggs identical in character is provable by a very simple experiment which has often been repeated. A newly-laid egg from a worker cell has been placed in a queen cell, which is a comparatively large, acorn-shaped structure usually dependent from the edge or bottom of the comb. The egg found in the queen cell has at the time been transferred to the worker cell. The two have been allowed to hatch and grow to maturity. But the worker egg in the queen cell has invariably developed into a fully equipped queen bee, and the queen egg put into the worker cell has always produced an ordinary, stunted, sterile worker bee. The experiment can also be made with hatched larvae,

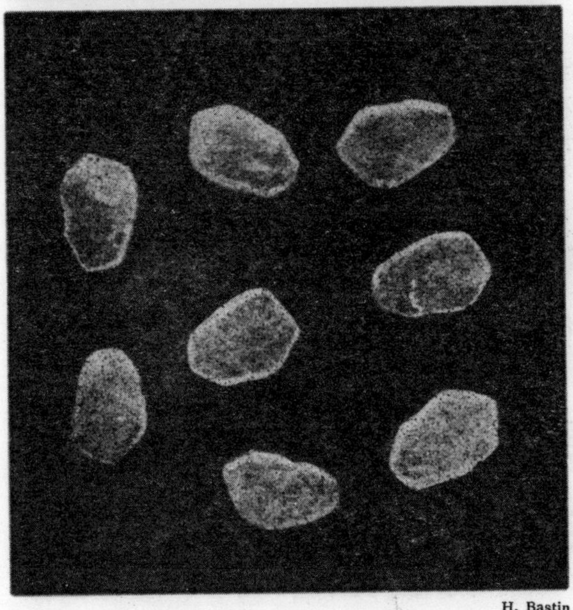

H. Bastin.

BEESWAX IN THE MAKING

When the honey-comb, which is formed of the substance called be swax, is to be constructed, the workers extrude wax particles from between the plates of their abdomens (top). The wax is at first hard (bottom), and it is then chewed to make it soft.

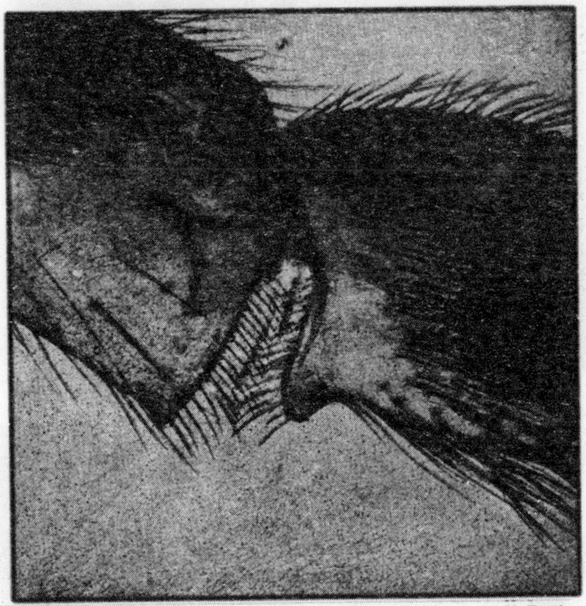

H. Bastin

BEE'S LEGS IN DETAIL

The hinder pair have each a joint (bottom), hollowed out and furnished with hair to form a basket for pollen. The top photograph shows two parts of the legs, the lower the pollen combs and the upper the pollen basket itself.

provided these are not more than three days old, and in every case the result has been the same.

The drones, or male bees, however, are derived from eggs differing vitally from the eggs which produce queens or worker bees. The mother bee must, and actually does, deposit a different kind of egg in the drone cells from that which she lays in the worker cells. Is this due to intelligent choice on her part? And if not, how is it brought about? It must be said at once that a definite answer to the question has still to be agreed upon between modern students of honey bee life. But the writer is of opinion that the matter can be explained in the following way

In order to understand the position, it is necessary here to go rather fully into the extraordinary system of propagation of species appertaining to hive life.

It is not a matter of the simple coition of the sexes. The mother bee of a hive meets the drone only once in her lifetime. The young virgin queen emerges from her cell, and spends a few days wandering about amidst the throng in the hive. The drones of her own hive take no notice of her, and, as far as is known, fertilisation of a queen by her own kindred never takes place, either within the hive or outside. Her single meeting with the drone occurs always in the open air, and, most probably, always at a distance from the home apiary.

There comes a day when the young virgin queen sets out upon the wonderful venture of her marriage flight. She breaks from the hive out into the sunshine, hovers for a few moments to mark the spot so that she will be able to find her way back again, then flies off straight across country swift and high. This occurs generally towards noon of a fine day when all the drones of the countryside are out and about, urged by the dominant instinct of their tribe. Their great, immensely powerful eyes soon detect the flying queen, and all and sundry at once give chase. The prize falls to the strongest and swiftest. A little later the young queen returns to her hive, and after a short time takes up her new duty of filling the brood-combs with eggs—work from which a whole new bee nation is now destined to arise.

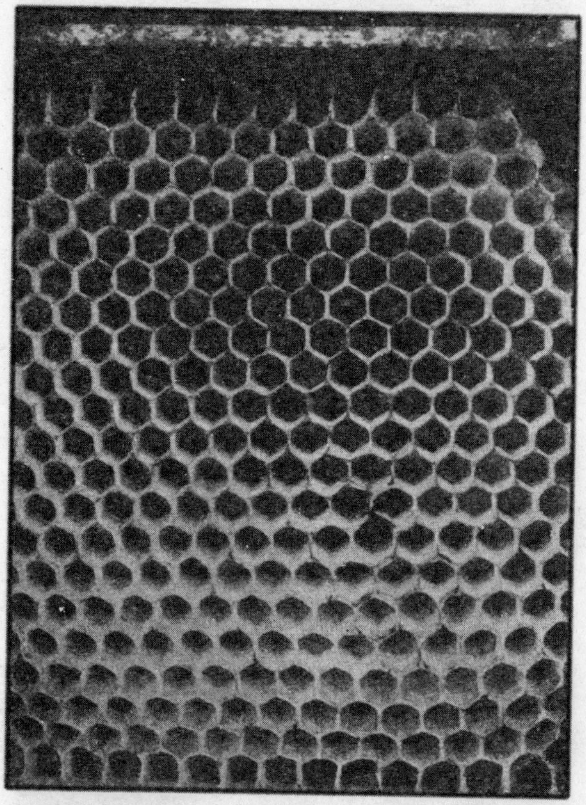

But if, from inclemency of weather at mating time, or from any mischance, the young virgin queen fails to have commerce with the drone, she is still capable of fulfilling part of the duties of a mother. An unmated queen is able to produce eggs which will hatch out into fully developed bees; but—and here is the significant point to mark—those eggs laid by a virgin queen bee will result in only drones, or males.

Now we must look into the question of what actually takes place when the foremost of the pursuing drones succeeds in overtaking the young queen during her marriage flight.

A normal coupling occurs. But the fertilising essence of the drone does not pass into the queen's ovaries. It merely fills a receptacle which exists for that purpose near the entrance to the oviduct or passage by which the eggs of the mother bee are extruded. Every egg laid by a queen bee remains unaffected as far as the drone is concerned, until the moment of its passing across the mouth of the spermathecal pouch just described. And then it either receives, or does not receive, the male fertilising germ. Those eggs which pass the spermathecal duct unimpregnated, result always in drones or male bees. And those which receive the germ develop invariably into female bees—queens or workers, according to the nature and amount of larval food subsequently supplied in the cells. From this it will

Sedgwick

BEES AT WORK IN THEIR THRIVING NURSERY

All day through the summer the worker bees are literally working themselves to death in the hive, for the average bee life is then about six weeks. Here we see one of the combs in a hive with the workers tending the breeding cells (bottom). The upper photograph shows a comb built except for one of the top corners.

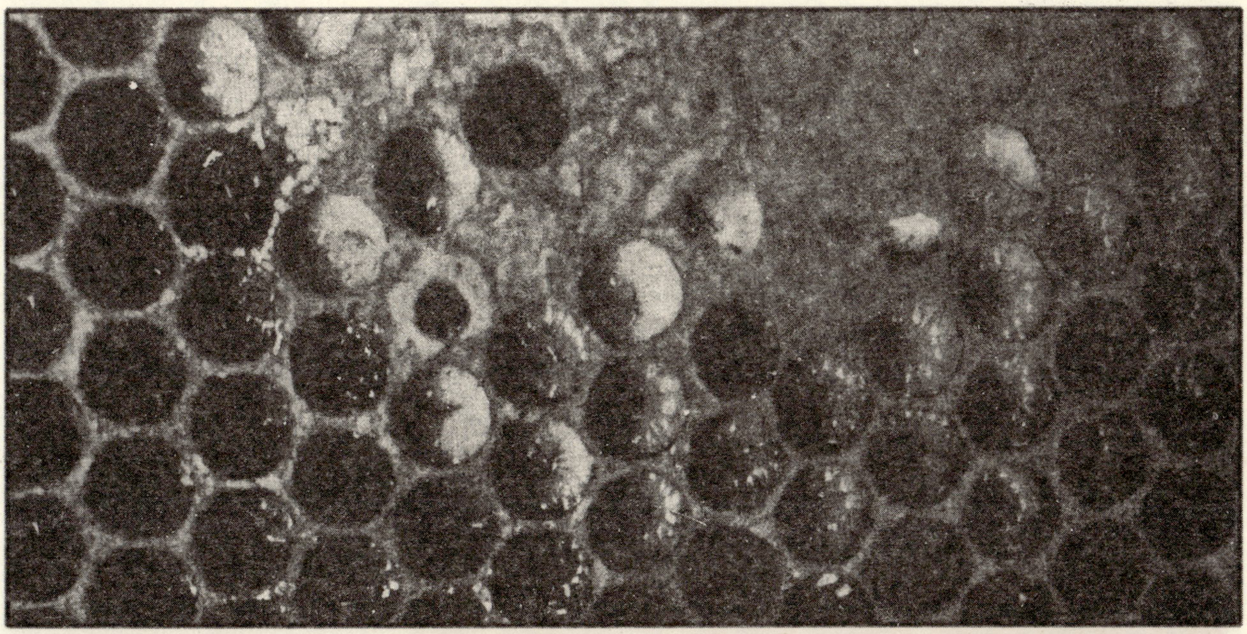

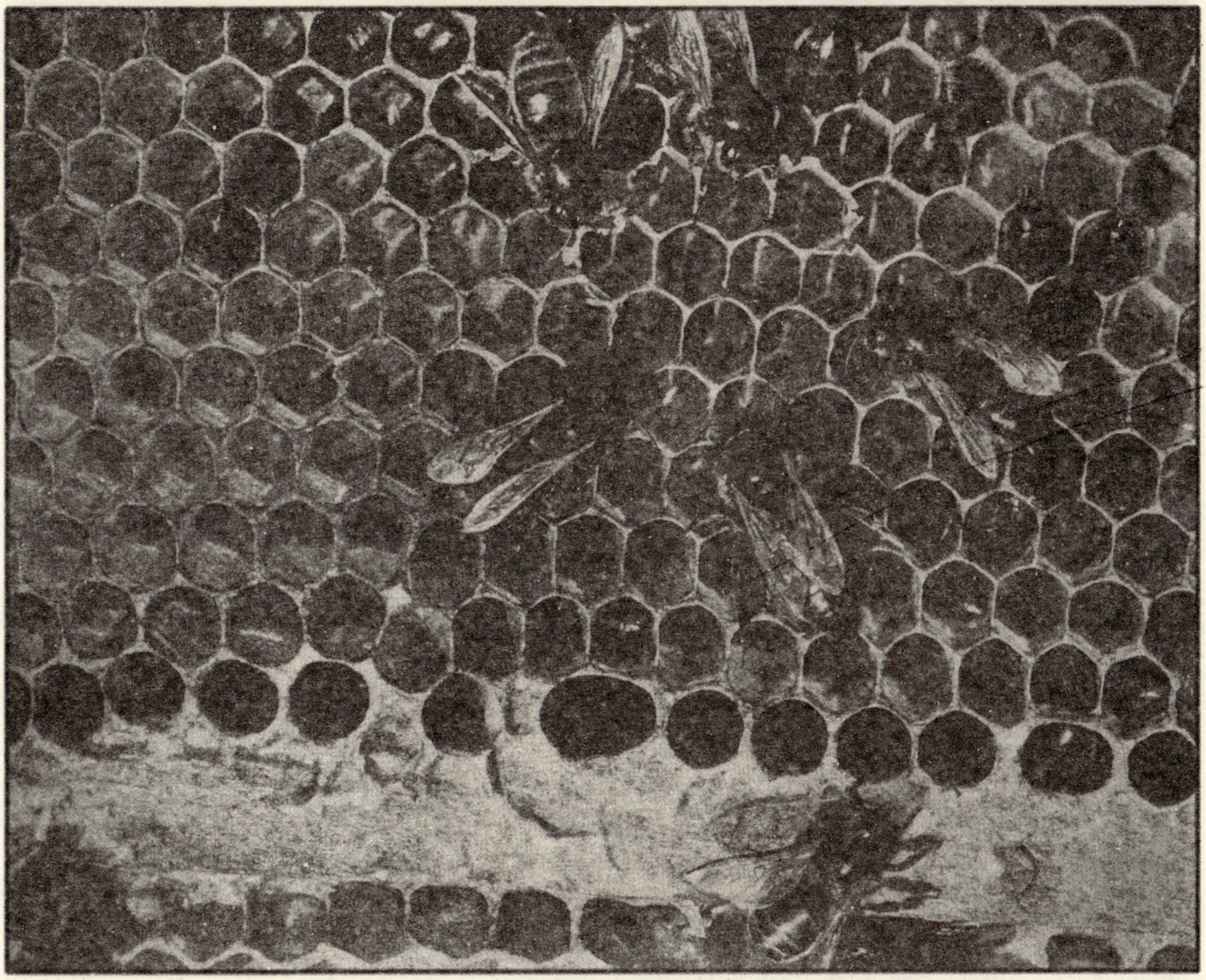

THE QUEEN BEE ON THE COMB AND THE GRUBS IN THEIR CELLS

Sedgwick

During the early summer the queen bee spends most of her time, not even pausing at night, in wandering over the combs (bottom) attended by servants who feed, clean and stroke her, depositing egg after egg in the cells. The term "queen" is really a misnomer. Mother bee is a more suitable name for this single individual of the hive is the mother of all its inhabitants. In the photograph she is the largest bee, and two of the attendants are beside her. The upper photograph shows some grubs half grown as they lie in their cells be at once seen that while the females of the honey bee race are derived from both mother and father, the males are the offspring of mother alone.

It has been necessary to go into these details at length because, unless they are known, the probability of what is now to be advanced cannot be appreciated. We have seen that a laying queen bee, passing across drone comb and worker comb in the course of her day's activities, stops at each empty cell, inserts her body therein, and deposits an egg, which we observe afterwards as a tiny white object like a microscopic grain of rice glued end-on to the base of the cell.

The drone comb cells measure about four to the inch, and the worker comb cells about five to the inch, measuring across the cells from side to side. Somehow or other only eggs which have had contact with the queen's spermathecal duct get into the small worker cells, and only eggs which have escaped that contact get into the larger drone cells. How is that state of things brought about?

In the opinion of the writer it is effected in a very simple, though none the less remarkable, way. When the queen inserts her body into the narrow worker-cell the abdomen assumes a necessarily straightened position when the egg is forced against the aperture of the spermatic receptacle, and thus becomes impregnated. But when the queen is using the larger, roomier drone cell no such constriction occurs. The body retains its normal, slightly curved posture, and the egg escapes untouched. If this be not a true explanation of the mystery, a mystery it will probably remain to the end of time.

In any general examination of this sort, however brief, into the communal life of the honey bee, interest cannot fail to be aroused at that master stroke of practical communism—the way in which the bee republics carry out the multiplication of individual colonies, as well as the multiplication of bees.

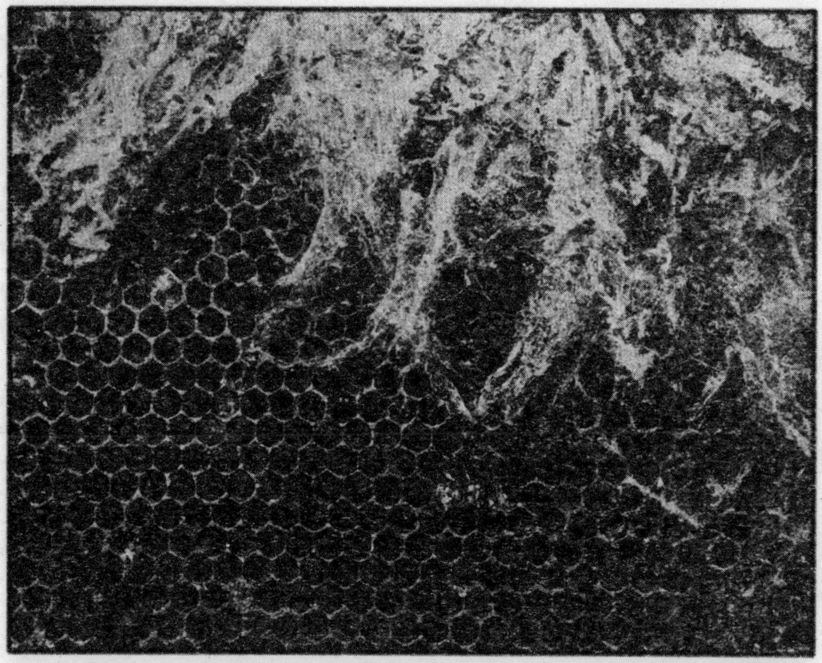

H. Bastin

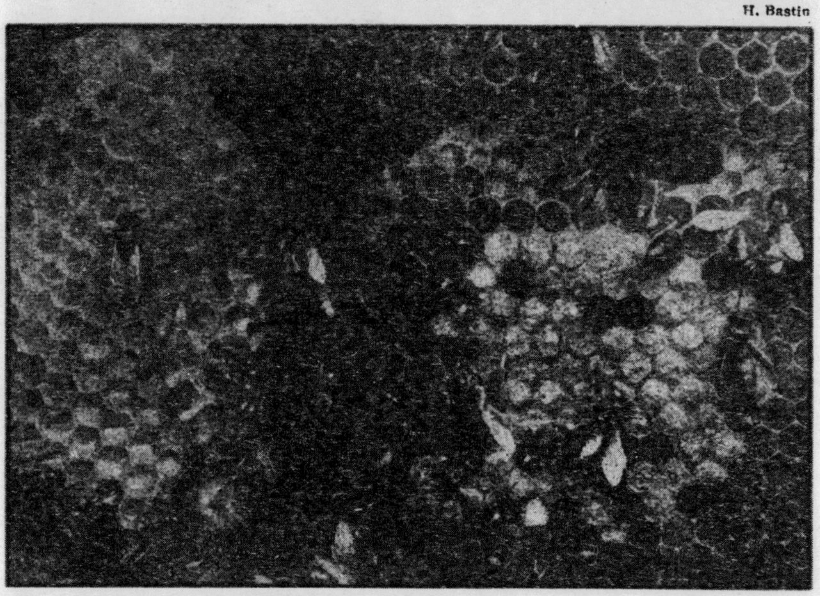

Sedgwick

ACCIDENT AND INVASION IN A BEE COMMUNITY

The life of a hive of bees is not, so to speak, all honey, for besides liability to various destructive diseases the community may at any time be attacked by various enemies. If the comb becomes damaged it is promptly mended (bottom), but a less easily remedied difficulty is the invasion of the wax moth caterpillars (top) which spin a web over the whole comb

EVERYONE knows that, in the height of summer, swarms leave the hives. A great number of the bees suddenly forsake the hive, fly about in a whirling, vociferating crowd for a few minutes, then gather together in a dense cluster somewhere hard by, generally upon a branch of a tree, where, unless interfered with by the beekeeper, the mass of bees will remain quiescent for the rest of the day and throughout the ensuing night, getting on the wing again some time during the following morning and then, as most usually happens, disappearing for good.

Without attempting an answer to the question, let us look into a bee-hive at some time before a swarm is due to emerge.

Up to that time, from the earliest days of spring, queen and worker bees have been straining every power together to produce a populous and prosperous state. There comes a day when the city is rich in labourers of all sorts. But as yet the population is wholly feminine. The males have been killed off in the foregoing autumn, because they are needed only for a few weeks in summer time, and the sternly utilitarian worker bee does not see why they should be sustained in idleness for the rest of the year. Now, however, the fiat goes forth that males are to be produced. The drone cells fill with eggs. Soon the deep, blustering voices begin to sound in the summer air. But something else comes to pass in the bee city. It is full now to the brim with winged people. It can expand no more. The common decision is reached—how, not the wisest among bee students has ever really divined—that the greater

The hive, finding itself overstocked with population, has sent out a certain proportion of its inhabitants to form a bee city for itself. In nature, this colony almost always establishes itself in some suitable place, most often a tree, at a considerable distance, as above described. But if the bee-keeper take the swarm, placing it in a hive of its own, and even stationing it close to the original home of the swarming bees, these bees will not return to their old hive. They have done with it, apparently forget all about it, and set themselves to furnish their new quarters as though the old home had never existed for them. In a month or two the colony will have established itself as a separate stock fully as large as the one from which it was derived.

Now what is this swarming procedure of the honey bees unless it be the carrying through of a policy of compulsory emigration—the adoption of a principle in citizen-science to which even the supposedly enlightened human race has not yet aspired?

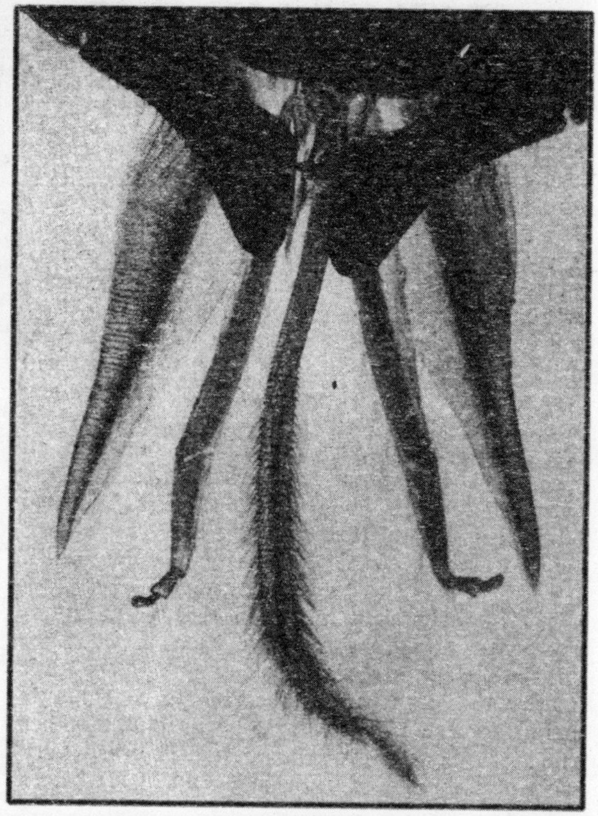

J. J. Ward

MOUTH PARTS AND PROBOSCIS OF WORKER

A bee's mouth (bottom) consists of outer and inner jaws, the tongue or proboscis, and on either side of it two labial palpi which form a case for the tongue when it is not in use. The tongue (top) has an end shaped like a spoon.

H. Bastin

TREASURE FROM A FOXGLOVE BELL

It is not always realized that a bee's body is covered with minute hairs. These catch the pollen as the insect moves about a flower. The pollen is then brushed off and moistened into a little pellet, and deposited in the pollen basket on the hind legs.

part of its inhabitants shall emigrate, to set up an entirely new commonwealth elsewhere.

What then happens cannot be too simply told, because it is so wonderful. At the time a hive begins its preparations for swarming, it may contain anything between 30,000 to double or treble that number of worker bees. Perhaps a little more than half of these, when the order is given to depart, will at once rush out of the hive to constitute the trekking host. The rest will remain busily engaged on the work of the city, going in and out, and, to all appearances, taking not the slightest notice of the frantic proceedings going on. It is difficult to explain this state of things on any other hypothesis than that every bee in the hive has long known which among them is to stay and which to go.

Be this as it may, it is certain that preparat ons tor the exit of the swarm have been in train for some time. The prospective colony must take with it a mother bee, or it will not be able to continue its separate life. And there must be no doubt of her fecundity. So, to give the outgoing bees every chance of making good in the independent life before them, it looks here as if the parent hive deliberately accepted a risk. Queen cells are now constructed, and young queens are raised. Several, indeed, may have come to tull maturity by the time, and even betore the time, the swarm issues. But they will not be permitted to emerge from their cells before the day chosen. Guards are placed over these cells, not only to prevent the young queens breaking out before they are wanted, but also to prevent the old queen getting at and destroying them, which she is always eager to do.

So things go on until the appointed day arrives for the departure of the swarm. And then it is the old queen, with her proved capability, known to be at the seasonal height of her egg-laying powers, who is sent forth with the swarm. The parent hive elects to remain queenless until one of the young virgin queens, who is now allowed her freedom, has survived the hazard of her impregnatory flight, and proved her claim to full motherhood. Then she is permitted to destroy all her still incarcerated rivals, the risk to the parent stock being now a thing overpast.

In the construction of the combs, either for the storage of honey and pollen or as nursery quarters for the young larvae, the honey bee displays perhaps an even more amazing ingenuity than is seen in any other of her works and ways.

And, first, as to the choice of building material. In beeswax, as we see it wrought up into comb, we have a substance fragile, delicate, light as air; and yet the combs are capable not only of supporting, but of suspending, a dead weight thirty times as great as their own. There was nothing obtainable in nature, we may be assured, of the same quality, or the wonderfully astute worker bees would have pressed it into their service. A bee-hive is a fortress with only one aperture as means of entrance and egress for all purposes. The space within is definitely limited. Economy of this enclosed area must rule every work. A storehouse had to be built. Cells for the nurture of the young bees had to be provided. The only way was to employ a material that, while of the strongest, would occupy the least space. This substance the bee finds in her own body in the wax which, for ductility, strength, and high resistance to heat, entirely surpasses any other material of its kind whatsoever that is known to science.

THE next stage in the problem of fitting up the interior of the bee dwelling was to determine the most suitable design for the structures needed, so that, while efficiency was secured, the utmost economy in space and material was also effected. On looking into a bee-hive it is seen that the interior is completely occupied by combs attached to the roof, and hanging down side by side to within a small distance of the floor-board, the combs being about a quarter of an inch apart throughout. Each comb consists of a double wall of cells hexagonal in shape, the cells being horizontally placed with their mouths opening outwards, and their bases meeting together in the centre of the comb. Thus one central vertical layer of wax is made to serve the purpose of closing the bottoms of all the cells in the comb, right and left.

It is evident that a considerable saving in material is here effected. In the first place, by making the cells six-sided in form, useless interstices between the cells, which would require to be filled with wax, are avoided. Then, in placing the two combined walls of cells back to back, not only is a saving made of the wax which would be needed for one entire set of cell bases, but the builders are enabled to reduce the width required for the whole comb. A glance at a piece of comb will immediately make this point clear. The bottoms of the cells will be seen to be closed not by a flat plate but by one of shallow pyramidal form, each cell base consisting of three diamond-shaped pieces joined together at their edges. This ingenious method of construction serves not only to add strength and rigidity to the comb, but it allows the pyramidal bases of the cells to be alternated, much as if the edges of two saws were fitted together. The result is that the total width of the comb, made up of two horizontal cells of the necessary length placed end to end, is visibly reduced, and a corresponding saving of material effected.

But by the adoption of this system of cell base construction, it is not only in the reduced width of the comb that saving in material is achieved; the weight of the entire structure can be safely lessened. If a piece of comb be held up against the light, it will be seen that the cells of one side do not coincide with the cells on the other. In a given cell, each of the three diamond-shaped plates of which its base is formed helps to close a different cell on the other side. The apex and three ribs of each hollow pyramidal cell base form foundation lines on which the cell walls on the other side of the comb are erected. Thus all cell walls throughout the comb rest on an arch, and all cell bottoms on a triplex girder. The result achieved by this astonishingly ingenious constructive system is that the quantity of material needed in the building of the comb can be reduced throughout to an absolute minimum. The thickness of the waxen cell walls and basal plates need be no more than will suffice to retain the honey or support the weight of the larvae. And this thickness has been found, by careful measurement of many combs, to be actually only the hundred-and-eightieth part of an inch. Is there anywhere, in the works of either nature or man, a more perfect example of the triumph of mind over matter?

Inevitably at this stage we are brought up against the old controversy as to the nature of the quality called instinct which is supposed alone to govern the lives of creatures other than man. The point comes up crucially in any and every attempt to deal with the marvellous commonwealth of honey bee life, and cannot be passed over here. It has been contended that there is nothing in the construction of the combs in a bee-hive, wonderful as it admittedly is, which warrants an assumption that the creatures building the combs are endowed with a higher order of intelligence than what is implied by the word Instinct. The fact that comb cells are found to be hexagonal, or six-sided, in shape, is asserted to be nothing out of the common, because, by a well-known law in nature, cylindrical or spherical objects brought closely together always tend to assume that form; and that, in fact, the cells of a honey-comb do so automatically by this law of mutual interference without any design on their makers' part. If a bottle be tightly filled with damp peas, it is pointed out, the peas, in swelling, will lose their round shape and take on a many-sided form.

Now this is quite true. But there is an essential difference between the swelling of the peas in a confined space, and the growth of the honey-comb, which takes place under perfectly free conditions. Moreover, one vital circumstance in the comparison is either overlooked or ignored. The peas are each separate, self-contained objects, and therefore capable of interfering with each other. But there is no such thing as a single, separate comb cell. Each hexagonal chamber in a comb shares its parts—its six enclosing sides and its threefold base—with no fewer than nine other such chambers with which it is in contiguity. And where there is no separate existence, there can be no mutual interference. The pressure theory, as accounting for the hexagonal shape of the comb cell, here obviously goes for nought.

But there is another circumstance in the method of construction of the comb by the bees, which, in itself, appears to be irrefragable evidence in favour of intelligent design rather than of what is called instinct, as actuating its construction. If a piece of comb which is in course of building be examined it will be seen that, while the upper part of the comb is finished with all its six-sided cells on each side complete to their rims, the extreme lower edge of the comb has as yet only the cell bases entirely laid in. This reveals the fact that, when comb-building, the bees make the six-sided bases of the cells first, erecting upon these, as upon a foundation, the hexagonal partition walls. Our own eyes prove to us that the hexagonal principle has existed in the minds of the builders, and is translated into fact in the making of the cell bases, before the walls are begun.

Yet, in disposing of this fallacious pressure theory in the construction of honey-comb, we only find that a greater mystery than ever has loomed above the horizon. For how did the astute little worker bee hit upon the hexagonal shape as the best for her comb? She could have made the cells cylindrical, but when fitted together in the comb these would have left useless interstices which would have had to have been filled up with wax. The hexagon has the double advantage of perfectly filling a plane surface, while being as nearly cylindrical as is needed to contain the round-bodied larvae. If we are not prepared to admit that it was some sort of attribute nearly allied to reason which led the honey bee to adopt the hexagonal form of cell we must at least concede something to those who feel that, in these days of increasing knowledge of the life of the bee and other creatures living in communities, the old, rigid dividing-line between reason and instinct is becoming more than a little shaky and ill-defined.

A. H. Willford

FEATHER DEVELOPMENT IN THE YOUNG BARN OWL, FROM NESTLING TO FLYING BIRD

When we come to examine the down on the young nestling we are reading part of the wonderful story of evolution. For the young bird, in the course of growth from embryo to fledgling, repeats the various stages of its development through the ages. And the story of this development goes back through thousands of centuries to the time when the growing tree of life divided one of its branches, the one to form the reptile and the other the birds. What were once characteristics of adult birds appear and are gradually discarded by each successive generation as it grows. On the left is a three-weeks-old bird, centre, a bird at six weeks, and right, at eight weeks. In other words, this is a repetition, in two months, of an aeon of development.

Chapter XXVI

The Childhood of Animals

By Frances Pitt

Author of "Woodland Creatures'

No stage in the life history of a wild creature is more interesting than its youth. Moreover, young animals, whether wild or domestic, are always a joy to watch, from a fluffy kitten playing with its mother's tail to a little seal sporting around its parent as they float in the sea.

Once, in the Shetlands, I was privileged to watch some seals and their young ones at home in a sheltered cove. They were the so-called common seal (*Phoca vitulina*), whose young ones are born in May, and as it was then the latter part of June, the youngsters were able to swim well. My friend and I lay upon the cliff top and gazed down into the little bay some hundreds of feet below. Great stacks of rock guarded the sanctuary, which was inaccessible to all save the wild creatures and the waves that rolled in, to crash in thunder upon a narrow beach. On this beach lay several seals with their pups beside them, and in the water were others, among them four old seals accompanied by young ones. It was very pretty to watch the little seals playing about their dams, as they all floated so contentedly in the green waves. One youngster kept playing about its mother's head, just like a puppy teasing a long-suffering old dog, but she paid no attention to it. Soon an old seal tried to take her baby ashore; she waited until a big wave came, when she let the breaker carry the two of them shorewards and wash them up the beach. The moment she felt ground beneath her she heaved and humped herself up the shingle out of reach of the succeeding wave, but her inexperienced child was not quick enough, and was carried back again. Turning round, the old seal saw what had happened, and quicker than can be told had dived in again. Once more she brought the little one shorewards, but again and again the baby was washed away. It seemed to enjoy playing in the waves, and it was apparent that it was having a useful lesson in water craft. Six times in all did that persevering mother endeavour to get her inexperienced pup up the beach, and at last it seemed to grasp the need to hurry, humping itself up the shingle at her side, to the shelter of a great black rock, where, high and dry, the old seal rolled on her side, and the baby, creeping up to her, proceeded to help itself to the refreshment which it no doubt needed. Thus they lay in the sunshine, unaware of the watchers so far above, and I thought about the way mother animals train their young.

We are accustomed to talking of animals as acting by instinct, and do not always realize the amount of education and experience the young animal has to acquire to fit it for the battle of life. Just as the human child has to go to school to acquire knowledge which will enable it to play its part in the world, so the wild creature, despite a considerable outfit of inherited impulses and predispositions to behave in a certain way under certain circumstances, has to learn how to get a living, and the best way to cope with the circumstances of life.

A chick, for example, when first hatched, has an inherited impulse to peck at anything which is bright enough to catch its eye, but it has no notion what is good to eat and what is not. It will as readily peck at a red thread as a red worm. It has to find out and learn from experience what is good to eat and what is not. The old hen does her best to teach her chicks what is good. When she finds any tasty bit she clucks to them, calls them to her, and by picking up and dropping the food, and again picking it up and holding it in her beak, demonstrates that it is good to eat. Thus chicks soon learn to discriminate, but there are many things they have to find out for themselves, such as the different kinds of grubs that are nice and those which are not. I offered some small chickens the black and yellow caterpillars of the magpie moth, which are usually avoided by insect-eating creatures, having evidently an objectionable taste. The chickens in their ignorance and innocence ran and picked them up, but they dropped them as hastily as they had seized them, and spent some minutes wiping their beaks. The caterpillars must have been very nasty, because the chicks remembered and refused them when offered the same larvae again two or three days later.

There was an otter cub that I saw experience a

E.N.A.

BEAR MEETS BEAR

When a small bear enters the world, usually in January or February, it is a complete replica of its parents on a small scale, unlike many young animals. Here we see a brown bear being introduced to an American black bear

Natural History N.Y

LITTLE KOALA AND ITS MOTHER

Australasia is the only haunt of the koala, which lives in the eucalyptus trees and carries its young when just born in a pouch like the kangaroo. Later the young one learns to cling to its mother's back, as we see.

similar unpleasant lesson. It was one of the two tame cubs which I had hand-reared and which was running free about the garden. The cub was turning over stones in search of slugs—a favourite amusement of the two otters—when she exposed a toad that had hidden itself beneath a brick. She was greatly delighted with her find, dragging the unfortunate toad from its hiding-place, and growling furiously at her sister when the latter came near, before carrying it off to play with and throw about. Of course, the toad immediately made use of its one and only defence, emitting that acid secretion which causes dogs such distress when incautious enough to pick a toad up. It was but a moment or two before the otter flung her treasure from her, and began to paw her muzzle and mouth. A second more and she was in a frantic state, rolling on the turf in great distress. It was some time before the pain subsided and her peace of mind was restored, but she never forgot the lesson, and in future handled toads with the greatest circumspection. Ever after a toad was taken by its toe, carried with care to the nearest water, and there washed until fit to eat.

In the otter, which is a remarkably intelligent animal, childhood lasts for some twelve months, during which the cubs go out fishing and hunting under the care of their mother, learning the ways of the river world under her tuition, and teaching themselves much river craft during their mad romps and wild games, for of all light-hearted cheerful youngsters otter cubs are the highest-spirited.

I know no more delightful sight than young otters at play, dashing through the water in porpoise-like dives, to catch one another up, face about as if in mortal anger, grab each other by the neck, and whirl over and over quicker than the eye can follow; only to part once more, and continue the mad chase from water to dry land, where one catches the other by the tail, pulls it up short, and the two tumble head over heels, to roll in a desperate embrace, before dashing back to the water, diving in, and splashing it far and wide as they roll, then turn and twirl till exhausted.

NEARLY all young animals play more or less, from the lambs in the springtime racing in the meadows and butting one another with lowered heads, to wolf cubs in their far-off forest den, or tiger cubs in the jungle. We can say that young animals are bubbling with the joy of life, and in considering the biological significance of play it may be added that it acts as a safety valve, letting off that superabundance of energy which is the prerogative of the young. The young creature, whether bird or mammal, wild animal or human child, is like a well-stoked steam engine; if it cannot let off steam sometimes something must burst, and play is the safety valve of the young animal; at

SLOTH BEAR WITH ITS BOTTLE

The will to live is well demonstrated in this photograph of a young sloth bear being artificially fed. The intense way in which it clings to the source of its food shows it determined already at this early age, to keep a grip on life the same time ensuring that everything shall run sweetly and be tuned up as perfectly as possible when it is called upon for the long steady work of maturity.

It may be taken as a rough rule that the more intelligent an animal is, the more playful and entertaining it is during its childhood; for example, the monkeys, especially the higher apes. And another rough rule is that the longer the average span of life of the individual, the longer it is reaching maturity, hence the longer its tutelage and the period it is dependent on its parents. Again the great apes are a good example, with the long childhood of the young and the dependence of the latter on the old ones. Taking both these rules together, we may add that the higher the creature the more important looms its childhood and early training, until we come to that of man, who starts life with the most meagre of instinctive outfits, and spends many years in preparation for maturity and the battle of life.

In contrast to man, the great apes, and other creatures with a long childhood, there are many animals in which the period of youth is reduced to a few weeks or months, and in which the time for play and education is likewise brief. Most of the birds, of course, grow up very quickly. The necessity of their hurried lives compels it. This does not allow them so much time to gain experience, but they have good outfits of instincts, so that in unexpected situations they are often able to act, as we do when we move habitually "without thinking"!

But what of the babyhood of birds? Well, first of all how it varies, from that of the helpless "squabs" of hedgerow birds, entirely dependent on the tender care of the old ones, to the self-sufficient chicks of the Australian "bush turkey" (the megapode, of which there are several species), which lays its eggs in a heap of decomposing vegetable matter, scratches this over the eggs, and leaves its treasures to be hatched in this natural incubator, taking no interest whatever in the welfare of its offspring. The latter, from the moment of hatching, can look after themselves, and never know what real childhood means.

How different the tender solicitude of most mother birds! If their chicks are only a short time beneath their care they, at any rate, spare neither love nor trouble while they have them, working their feathers to tatters to supply them with food. The most devoted of all are, I think, peahens. The peafowl not only takes the greatest care of her newly-hatched chicks, but, literally, keeps them beneath her maternal wing for an exceptionally long period. It is a most amusing, not to say ridiculous sight, to watch a peahen taking her nearly full-grown chicks up to roost at night. She flies up first, calling her family to follow, which the two or three youngsters hasten to do, when they creep to her side, cuddling close to her.

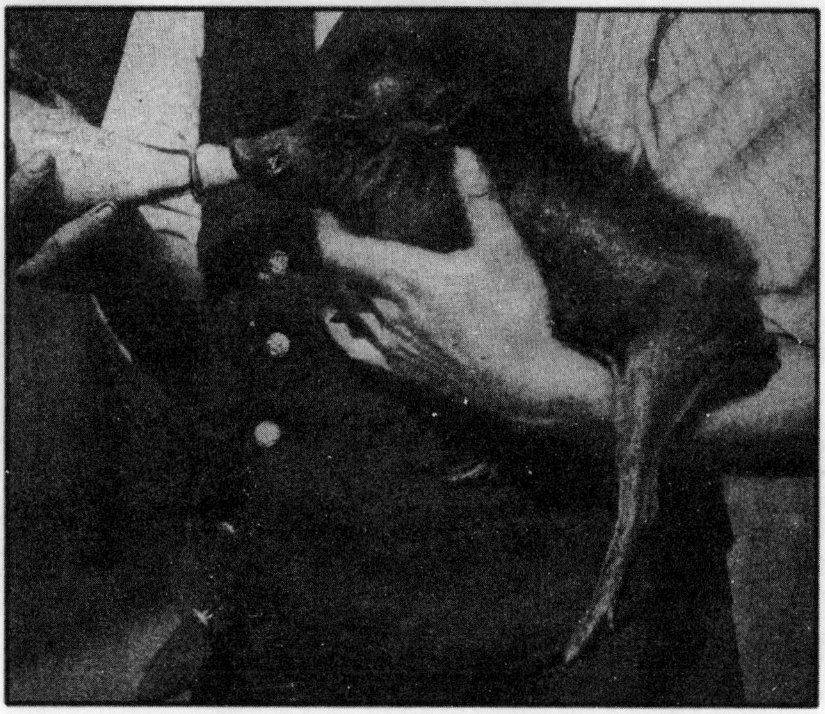

DRY-NURSING A WART HOG AND A LION CUB

Often it is necessary to bottle-feed young animals at the Zoo and here we have a young wart-hog (bottom) taking its nourishment from the keeper, while above is a lion cub gripping its bottle in a determined sort of way. Notice that the lion cub is striped when young like an adult tiger. These stripes gradually disappear with growth

Neville Kingston

BISON CALF AND A YOUNG LLAMA WITH THEIR MOTHERS

Among the characteristics of the bison—often quite wrongly given the name of an entirely different animal, the buffalo—is the shaggy head. This, it will be noticed, is not possessed by the calf, which in consequence exhibits quite a different physiognomy from that of its parent. The upper photograph in this page shows us a young llama which is very unlike its parent, but much more resembles a very long-legged kid Its colour, too, is different. In both these cases there is a contrast to animals like the bear, which resemble their parents from the start

Neville Kingston

WILD HORSE WITH A SHORT INFANCY AND PECCARY WITH A LONG ONE

Peccaries, like the wild pigs, go about in herds and are afraid of very little. Therefore the young can afford to remain helpless for two or three weeks. They are usually born in some fastness in rock or thicket, and there may be ten in a litter. The upper photograph shows a collared peccary from South America. In the lower photograph we have specimens of the Mongolian wild horse—a mare and her foal. Wild horses lead a nomad life and the foals must be able to follow their mothers almost at once and grow up quickly.

Neville Kingston

LEOPARD AND LION CUBS, DOCILE ONLY WHILE YOUNG

Maturity is reached by the leopard (bottom) in about two and a half years and by the lion (top) in about five years, that is to say that growth may continue until such a period after birth, although reproductive powers are developed earlier. The cubs of both these dangerous animals are naturally playful and affectionate in youth, and this state of things holds good in captivity. But when full grown the natural tendency to be fierce in an unfriendly world usually gets the better of their friendly feelings towards man at some time or other.

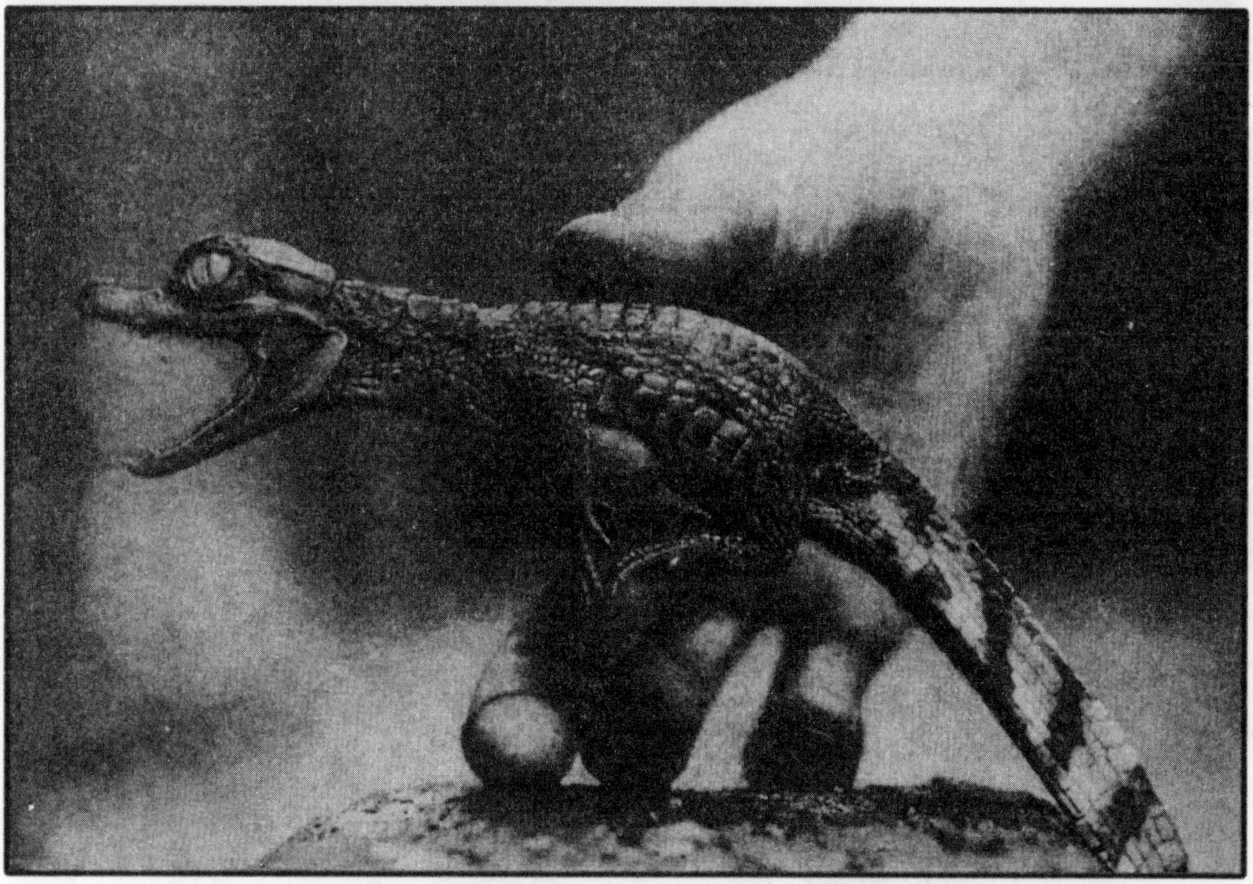

HOW ALLIGATORS AND SCORPIONS LOOK WHEN YOUNG

At ten months many animals are adult, and many more three parts grown. But the alligator is slower in development, for it is comparatively long lived, and has only reached the size we see here ten months after hatching. (The birth of a crocodile, the alligator's near relative, is the subject of the colour plate facing page 96.) Maternal care hardly seems to go with anything so unpleasant as a scorpion, yet the mother carries her young family about on her back (top) to which the little ones contrive to cling securely.

WHEN THEY ARE VERY YOUNG: BEAST AND BIRD CHILDHOOD

Young rabbits grow very quickly, and begin to breed and produce more and more rabbits at about the age of six months. All this is necessary for the continuance of the race of rabbits, which are a convenient form of food to so many beings from man to weasel. Three young ones appear in the lower left hand photograph. Hares (bottom right) take a little longer to grow than rabbits and are not properly adult for about fifteen months, though they are ready to pair in twelve. During the first year they are called leverets (a name derived, through the French, from the Latin word for a hare, while "hare" is from the Anglo-Saxon). The upper photographs show (top right) young willow warblers and (top left) infant thrushes.

is the same in the case of the puma, which suggests that these animals are descended from beasts that were spotted or mottled. A similar change is seen in certain young deer, which begin life beautifully dappled, and then lose their spots; but in their case it is possible the spotting may be an instance of protective adaptation, serving as camouflage when the dam has to leave her new-born fawn hidden in the undergrowth. Whether this latter argument accounts for the striped young of animals, such as the tapirs, is another question, but the prevalence of stripes and spots among these

one under either wing, she spreading her wings so as to cover her great offspring now almost as big as herself. This she does every night until the succeeding spring, and I have seen an old peahen trying thus to protect a big cockerel who was larger than herself. The childhood of the peacock is certainly a lengthy one compared with the brief one of the majority of birds, but it must not be forgotten that he takes some time to grow up, not acquiring his adult plumage until three years old, and only then developing the full glory of his eyed train. He lives, however, to a good old age, as is usually the case with creatures that are slow to reach maturity.

It is the same with many of the gulls, such as the great black-backed gull, which passes through several seasons as a grey-brown speckled bird before assuming the well-known white livery with dark mantle.

There is a common saying among biologists that the individual recapitulates the history of his race—that is, that in the course of his life he passes through the stages that have marked the evolution of his species. In many instances this recapitulation is blurred by the need of special adaptation of the young to their environment, but in other instances we can discern it more or less plainly, as in the grey-brown plumage of immature gulls and the speckled feathers of the young peacock. There is every ground for believing that in these cases we are getting glimpses of the ancestral plumage of the gull and of the peacock, that the snowy feathers of the one and the gorgeous-eyed plumes of the other have been evolved from quite ordinary beginnings.

This wearing of old-time clothes by the young is also seen in other and widely divergent species, even among the mammals, such as young lions and tigers. Here we have a queer contrast not only between youth and age, but between cubs of these comparatively nearly related animals. Tigers, as we all know, are handsomely striped, yet tiger cubs are born with plain coats, only developing their characteristic markings as they grow older. Now lions, with their plain jackets, start life with decorations, the baby lion bearing marks on its coat! It

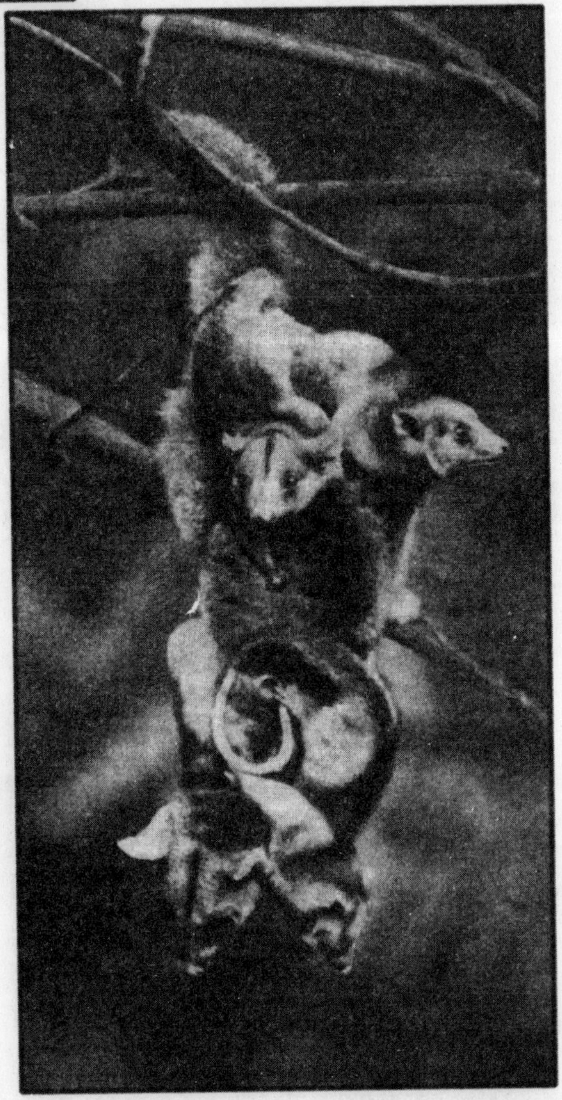

F. W. Bond

OPOSSUM AND HEDGEHOG FAMILIES

Such animals as take their young about with them have each found the best way of doing this. Below is an opossum, a liver in trees, with offspring securely clinging to its back Above is a hedgehog taking its six children for a walk.

Keystone

IBEX KID CONFINED IN NATURAL SURROUNDINGS, AND THE BLACKBOK

The young of ruminants or cud-chewing animals are subjected to a life where early activity is imperative. Such animals as the ibex (bottom) or the South African blackbok (top) have often to travel long distances for water and depend on their speed and agility in escaping from enemies. Also the feeding grounds have constantly to be changed and so we find that kids are soon able to follow their mothers among the rocks and crags of their mountain homes. The ibex, formerly common in the Alps, is found in Central Asia, Arabia and Abyssinia.

RHINOCEROS, ELEPHANT AND WALRUS IN THEIR YOUNG DAYS

'hile it has been naturally difficult to study the habits of the wild rhinoceros, it is known that the young take a long time to mature, and ecimens of six or seven years old have been seen still running with the mother and suckling. The elephant does not use its trunk for inking or feeding until it is some weeks old, and is active very soon after birth. But the mother uses her trunk constantly for stroking her little one. A young walrus (top) is easily tamed, for it is very dependent in early years, and in the wild state stays long with its mother.

creatures lends support to the idea. But the markings are lost as the young animals proceed with the business of growing up.

REVERTING to plumage changes in young birds, with their striking contrasts, often more striking than those of the spotted lion cub that becomes plain, or the plain tiger cub that becomes striped, what could be more surprising than the change of the dingy brown cygnet into the snowy swan. Here we almost certainly have a recapitulation of the history of the race, and of the evolution of a white bird from what was originally a grey-brown one. But does this equally apply to the case of the black swan, for here the facts are reversed? In the latter the cygnets are white to start with and become black as they grow older! Whether this is adaptation, or recapitulation, I cannot say. However, there are many and obvious instances of special adaptation among young birds, especially among the downy chicks of such species as nest in the open, whose young leave the nest soon after hatching. The young golden plover is a good example. This chick leaves its nursery as soon as its down is dry, following its parent out into the heathery waste, where danger stalks abroad in the shape of raven, hawk, fox, and wild cat. Here its only protection is invisibility, and thanks to its coloration it is invisible. When anything alarms the parent, she utters a danger cry, at the sound of which the chick crouches flat, remaining as motionless as a stone. The old bird flies off, trying to draw the enemy after her, even feigning injury to do so, but the little one still lies as if frozen, and with its perfect adaptation of colour and markings blends admirably with the ground where it rests.

I was once hunting for young golden plover, and had been doing so for half an hour, the distress of the old birds assuring me I was close upon the chicks, when I almost stepped on what I thought was a small tuft of green sphagnum. It looked like a bit of moss lit by sunlight, but just in time I realized it was a plover chick! Its lovely golden green and black-spotted down so exactly resembled the play of light and shade on moss that it was bound to be overlooked. It was the merest accident I had not overlooked it and stepped on it!

F. W. Bond

TENTACLED SNAKE WITH NEW-BORN OFFSPRING

Birth finds the snake already equipped for life, and, save in one or two species, there is no parental care devoted to it. The young are exact duplicates of their parents except that in some species the markings may vary. Altering conditions, especially of temperature, affect the growth of individuals so that it is practically impossible to judge the age of a snake, not in captivity, by its size. The photograph shows the young of the small tentacled snake shortly after birth, with their parent.

Neville Kingston

eat. The speculative elder can mark the dress, behaviour and inherited aptitudes of young creatures and thereby learn something of the history of the race; though he must not forget that special adaptation plays its part among young as well as elders, for natural selection is a force that bears equally on all ages, and even upon the joyous play of the carefree and delight fully irresponsible young wild animal.

The biological significance of play, as already hinted, is unquestionably pre paration for later life, and the tuning up of the brain and muscle ready for the calls that will then be made upon them. Hence it follows that play generally takes the form of mock com- bats, or mimic hunting, foreshadowing the later activities of the animal: yet in the young unsophisticated creature there is a certain element of joyousness, a bubbling over of vitality, which seem above and apart from such businesslike play

The whole question of this urge in adolescent animals to play is dealt with specifically in Chapter XVI entitled Playtime Among the Birds and Beasts which, with the present chapter, comprises an examination of an important phase of animal life. This phase is one which will go far to help us in the study of the wild children of Nature

It is the same with other chicks which resemble their surroundings; red-brown woodcock chicks among oak leaves; young gulls in iron-grey upon the grey rocks; snipe chicks dressed in tortoiseshell down to resemble the peaty-black mud of the bog; lapwing little ones in their grey and dark grey camouflage which just resembles the shadows between the herbage on the meadow; and many a score of other young birds that are specially dressed for hiding.

Then at the opposite extreme are young birds that begin life in holes or sheltered nests, and have no use for downy garb or camouflage effects, such as the naked squabs of the wood-peckers and kingfishers, which lie safely in the dark until they can assume the dress of maturity and fly forth into the world fully equipped as perfect or nearly perfect editions of their parents.

W. S. Berridge

DINGO PUP AND TIMBER WOLF CUBS

About six or seven to the litter is the general rule for dingo pups, the offspring of the wild dog of Australia. They are frequently born in hollow trees. Young timber wolves, natives of North America, undergo a course of maternal care, being educated to catch their food and beware of danger.

Thus, from this brief survey, it will be seen how various is the childhood of animals, from the long adolescence of a young elephant under its mother's anxious care, or that of a young chim-panzee in its family circle, each having to gain experience of the world and learn how to make its way in life, to the brief upbringing of a little bird, with its considerable outfit of inherited instincts, but which, even in its short childhood, has much to learn. The human child can certainly console himself, or herself, for long hours spent at lessons with the thought that every little creature has likewise to go to school: whether it be a young otter learning that toads are nasty, or a chick finding out that red thread is not good to eat.

W. S. Berridge

STOAT AND WEASEL CUNNINGLY CLAD ACCORDING TO THE SEASON'S CHANGE

Both upper and lower photographs on the left are of the stoat and those on the right of the weasel. The former is slightly larger than its near relative the weasel and, whether in its winter coat of white or in its dark summer fur, the tip of the tail is always black. In Scotland and the North of England the stoat turns white in winter, but this change becomes rarer as the more southern counties are reached. The animal is called the ermine when white. The weasel is the smallest and most ferocious, and also the most often seen of its race, and though small enough to invade the galleries of field-mice will attack a rabbit, which is far bigger than itself. In summer its coat is light yellowy brown with white underparts.

Chapter XXVII

Animals that Change their Clothes

By Dr. H. Graham Cannon

Professor of Zoology, Sheffield University

CLOTHES play a very important part in our lives. To be comfortable we must be properly clothed. If our clothes wear out we must buy new ones. If we grow out of them we must obtain a larger size. When winter comes we must put on our thicker garments and for each occasion there is an appropriate suit of clothing. Now, animals do not wear clothes, but, if we consider their skin, their shell or covering of feathers as their clothes, we shall see that a great many animals are capable of changing their clothes for different purposes and occasions, just as we are ourselves.

First comes the case where an animal's outer covering wears out. We are all familiar with the moulting of a dog. At certain seasons of the year the hairs become brittle and have to be replaced by new. Each hair grows out from a root at the bottom of a little pit in the skin. At the moulting season the hair ceases to grow, breaks off at its base inside the little pit and another new hair begins at once to grow out in its place. This pushes out the old hair, which then falls off. The old hairs are thus pushed out by the newly-growing ones, just as our own milk teeth are forced out by our permanent second set. A very striking example of moulting can be seen in the wild sheep, which are to be found in any big zoo. The wool is thrown off in thick, tangled patches, and gives the animal a very untidy appearance until it has all been cast and the animal stands all handsome in a spotless new woollen suit.

In some cases the hairs, which grow after a moult are quite different from those that they replace. For instance, the fur of a young tapir is marked with brown and white stripes running the length of the body, but after a year of life it moults and puts on a totally different coloured coat, black fore and aft and greyish in between. There are many other cases of animals which are born in a suit of baby clothes but which later put on their grown-up suit.

Among birds, moulting is perhaps even more marked than among mammals. The feathers of a bird are made for very hard wear and tear, and it is not surprising that they have to be replaced periodically. Moulting is usually a slow process, so that meanwhile the bird is not put out of action, but in some cases, as, for instance, in certain geese, the feathers fall so rapidly that, for a time, the birds are unable to fly. Now, birds, in addition to feathers, are covered in certain places by scales, for example, the legs of a fowl. Claws are modified scales, and in the grouse these are moulted and replaced by new just as are the feathers. The bill of the puffin is partly covered by scales, and the outer parts of these are shed annually.

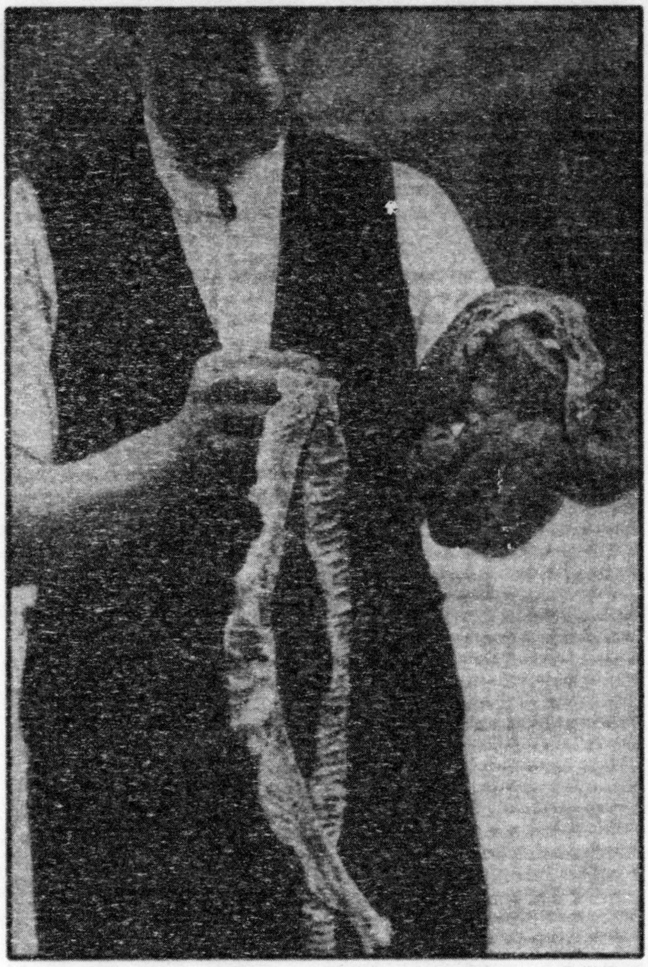

F. W. Bond

BULL SNAKE AND ITS OLD SUIT

Every now and then snakes have to shed their skins, and this they do by rubbing themselves against tree trunks or stones, when the skin splits at the mouth and the snake glides out in a new skin, incidentally turning the old one inside out in the process.

Up to now we have dealt with cases where the clothing wears out, but, more often than not, especially when we are young, we have to obtain new clothes because we have grown out of our old ones. This often happens in the animal world. In newts and frogs, for example, the outermost layer of skin consists of a few layers of flattened cells which are not, in the strict sense, living. They are horny, and not very elastic, and, as a result, the whole outer layer is cast periodically while the animal is in process of growing.

In the frog the skin usually splits down the back, while in the newt it splits round the mouth and the animal

TWO SHELLS BUT ONLY ONE CRAB

Growing too big for one's clothes always causes a certain amount of trouble, and the crab goes through a critical time when it needs a new suit. The complete outer covering, legs as well as shell, is cast so that we get the crab, as here, and a complete but empty replica beside it. But the new shell is very soft and no protection, and so the crab must hide in some sheltered nook for a day or two while the new armour hardens. In the photograph the empty shell is on the left and the specimen is of the edible crab.

wriggles out of its "shirt." The cast skin of a newt may sometimes be seen in an aquarium looking like a transparent ghost, but usually both frogs and newts are economical, and eat the skins as soon as ever they are cast.

SNAKES and lizards are covered with scales which are embedded in the skin. These are covered by a thin, transparent, horny layer which is shed or sloughed periodically, just as in the case of the newt. A difference must be noted here between this sloughing and the moulting of a bird. The scale of a lizard must be compared with a feather, in fact, some authorities consider that the bird's feather evolved from the reptilian scale. Now, in the case of a lizard, only the thin outer covering of the scale is shed while it is the whole feather that is cast at the time of a moult.

There is a very large group of animals called the Arthropoda, which includes all insects, spiders and crustacea—the shrimp and crab group. In these animals the whole outer covering has become hardened to form a rigid armour. In places it remains thin and flexible, so that the body and limbs can be moved by the muscles which are attached to its inner surface. In fact, the arthropoda can be considered as animals whose skeletons are on their outsides instead of deeply embedded in the body, as in us. The basis of this external skeleton is a substance called chitin, and it is produced or secreted by the actual skin, which lies immediately inside it. Except at the thin joints of the body it is often reinforced by salts of lime.

Now, in the case of these animals gradual growth as in a mammal or bird is obviously impossible. The result is that the life of, say, a crab, is simply a succession of moults, the crab in between the moults growing too large for its own shell. Between the moults the tissues of the body tend to increase in bulk, but cannot owing to the rigid shell, until at last the latter bursts and the body inside escapes clothed only in its real, thin, flexible skin. It immediately swells and begins to lay down once again on the outside of its skin the reinforcement of chalky chitin. The growth of an arthropod can thus be compared to walking up a flight of steps while the growth of a mammal is a process which rather resembles walking up a gradual slope.

Animals That Change Their Clothes

Immediately after moulting, the arthropod, especially a form with such a hard skeleton as a crab, is a very helpless creature. It has not only lost its protecting armour but has lost the rigid support for its muscles. It is not surprising then, that when a crab is about to moult, it discreetly retires into some narrow crevice where it is hidden from its enemies. These "soft" crabs are much sought after for bait, and can often be found under rocks sitting by the side of their cast-off suit, now too small.

In many of the arthropoda the young forms or larvae are totally different in appearance from the adult. For instance, the barnacle, which is found on rocks all round our coasts, is a small, limpet-shaped crustacean. It remains fixed throughout its adult life to the stone. Its larvae, however, are quite different. The egg of the barnacle hatches as a minute triangular larva called the nauplius, which swims about in the sea. After several moults, during which it increases in size but retains the characteristic triangular shape, it throws off its naupliar shell and emerges as a totally different shaped larva, the cypris larva, which looks like a minute mussel. It is a bivalve, that is, it has a pair of shells which fit together and enclose the rest of the body and limbs. This now comes back from the sea with the incoming tide and settles down by its front pair of legs on the rocks. Here the larvae remain for a while and can be seen high and dry between tide-marks scattered over the rocks as little oval, glistening bags among the older barnacles. When the tide comes up again the larva finally moults, throwing off its bivalve shell and emerging as a minute but perfect adult barnacle, condemned for the rest of its life to sit on the same piece of rock.

Now in these cases, when the nauplius changes to the cypris, or the cypris to the adult, the hard external shell serves as something more than mere clothing to the body. It serves as a box inside which the whole body can be reorganized. The cypris larva immediately after it has moulted from its previous naupliar stage fits its new outer chitinous covering as a hand fits a glove, but, once this shell has hardened the real cypris larva inside proceeds to reorganize itself into the form of the adult. Thus, if a cypris larva which has already settled down on the rocks is examined by means of microscopic sections it is found that inside the cypris shell there is folded up in a most complicated manner a perfect adult.

Many such stories could be told. The crab, for instance, goes through a similar series of changes of shape during its growth from egg to adult. The butterfly, another arthropod, is a very familiar example, but this case is somewhat different from the barnacle story. The egg of the butterfly hatches and the young caterpillar grows to its full size by a series of moults. It increases in size at each moult but does not perceptibly alter its shape. It then pupates, that is, it contracts, its skin hardens and it goes into an inactive resting stage called the chrysalis or pupa. Now, inside the pupal case a complete rebuilding of tissues takes place and the butterfly is formed, beautifully folded up, and finally after some time it emerges as the adult insect. In this case the change of body form is so great that the larva has to go into

Neville Kingston

F. Martin Duncan

HOW THE LOBSTER DISCARDS ITS OLD CLOTHES

Lobsters have to shed their tough armour plates just as crabs do. Such rigid coverings do not allow for more than a limited amount of growth. Our bottom photograph shows, not a lobster but the deserted shell of one as it was found one day on the floor of one of the tanks in the Aquarium at the London Zoological Gardens. Above is the lobster itself.

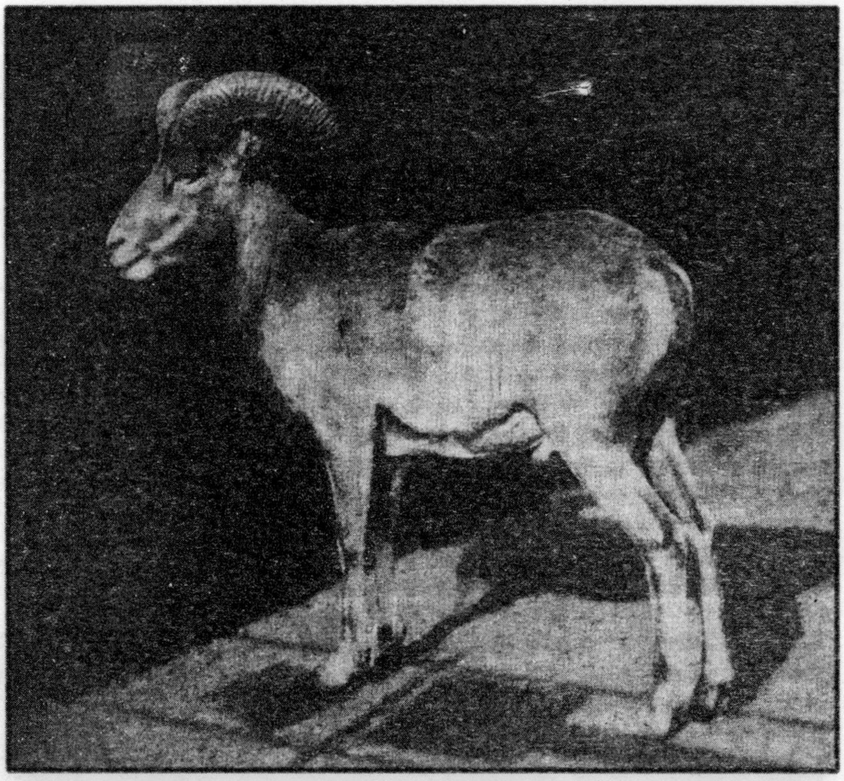

W. S. Berridge

CHANGING APPEARANCE OF THE MOUFFLON FROM CORSICA

This species of wild sheep is found only in the Mediterranean islands of Corsica and Sardinia. It lives in flocks in the very highest parts of the hills and is very timid. The winter coat (bottom) includes heavy festoons of hair on the chest, while in the summer a change suitable not only to the climate but the altered light conditions is made (top).

a resting stage in order to carry out the necessary alterations. It is like a ship going into dry dock for refitting. The machinery must be altered from the crawling mechanism of the caterpillar to the flying machine of the butterfly, and so the clothing of armour is used as a box in which the transformation can be carried out undisturbed.

But these are not the only reasons for the persistent moulting of the arthropod. Chitin, which, as we have already seen, forms the basis of the shell, is a complex compound of ammonia. Now substances distantly related to ammonia are being continually produced in the animal body as waste products resulting from its activity and, by some means or other, they must be thrown out or excreted from the body. The arthropod is an economical animal and uses them to assist in the production of its chitin. Moulting of an arthropod is one of its methods of excretion.

We have now considered cases of animals which change their clothes either because they have worn out or because they have become too small. It constantly happens that in some animals and birds the time taken for the clothes to wear out agrees closely with the seasons. A new coat grown in the spring is ready to be cast off at the beginning of the next winter. In these cases the winter coat may differ from the summer coat and, in fact, may be particularly suited to the cold snowy months of winter. Thus the stoat, which is brown in summer, sheds its coat for a pure white suit at the onset of winter. The mountain hare behaves in a similar manner. Strangely enough, in both these animals one small part of the body remains the same colour throughout winter and summer. In the stoat the tip of the tail and in the hare the tips of the ears remain black.

This seasonal change is not confined to mammals. It is

Animals That Change Their Clothes

Now while the protective value of these white winter coats from the point of view of camouflage may be questionable, there are many animals which have a remarkable power of adjusting their colour and general appearance to fit in with their surroundings. That is, they do not actually change their clothes but appear to do so.

Perhaps the most popular example is the African reptile, the chameleon. The marvellous way in which this creature can change its colour to harmonise with the foliage on which it is crawling is so well known that it has even given rise to fable in the story of the

W S Berridge

ARCTIC FOX READY FOR SUMMER AND WINTER WEATHER

Common all over the Artic regions is the small Arctic fox, which in the summer time (bottom) is black. In size it is inferior to the Common fox. The fur is exceptionally soft and thick, and when the winter arrives the whole coat turns white (top) and an extra coat of shorter fur is grown underneath. In the spring this under-fur comes off in patches

shown in many birds. The ptarmigan moults three times a year. During the summer it is brownish like the grouse, in the autumn it moults and develops a greyish plumage, while in the winter it turns white. This winter whiteness is obviously of use to the animal in making it inconspicuous against a background of snow, but the value of this camouflage must not be overrated. The country in which these animals occur is not always or completely covered with snow during the winter months and a white hare standing out on a ploughed field is as conspicuous as any animal can be. There is, however, another value in the white winter coat. Mammals and birds are warm blooded creatures, that is, their body temperature is higher than that of the surrounding air and is maintained practically constant throughout the year. Hence they always tend to lose heat into the surrounding atmosphere and, as this heat is lost, so more heat has to be generated from the food inside the body. Now a hot body loses heat much faster in a cold room than in a hot one. A kettle of hot water will cool much more quickly in an ice chest than in a hothouse. Hence mammals tend to lose heat more rapidly in the cold winter months than in the summer. A white object loses heat by radiation less rapidly than one of any other colour. Hence the value of the white coat is that it minimises the loss of heat by radiation and so efficiently economises the natural fuel of the body.

unfortunate chameleon which, when placed on a Scotch plaid either died or burst: but accounts differ. A better example, however, one which we can see in our own countryside, is the common frog. Whether it be found sitting at the bottom of a pond or hiding under the shelter of a rock it has usually managed to regulate its hue to resemble very closely the general tone of its surroundings. The common flatfish, the flounder, is another very good example; in fact, it is extremely difficult to make out a flounder lying quite still on a gravelly bottom. It is so expert that it can regulate its own mottling to fit in with the coarseness of the gravel or sand on which it is lying. If it is placed on a pure white background it will become very pale. If now, it is placed on a black background it darkens immediately. On a white background covered with black spots, provided the spots are not too large it even makes a fair attempt to copy the background.

How are these changes brought about? The colour of both frogs and fish is due to the presence in the skin of a large number of mobile cells containing pigment granules. The cells can expand or contract, can press nearer the surface or retract from it. The pigment may be black or red, yellow, or of an opaque whitish reflecting nature, and all the colour changes are brought about simply by the re-arrangement of these pigment-bearing cells. When the animal darkens the black cells expand or come nearer the surface and conversely retract when the animal blushes paler. In the case of the fish, there is certain evidence that the pigment cells are each controlled by a minute nerve, although this may not be the only control. Thus in a turbot in which a big nerve in the head region had been severed, the skin round the jaws supplied by that nerve remained permanently dark when the fish was placed on a white background. The severing of the nerve cut off the pigment cells from the stimuli which normally passed down that nerve from the brain, and hence no message reached them when the background was changed.

W. S. Berridge

Neville Kingston

HANDSOME ANIMALS GROWN UNSIGHTLY WHEN CHANGING THEIR CLOTHES

When the musk ox (top), which is found in the extreme north of Canada and Alaska, moults it presents a very sorry appearance with its old coat hanging in wretched tatters above the new spring suit. Similarly, when the Arctic fox (bottom) is in the transition stage between warm and cold outfits a once graceful animal looks really dejected. The new coat, dark grey to black, can be seen on the hind quarters, where the winter coat of white has quite gone. But the rest of the animal is still in the half-and-half stage.

What causes the stimuli to leave the brain? This finds an answer in the fact that a blinded fish shows no colour change. The chain of events seems to be that the background is reflected in the eye. This sends a message to the brain and, from this centre, appropriate messages are relayed through certain nerves direct to the pigment cells and bring about the colour adaptation. It must not be thought that this is the complete story; there are, undoubtedly, other ways in which the extraordinary colour responses may be brought about.

In the frog there is no definite evidence that the pigment cells are under a direct nervous control; in fact, experimental evidence suggests the reverse. The controlling mechanism here seems to be primarily through what is termed an 'internal secretion.' An internal secretion is a substance produced in one part of the body and carried by the blood stream to other parts where it produces some definite effect. Thus the thyroid gland produces a substance which affects growth in all parts of the body. There is another small gland called the pituitary body, which is situated at the base of the brain. In mammals the internal secretion of this gland also regulates growth, especially that of bones, but in the frog this same secretion is an important factor in the control of colour response. By a very delicate technique it is possible to remove the pituitary rudiment from a tadpole. An individual so treated remains permanently pale, but on injection of an extract of pituitary body it becomes at once much darker. The effect wears off after a time and the experiment can be repeated. An interesting point is that this effect can be produced whether the extract be obtained from the pituitary of a frog, a mammal, a bird or a fish.

W. S. Berridge

WILLOW GROUSE, WINTER AND SUMMER

This bird is the European, Asiatic and North American representative of the red grouse which is found only in Great Britain. The willow grouse changes its plumage in winter, when it is dove-white (bottom). In between the changes it is mottled (top)

ANOTHER group of animals showing very marked colour changes is the Crustacea. There is a very beautiful prawn called hippolyte which swims about among seaweeds and it is found that those caught above brown weeds are always reddish brown, while those from green weeds are bluish green. Further, if the green forms are kept in an aquarium with the brown weed they adjust their colour accordingly, usually at once. At night, fishing over the same weeds, all the prawns would be found to be a beautiful transparent blue. There is thus a daily change: during the day the prawns match their surroundings, but at dusk they put on their night clothes. The colour cells of a Crustacean are more complicated than those of a frog; they may contain pigment granules of more than one colour so that the same pigment cell, by spreading out within itself one set of granules and retracting another, may at one time appear, say, yellow, and at another, red. Further, these cells appear to be affected directly by the light falling on them. Thus, in a blinded prawn or in isolated pieces freshly cut from a prawn, the colour change is still obtained. However, if the prawns are kept continuously in a bright light they still show, to a certain extent, their normal nocturnal transparency. Thus, in addition to the direct effect of the light, there must be some daily rhythm in the animal or in the pigment cell itself which causes it daily to expand and nightly to contract.

There are other animals which can very rapidly change their appearance but in which the colour change may not be of any value as a camouflage. The octopus, for instance, if disturbed in an aquarium, may blush immediately a deep purple brown and then, as suddenly, lose its colour. It is difficult to say what is the value, if any, of this emotional colour change, but we must not forget that, before we can say that this is not some sort of camouflage, we must place ourselves in the position of the enemy or the prey of the octopus, and try and visualise what such a sudden change would look like when viewed underwater from the rocks among which the octopus lives.

In India there is a group of chameleon-like lizards called *Calotes* which show a very marked emotional colour change when fighting or courting. The male, when courting the female, develops a conspicuous dark patch on either cheek, but when he is driven off and captured the black spots are found to have disappeared. This case should not appear so strange to us when we remember that some of us may blush

W S. Berridge

FINDING NEW CLOTHES INSTEAD OF GROWING THEM

Since the hermit-crab is not protected on its hinder portions by a shell, it finds one deserted by its original owner and uses that. As it grows, successive shells are discarded for larger ones. Here are (bottom) a hermit-crab in a whelk shell and (top) a crab which has left one shell and is seeking another. During the transition stage the crab, whose body is very soft, is in a perilously undefended state.

furiously, or, maybe, go deadly white, when engaged in an exactly similar occupation.

These emotional colour changes lead on to those marvellous cases of breeding display found among birds. In many birds, the male, at breeding season, moults and develops a special breeding suit of feathers, and in this new garb attempts to attract the hen bird. But he is not content with merely a change of clothes. He parades and dances and strikes all sorts of grotesque attitudes so that, like a quick-change artist, by continually putting on new garbs he flatters and entices the female audience. The peacock, with its gorgeous tail spread and its head thrown back, appears a different bird from the graceful cock walking sedately. The cock bustard, at the height of its display, is hardly recognizable as a bird. Every feather seems to be turned over into the middle of its back, its throat is distended to an enormous bag, and its head is lost in the pillow of feathers on its back. The argus pheasant spreads out its wings and brings its tail forward so that together they form one broad sheet of beautiful feathers, but the bird's head and neck seem to have disappeared completely. Actually, the head is thrust back underneath and behind one of the wings, and the cock keeps one eye on the hen, staring through a minute gap left between the wing and the side of the body.

THESE gorgeous displays are not, however, always harmless parades in front of the hens. In the case of the black grouse the males gather together and combine their displays with actual fights in front of the usually uninterested hens. And this brings us finally to the cases of animals which put on special clothes for fighting purposes. In the ordinary deer, the male grows its magnificent antlers, and their only real use seems to be for fighting. At breeding seasons the males become very aggressive and fight each other, using the lower branches of the antlers to stab at their rivals. It must be admitted, however, that they are not very efficient weapons, and the hoofs seem to be much more effective. Each year the antlers grow anew and each year an extra branch or tine is added. Towards the end of the year the blood supply at the base of the antlers becomes cut off, with the result that this region becomes brittle and the whole antlers break off at the base.

At the outset we enumerated a few of the reasons why we change or obtain new clothes. From the cases we have so briefly considered it is evident that we are not supreme in our sartorial efforts. What is to some of us a matter of grave importance and, to most of us, of great expense, is to the other animals part of their everyday life. They may be provided annually with one, two or even more suits, or they may possess a coat which outrivals the wardrobe of the most expert quick-change artist. With them their clothing is part of themselves, a legacy from their ancestors.

This legacy benefits different animals in different ways. One changes its clothes because it needs to harmonise with its surroundings for the avoiding of hungry enemies; another because it has grown too big for its old suit, and yet another for the purpose of adapting its natural covering to the seasonal variations of the weather or to the needs of courtship. Each of these changes is a marvel, both in purpose and in method, of the wonderful animal world.

Facing page 280 (Vol. II)

F. Schensky

COMPASS MEDUSA DELICATELY UNDULATES THROUGH THE SUMMER SEA

Chapter XXVIII

The Wonder of the Seashore

By Mrs. E. W. Sexton

The Marine Biological Laboratory, Plymouth

The seashore—where the earth and ocean meet—the very name is a magic casement opening on a wonderland of life and beauty.

Life is the most striking character of the shore. Nowhere else in the whole world is it to be found in such infinite variety and such amazing profusion as on this narrow strip of land between tide marks, and yet nowhere else are the conditions so complex and the problems of existence so acute.

Take any typical shore animal, such, for instance, as a sponge which is fixed to the rock, or a sea anemone capable only of limited movement, or even a shore crab able to move about on the beach, and innumerable questions spring up. How is it possible for them to endure daily the twice recurring ebb and flow of the tide, the exposure to the sun, wind, dust or frost, followed by complete submersion? Land animals breathe dry air, sea animals breathe air dissolved in water, but the shore population has to spend half its time on land and half in the sea. What kind of breathing apparatus can such creatures have?

How can they guard themselves against wave shock? Sometimes the tide "comes silent flooding in," but what about the gales when the waves break in thunder and hurl huge boulders on the shore and against the cliffs? How can any living thing escape then?

And again, how can they protect themselves from questing enemies, the birds which hunt on the shore when the tide is out, and the voracious fishes when the tide is in? Then the question of food: how can stationary animals get it, and how can they propagate their kind and ensure a start in life for their young? There is no end to the problems, and the more we explore them the more wonders are revealed.

C. J. King

BARNACLES CAST UP BY THE TIDE

Attaching itself by a long fleshy stalk to any driftwood it can find the barnacle feeds by protruding certain feathery feelers and drawing in the minute organisms with which the sea is filled. In old days sailing ships were much handicapped by the thousands of barnacles on their bottoms

We have in the United Kingdom, compared with the total area, a coastline of great length, about 7,906 miles. The tidal zone alone—that is, the part lying between high and low water marks—has been estimated at 620,000 acres. As on the land so in the sea, the life of the animal is primarily dependent on plant life. The food of the fishes is really, though indirectly, derived from the floating "sea meadows," immense fields consisting of untold millions of microscopic plants drifted along by the winds and currents near the surface of the sea. And on the shore, wherever a foothold can be found, are the fixed seaweeds, each type of shore with its own particular community of plants, and each community with its associated animals seeking food and shelter. The vegetable feeders, like limpets and periwinkles, live directly on the weeds, and the predatory animals follow to feed on the vegetarians. It is the same in the sea meadows—where incredible numbers of tiny animals, copepods, little crabs, jellyfishes, baby sponges, newly-hatched fishes, swim and feed among the plants; following these come the bigger fishes, and then the birds, taking toll of all on the shore and in the sea. The microscopic floating life of the sea is known as plankton, from a Greek word meaning 'that which is drifted.'

Following the tide down from high water mark to the water's edge it is interesting to note the different series or "zones" of plants and associated

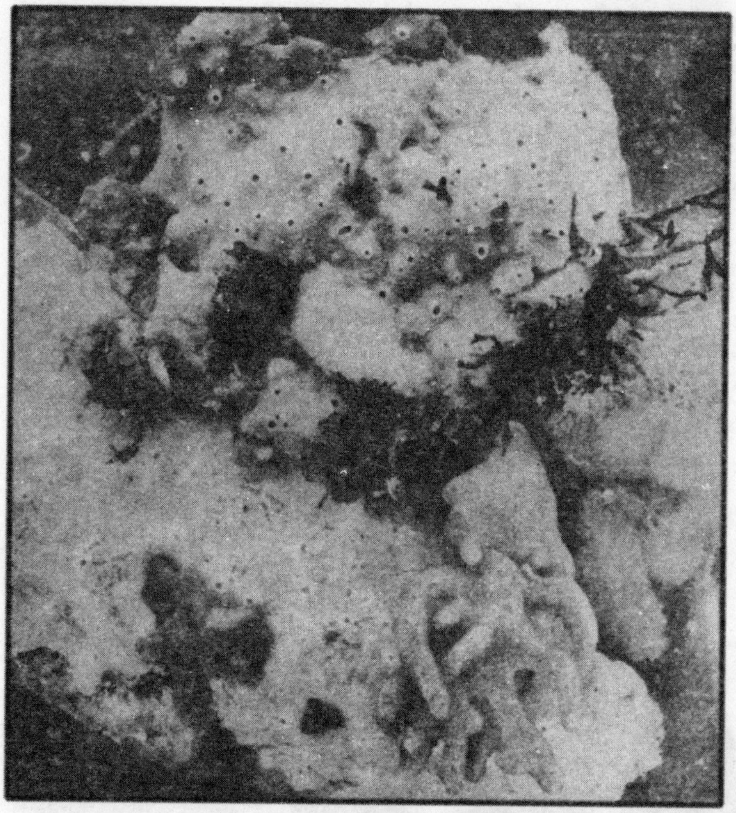

animals that we meet. First, on the highest part of the beach, only reached by spring tides and spray, the channelled wrack (*Pelvetia*) is the predominating seaweed. Here most of the inhabitants, limpets, periwinkles, dogwinkles and acorn barnacles, are protected by heavy solid shells and wonderful devices for shutting themselves in and keeping moist till the tide returns. The limpet, for example, makes a pit or "scar" in the rock, the exact size of its shell, and settles tightly into it; the periwinkle has a little shutter or lid with which it closes the entrance to its home; while the acorn barnacle builds a hinged roof to its house and shuts it as the tide ebbs.

Lower down the shore many varieties of seaweed flourish, but the prevailing types are the *Fucaceae*, such as the flatwrack; bladderwrack, with numbers of round air bladders in pairs on the fronds; knobbed-wrack, paler and with larger bladders; and notched-wrack. This "fucus zone" merges into the oarweed or laminaria zone, which is only uncovered during low spring tides. The name of tangles is often applied to laminaria. A vast number of settlers inhabit these regions—sponges, sea firs, anemones, corals, starfishes, bristleworms, crabs, prawns, shore fishes—all different in structure, habits, weapons and ways, but alike in having life histories so varied and amazing as to read like fairy-tales. It seems incredible, for instance, to find a microscopic swimming animal about the size of a pin's head, settling down and starting a colony, and a colony, moreover, in which division of labour is carried to a remarkable extent, with different members allotted to different duties. Yet this is what the tiny hedgehog hydroid (*Hydractinia*) does. Its colonies are usually made on shells inhabited by a hermit crab and, with a lens, the individual polyps can be watched at work; some are employed in catching the food and distributing it to the colony; some, much smaller, produce and carry the eggs; while others around the margin guard the whole, coiling and uncoiling and lashing to and fro when touched.

Again, who would expect to find a mutual benefit association between creatures so diverse as a crab, a worm and an anemone, to give one instance?

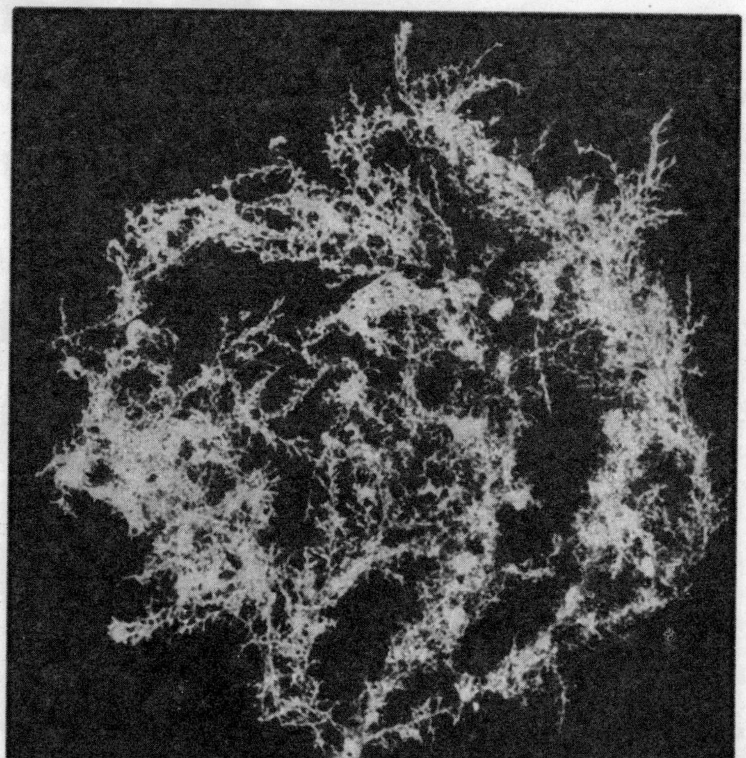

C. F. Gill

FOUND AT LOW TIDE: HYDROIDS & CRUMB-OF-BREAD SPONGE

On rocky shores we may discover a substance looking something like buff-coloured bread. This is the crumb-of-bread sponge which is a colony of minute creatures living and getting their food in this their wonderfully made commonwealth. The hydroids (bottom) also live in a colony which we may find attached to some seaweed.

Schensky

SEA ANEMONES, LOVELY FLOWERS OF THE SEASHORE, BLOOMING UNDER WATER

It is lucky for the observer that the sea anemone prefers to live in clear water fastened to hard, insoluble rock, because in these conditions its beautiful form and colour are seen to the very best advantage. Between high and low water marks, upon a shore which is covered with rocks, many of the loveliest varieties are to be found in the pools, growing like brilliant flowers in a submarine rock garden. We have a particularly beautiful form in the thick-horned anemone (bottom), while the upper photograph shows the widowed anemone.

Schensky

CURIOUS SEA CUCUMBER THAT DISCARDS PART OF ITSELF WHEN FOOD IS SCARCE

Among the rocks along the south coast of England lurks the sea cucumber, and it may be discovered when the tide is low. Its appearance is as deceptive as its name, for although it looks like a sea plant it is really allied to the sea urchin. It has a soft body, which it contracts and expands to move itself about, and about the mouth are ten branches, or stalks, ending in leafy-looking appendages. From the body protrude a number of sucker feet. The sea cucumber is remarkably adaptable to circumstances, for if it encounters a food shortage it very readily parts with portions of itself—the stalks about its mouth, the mouth itself, and even the intestines—only to replace them when times are better again.

The photographs by F. Schensky in this and other pages are reproduced by permission of Dr. Werner Klinkhardt, Leipzig, from Animal and Plant Life in the North Sea, published by the Biological Station, Helgoland

Schensky

SEA ANEMONES GROWING AS THOUGH IN A SUBMARINE ROCK GARDEN

Among the crevices of rocks, especially along the coasts of Dorset, Devonshire and Cornwall, this beautiful anemone, the sea-pink, may be found clinging a short way above the low water mark. It has a way of flattening itself against the background so that it much resembles merely a soft incrustation of the rock to which it is fixed. The colour varies from salmon pink to orange brown, and perfectly white specimens also occur. Its tall stalk or body and its many short and delicate tentacles give it the appearance of some strange flower in a rock garden.

The hermit crab lives in an empty whelk shell, with a worm tenant inside and a big stinging anemone outside. The crab's gain in the partnership is evident. It is a dainty morsel for a fish, but with the anemone prepared to shoot out masses of long, stinging threads on the slightest provocation it would take a braver enemy than a fish to risk an attack. The anemone and the worm profit by sharing the crab's meals, the worm gliding down the big claw and helping itself as the crab tears up the food, while the anemone bends down and collects its food behind the crab.

And then—to take another "fairy-tale"—what of the extraordinary method called "alternation of generations" employed by some of the stationary animals, by means of which they spread their young and give them a better chance in a new district? One of the hydroids (*Syncoryne*) lives fixed on rocks and seaweeds, and produces buds in the form of tiny jellyfishes or swimming bells, which swim up to the surface of the sea, there to be carried away by waves and currents, sometimes to a considerable distance before they scatter their eggs. The young which hatch from the eggs soon go down to settle on the bottom and develop into the fixed, tree-like hydroid again. And so the alternation continues, one generation, fixed, gives rise to the swimming bells, the next, swimming, produces the fixed again.

This same method can be seen in a small bristle-worm (*Procerastea*) living with the syncoryne, or rather, at the syncoryne's expense. The worm looks like an inch of yellow sewing cotton, but although so small, it has fifty to sixty segments in its body, and a head with long feelers, four red eyes and a sharp proboscis. It makes a thin transparent tube on the stem of the hydroid just behind a polyp, and there lies quietly until the polyp has fed, then as soon as a good meal has been collected, it darts out its proboscis and pumps away the whole of the food, leaving an empty, hungry polyp to collect a fresh supply for itself.

Procerastea multiplies in several ways. The parent worm may develop a "bud," which will eventually grow into a complete worm with long swimming bristles, very different in appearance from the parent. The bud breaks away when mature

SEA-URCHIN, ONE OF NATURE'S MARVELS OF CONSTRUCTION

The shell of the sea-urchin is wonderfully made, being built up of a number of interlocked plates which are protected by spines, so that the shell has rather the appearance of a hedgehog. The sea-urchin moves along the sea bottom, mouth downwards, by means of its spines, which it can move, or by a number of tubes, like those seen on the underside of a starfish, which protrude between the spines. In some large specimens, which may measure twelve inches round, there are nearly 5,000 spines. The mouth is furnished with five teeth.

and swims up to the surface, where the eggs are scattered and the young hatched. These sink down to the bottom and grow like the first generation.

But procerastea has another and much more remarkable way of reproducing itself. It can break itself up into fragments, and then grow new heads and new tails to all the pieces! A similar process of regeneration can be seen in many of the larger shore animals. Anemones sometimes tear at the base as they move over rocks, and these torn pieces grow into complete anemones again. Starfishes are able, in a difficulty, to throw off one or more of their arms, and then grow new ones to replace them. The "comet" starfish is only a common starfish which has lost or thrown off four of its arms, and left itself with one long arm and the disc. A brittle star can break into fragments, leaving only the disc, and even then can grow afresh. Crabs and lobsters, too, are often found with one or both of the big claws missing, either broken in one of their frequent battles, or injured and thrown off by the animals themselves. At the time of the next moult, a new limb is grown.

We cannot go very far on the beach without meeting the ubiquitous sponges, encrusting and sometimes eating away the rocks, and growing everywhere, even on crabs and oysters. Sponges are very low down in the scale of life, and look so much like vegetable growths that they were not recognized as animals for a long time. They begin life as tiny, free-swimming larvae, but soon settle down and start growing colonies. Each individual is shaped like a hollow vase with a large hole at the top, and numerous small holes or pores round the sides. Through these pores a current of water enters, bringing food, and air to breathe and flowing out again by way of the large hole. A remarkable arrangement of cells in the body of the sponge generates and maintains this current, each cell having a fine whiplash hair which keeps up a constant beating in the direction of the outgoing stream. The velocity of this current in some species has been recorded as two or three inches a second. The movement can be easily seen on putting a piece of living sponge in a dish of sea water and dropping a little powdered chalk over one of the holes in this unexpectedly energetic organism.

Schensky

BED OF OYSTERS AND THE STRANGE WARTY SNAIL

When the Romans reached Britain, one ot the things which commended the island to them was its excellent oysters. Since then oysters have been extensively cultivated, but while a wild or native oyster reaches full size in about four years, the oysters on artificial beds take about three years more to reach maturity. Each one produces from 600,000 to 1,800,000 eggs every season. Above is a warty snail with the broad white band of spawn that it produces. This is of most delicate beauty and measures several times the snail's own length.

Schensky

SCAVENGERS OF THE COAST THAT SOMETIMES GET LEFT BY THE TIDE

Any decomposing flesh is eaten hungrily by the lobster, who thus performs a most useful service in helping to prevent the shore from being littered with putrefying matter. Big lobsters keep to the deep water, but occasionally one may be encountered in some rock pool where it has become temporarily imprisoned by the outflowing of the tide. But small lobsters may be quite often seen, sometimes entirely out of the water in some cranny. The lobster swims backwards by doubling itself up suddenly and giving a forward sweep to its tail.

Schensky

HOW SPIDER AND HERMIT CRABS PROTECT THEMSELVES

Our lower photograph shows one of the strange spider crabs, seen on the left. It is very clever at disguising itself so as to be almost invisible. Next to it is a hermit crab, which also forms the subject of the upper photograph. This crab is also called the soldier crab, and it has received these names because, having no shell of its own, it must go and find one belonging to something else, such as a winkle or a limpet. When it has grown out of its first small shell it is liable to covet one belonging to another crab and to fight for possession.

Sponges make a framework of minute needle-like spicules of lime or silica, or have a horny skeleton like the bath sponge. That and their disagreeable smell render them distasteful to most other animals. The commonest British species is the crumb-of-bread sponge (*Halichondria*), so called because when cut through it is seen to be full of holes like well-risen bread. Its sharp, curved spicules are made of silica, each about a two-hundredth of an inch long and one five-thousandth of an inch wide. It varies in colour, green, brown, or yellow, and in shape from a thin encrusting layer to large masses several inches thick. Another sponge, well known because of the immense destruction it causes, is the boring sponge (*Cliona*). It penetrates limestone rocks, causing them to crumble away, and is a perfect pest on oyster-beds, burrowing into and perforating the shells.

One of the most beautiful sights of the seashore is a rock pool, with its fairy world of miniature forests and living flowers. It is the home of the polyps, loveliest of shore inhabitants, and here in their full perfection we find the tiny, fragile, delicately-tinted builders of the sea fir and coral colonies, as well as the bright, flower-like sea anemones.

THE " miniature forests " of the sea firs were long thought to be seaweeds, and it was only about a hundred years ago that a doubt arose as to their plant nature. Then the name of zoophyte was given, meaning " animal-plant." Later they were recognized as true animals and called hydroids (from their resemblance to the fresh water polyp hydra), and the plant structure was seen to be merely a horny protective sheath covering the stems and forming the little cups at the sides of the branches in which the polyps dwell. From these they rise as the tide flows and expand their tentacles in the search for the minute creatures on which they feed, and into them they retreat as the water ebbs again. A living sea fir colony is a revelation of beauty, its branches starred with crystal polyps each " at the diamond door of his house in a rainbow frill." Some are phosphorescent, like the obelia on oarweeds (*Laminaria*), which glows with a bright, opal-green light when the fronds stir in the darkness. There are innumerable species of hydroids ranging from an inch to a foot in height.

All the polyps, hydroids, jellyfishes, anemones and corals, are armed with very powerful weapons in the shape of batteries of stinging cells, which can be shot out with great force, to paralyse the prey or stun an attacking enemy.

In the beadlet anemone, the commonest of the British anemones, the stinging batteries can be easily seen behind the tentacles as a circle or necklace of shining blue beads, each bead containing a battery. Some anemones have additional weapons, called *acontia*, long threads crowded with sting cells which they shoot out in masses from the mouth and sides. The threads are as much as six inches long in the parasitic anemone, so it is not to be wondered at that fishes give a wide berth to the hermit crab which carries one of these protectors. Fortunately the stinging-barbs are too weak to be able to penetrate the human skin.

SEA anemones are a never-ending source of interest. Anemones are found in the greatest numbers in places like estuaries, where the currents bring a continual supply of food, for, in spite of the dainty appearance of these creatures their appetites are enormous and nothing comes amiss to them. They differ in habits ; the beadlet wanders over the rocks even up to high water mark, where it can be found under the seaweed closed into a small red lump waiting the return of the tide ; the daisy anemone likes the rocks ; the vestlet (*Cerianthus*) makes its " vest " or coat-covering in the mud ; while the hermit crab anemones choose a shell in which a hermit crab lives. The big whitish Parasitic anemone (*Adamsia polypus*) is usually associated with the large hermit or soldier crab (*Eupagurus Bernhardus*) ; the velvet cloak (*Adamsia palliata*) which looks like white velvet spotted with red, lives with the little hermit (*Eupagurus Prideauxi*). Tiny brilliant Jewel anemones (*Corynactis*) can be found about low water mark in clusters on the vertical faces of the rocks, scintillating in all shades of colour, from rose, lilac, emerald, orange and scarlet to pearly white.

Little sea-gooseberries, or iridescent fireglobes, are sometimes to be found in rock pools, brought in by the tide. They look like delicate transparent globes, colourless when at rest, but gleaming iridescence as they swim. The two long tentacles are seen sweeping the sea for prey, but they can be drawn right back into two deep pits in the body. Each tentacle is covered with sticky cells called " glue cells " or " lasso cells " which contain spiral threads and catch the prey by entangling it.

WE cannot go far between tide marks without meeting some of the Echinoderm family, which get their expressive name " prickly skins " from the spines, or prickles, of carbonate of lime. The sea-urchin, feather-stars, and brittle-stars have hard skeletons of lime ; starfishes a limy framework covered with a leathery skin ; while the sea-cucumbers have soft bodies, but numerous limy prickles in their skins which make them rough to the touch. Anyone picking up the prickly ball of a sea-urchin or the flat five-rayed starfish might well wonder how such helpless-looking creatures could possibly move, but put them down in a rock pool and in a few minutes the riddle solves itself. Down the sides of the urchin and under each ray of the starfish hundreds and hundreds of tiny delicate tubes appear, stretching out and feeling round until they touch something, to which they fix themselves by the " suckers " on their tips. These are the tube-feet which are kept filled with water by mechanism inside the animal, and can be pushed out or drawn back at will.

The sand-urchin, which makes a burrow eight or nine inches below the sand, has another use for some of the tube-feet round its mouth. These are of

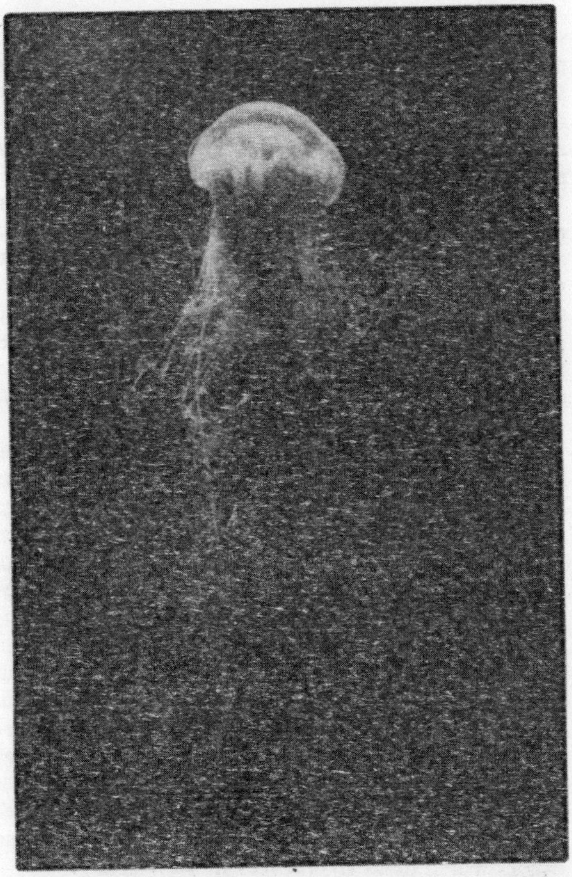

Schensky

MEDUSA OF THE SEA

This beautiful jellyfish is the cornflower-medusa. The medusas are named after Medusa, the Gorgon, whom Perseus, the Greek hero, slew. The long tentacles of the jellyfish are reminiscent of the Gorgon's hair, which consisted of snakes.

enormous length and can be pushed up to the surface where they collect minute creatures for food.

The edible sea-urchin's masses of eggs are used for food in many places; one female it is calculated will produce twenty million eggs in a year. The small purple-tipped urchin is common under stones, but difficult to find owing to its curious habit of dressing itself in bits of seaweeds and shells. Besides the "five-fingers" starfish common on the beach, we can find the red and white sun-star with twelve or fifteen rays; the big five-pointed scarlet cushion-star; the starlet (*Asterina*) or small greenish-yellow cushion-star, in the rock pools; brittle-stars and sand-stars, called snake-tails from their wriggling snakelike movements; and occasionally a feather-star cast up by the tide, with its arms covered with rosy plumes.

The sea worms are often despised because they are "worms" but it is only a case of "giving a dog a bad name." To anyone with patience enough to watch them as they come out of their hiding places their gorgeous colouring and graceful movements will be a delight. It is not possible to give any idea of these in a photograph. It seems difficult to believe that the sea-mouse, or gold-mouse (*Aphrodite*) is a worm at all when we look at its mouse-coloured furry back, and the fans of iridescent hairs on its feet, shining green and gold like a humming bird's plumage.

Another, the fan worm (*Myxicola*) makes a gelatinous tube in which it lives, embedded in the mud, expanding its beautiful crown of feathery gill-filaments above the entrance in search of food, but shrinking back at the least alarm.

Many worms build dwellings for themselves. The quill worm (*Hyalinoecia*) makes a transparent tube just like a goose quill about three or four inches long, with valves inside, which allow of its coming out but prevent other worms entering. The sand mason (*Terebella*) collects sand grains, mixes them with mucus, and uses its lips as trowels to plaster them in position. Its tubes stick straight up, about an inch above the surface, each with a fringe of branching sandy threads at the end. The common lob or lugworm (*Arenicola*), used as bait by fishermen, forms U-shaped burrows one to two feet deep, and works down by swallowing the sand in the same way as earthworms do, throwing out the castings at one of the tube entrances. As many as three to four millions have been found on a mile of beach between tide marks. The boring worm (*Polydora*), about half an inch long, is a most destructive creature, which bores U-shaped tunnels or burrows in rocks or oyster shells. If danger threatens at one end of its tunnel it can turn round and escape by the other.

Everyone knows the Crustaceans, partly because so many of them, like crabs, lobsters, prawns and shrimps, are used for food, and partly because it is impossible to spend any time on the shore without

C. F. Gill

MARINE WORM

There are many worms of the sea that are not at all worm-like in appearance, and this one, which frequents the shore, is the fan worm. Most worms possess a nervous system, and these have a digestive tube and a mouth provided with horny jaws

Mussel

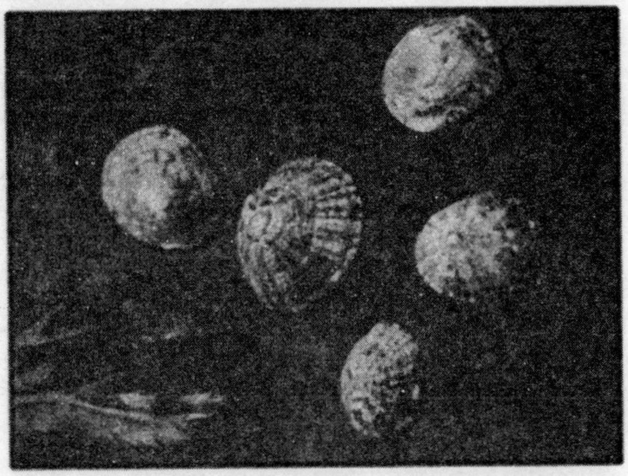

Limpets

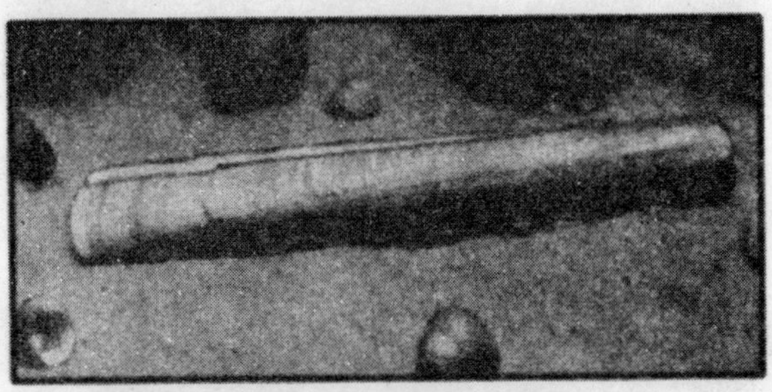

Razor shell

Whelk

SEA SHELLS OF THE SHORE

Shell fish form one of the staple articles of diet for fish as well as man. All those seen here may be found on beach or rock along the coast of Britain. The most curious looking is the shell of the razor fish, which spends its life buried upright some distance down in the sand. The photographs are by S. C. Johnson.

some of the family intruding themselves on our notice, the sandhoppers on the sand, or the agile shore crabs on the shingle. They go through several changes before full growth is reached, and as the hard skin or shell will not allow of stretching to meet the growth each change must be prefaced by a moult.

Prawns (*Leander*) and shrimps (*Crangon*) are often confused one with the other, although they are really quite different, and live in different localities, the prawn in rocky places and the shrimps on sandy shores. The prawn has a long beak or horn in front, and both pairs of its feelers are long and delicate, while the shrimp has a very short horn and large scales at the base of its second pair of feelers, which it uses as shovels in burying itself when alarmed.

The chameleon prawns (*Hippolyte*) change their colour in a very striking way, red, green, or brown, to match the seaweeds among which they dwell, and even vary their markings, blotches, bars, or fine lines, according to the character of their surroundings. Innumerable crabs are to be met with on the shore. The common shore crab may be seen scurrying along amongst the shingle, the large purple swimming crab hiding among the stones, small edible crabs tucking in their legs and shamming death as soon as they are disturbed, whilst deep in some dark hole a lobster may be discovered guarding its chosen home. Some have very curious habits, like the hermits, which live in empty mollusc shells, the pea crabs, which hide in the shell of a living mussel, and others which dress themselves in seaweeds.

The whole shape of the hermit has been altered by its mode of life, the tail end being soft and twisted spirally so as to fit into the coils of the shell it inhabits. The soft-bodied little pea crab (*Pinnotheres*), which lives as a parasite inside oysters and mussels, sharing their food, gains shelter from its enemies, and neither harms its host nor is harmed by it.

SANDHOPPERS (*Talitrus*) are almost too well known, leaping and springing in the sand, or making shallow burrows in it. A near relative of theirs, the spectre shrimp (*Caprella*), can be found on the hydroids and small seaweeds, moving about like a looper caterpillar, or holding by its hind legs and standing straight out just as a stick insect does. Another relative, the Jassa, is found all over the world, building its tiny nests among the growths on rocks, buoys or piers, or on the bottom of ships.

The oarfooted crustaceans or copepods form a very important part of the " chain of life " in the sea. They feed on the microscopic plant life, and in their turn provide food for the fishes. Curlfooted crustaceans of various kinds occur in immense numbers. One, the rock barnacle (*Balanus*), often called acorn barnacle, because of the fancied resemblance to an acorn, covers the rocks in many places with sheets of tiny white cones. Each cone consists of six hard limy plates fastened to the rock, and has a hole at the top roofed over with a lid made of four movable valves. The noise made by the continual movement of the thousands and thousands of little roofs can be clearly heard if one listens ; 2,940 barnacles have been counted on a square foot of rock.

A young barnacle begins life as a swimming larva about the size of a pin's head, eventually settling down in a suitable spot and there cementing itself, head downwards. It changes its shape and develops the curling tendril feet with which it sweeps the water for food as if with casting nets.

DRIFTWOOD covered with ship barnacles (*Lepas anatifera* ; goose-bearing) is often cast up by the tide. A young ship barnacle begins life similarly to the acorn barnacle, but settles on some floating object and grows a long fleshy stalk, sometimes more than a foot in length, with the body at the end. The shell is made of five limy plates, and through the slit-like opening the feathery curling tendrils are constantly pushed out. Ship barnacles are often called goose barnacles because of the old belief that they were the young of the bernicle or barnacle goose. Probably from being so often found on drifting wood, they were supposed to grow on trees, to drop off into the water and to hatch as young geese.

Molluscs are found everywhere in vast numbers, in spite of the legions of enemies which pursue them. Some, like the sea slugs and the octopus and cuttle-fishes, have no shell ; others make shells for themselves of carbonate of lime, and it is interesting to note how the shape, size and solidity of the shell vary with the conditions in which the builder lives. A cockle has developed a stout shell, almost globular in shape, to resist the pressure of the shifting sand as it burrows near the surface. A razor shell, on the other hand, driving a deeper burrow, has a long, flat shell to allow of a more rapid passage through the sand. Dogwinkles (*Purpura*), which live on a coast exposed to heavy breakers, make shorter and much more solid shells than the dogwinkles which live in sheltered places.

" To cling like a limpet " is a common saying, and it has been calculated that a force of seventy pounds is needed to move this small resisting object from a rock, but birds know that if they take a limpet unawares a sudden blow will dislodge it. Limpets, strange as it may seem, have a strong " homing " instinct, and always return to their pits or " scars " after a foraging expedition by following the track made on the outward journey. The noise they make feeding can be distinctly heard as they mow or scrape the weed off the rocks with their long tongues. The tongue of a limpet has been called a " living file." It is covered with about two thousand strong hooked teeth, which as they wear down in front are replaced by new ones formed behind.

Periwinkles, like limpets, also feed on seaweeds, and have even longer tongues, and nearly double the number of teeth.

The mussel (*Mytilus*) spins a " byssus " or attachment of silky-brown threads on the rock where it settles, which it lengthens if the mud rises and threatens suffocation, or breaks when it wants to move to a new place. Tiny pearls are sometimes

Whelk's eggs

Eggs of Skate

Eggs of the Sepia

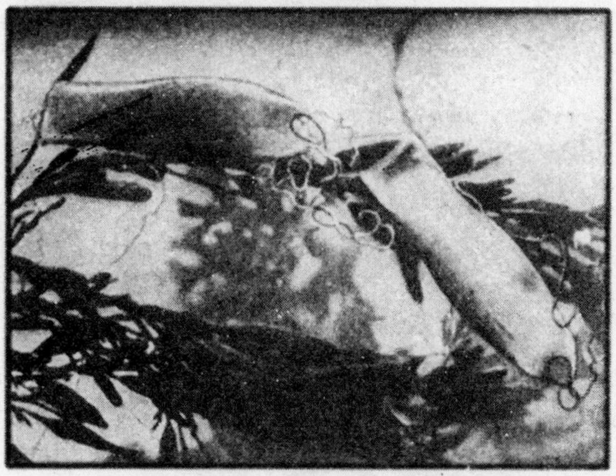

Dog-fish egg

QUEER EGGS OF QUEER FISH

No one would imagine that the thing which looks like a black purse, with four strings, is really a case for skate eggs, or that what looks like a mass of some cooked cereal is really a clutch of whelk's eggs. Both are very common along high-water mark. The photographs are by W. S. Berridge and F. W. Bond

A. H Willford

BLACK-HEADED GULL COMES BACK TO ITS NEST

Britain's coast varies in physical character tremendously, and each variation has its own particular features of special interest. Where the seashore is bordered by sand dunes marram grass is planted to bind these hills of otherwise shifting sand together. The gulls which nest along the shore often lay their eggs in the open, so that part of the sand seems covered with pebbles. The " camouflage " is indeed perfect. But this black-headed gull has found a ready-made nest in a clump of marram grass and has laid her eggs there.

found in mussels, formed in the same way as are the oyster's pearls.

The oyster (*Ostrea*) is the most important of the molluscs used for food and is extensively cultivated. An oyster has from one to two million eggs. It discharges the young "spat" into the water, where they swim freely for about two days before they settle down for life. They look like tiny specks, about the size of a pin's head, each enclosed in two transparent shells. When they sink to the bottom they fix their shells on rocks or stones by the lower valve, and there remain incapable of motion. An oyster takes four years to grow to a marketable size.

King & Son

A. H Willford

BUSY BIRD LIFE ON THE COAST

Below is a remarkable photograph of a common tern arranging her eggs with her beak preparatory to settling down to incubate them. Above we see a collection of razorbills and puffins collected on a rock. Most of the puffins, which are distinguished by their thick beaks, are lower down on the rock; while the razor-bills are outlined against the sky.

Razor shells are good for food, too. They are sometimes called spoutfish, because of their habit of shooting out a jet of water as they sink rapidly down their burrows.

The rockborers (*Saxicava*) and the large phosphorescent piddocks (*Pholas*) are very destructive, honeycombing the rocks with holes and tunnels like auger holes four to six inches deep. Their thin, delicate shells are covered with strong prickles.

A near relation of the piddocks, with an even worse reputation, is the shipworm or teredo, known from earliest times for the damage done to shipping and to all submerged wooden structures like piles of bridges, piers and wharves. It usually bores with the grain, and only changes its course to avoid a knot in the wood. The shipworm lines its long tunnel with a limy tube, and pushes out its "siphons" through the entrance of the tunnel, one taking water in and the other discharging the waste water and wood.

The sea slugs or Nudibranchs (naked gills) are very beautiful, delicate creatures of a wonderful variety of shape and colour. Each begins life with a tiny shell and later casts it off. The best known is the yellow sea lemon (*Doris*), about three inches long, often found on the crumb-of-bread sponge. Its strong tongue, set with about six thousand teeth, is used for scraping the surface of the sponges for a supply of food.

The octopus (*Polypus*), cuttlefishes (*Sepia*), and squids (*Loligo*) are the most highly organized of the molluscs. They are strange-looking creatures with curious bag-shaped bodies, eight or ten long writhing "arms" beset with suckers, staring black eyes, and mouths like parrot beaks. The animals themselves are seen occasionally in rock pools, and the egg-masses are abundant in the summer months. The octopus lays thousands of eggs, attached to a central stalk, fixed on rocks or stones. The cuttlefish attaches its masses of black eggs called "sea grapes" to seaweeds, while the squid's eggs or "sea mops" are buoyant, and made up of numbers of long jelly-like sheaths, filled with eggs. One sea mop contains about forty thousand eggs.

In the rock pools and under stones many interesting fishes can be found lurking in crevices or attending to their family cares. Some haunt sandy places, like the sand goby which makes a nest by heaping up sand around an empty shell, and hollowing out a pit underneath. The eggs are laid on the inner side of the shell, and then the father mounts guard, driving away all intruders and fanning vigorously with his fins to keep water in circulation over the eggs.

THE butterfishes, male and female, take turns in guarding their eggs, and coil themselves around the mass. Sometimes they push the eggs into the holes bored by the piddocks, and mount guard near by. They are often called "nine-eyes" from the row of black spots on the back, or "butter eel," because of their shape and exceeding slipperiness.

Sticklebacks' nests are well known. The male makes a nest as large as a man's fist in the growing seaweed by spinning a silky elastic thread, and then swimming round and round the weed, binding it with the thread. The wrasses, too, make nests of seaweed to hold the eggs, and guard them while the young are hatching.

The common blenny or shanny is a very active climber, getting easily about the rocks by means of its large, fan-shaped breast fins. It eats the acorn barnacles, biting them off with its sharp teeth. Another quaint little fish is the father lasher (*Cottus*) or bull-head, so called from its habit when irritated of swelling and erecting two spines like horns on its head. It lives in rock pools and amongst the tangles.

Quite a number of insects frequent the shore, and are exceedingly interesting from the point of view of adaptation to an amphibious life. Fleshflies, black-flies (*Coelopa*) and midges swarm among the jetsam on the beach, where the heat of the decaying weed helps the hatching of the eggs. One of the most abundant kinds is a tiny wingless blue-black spring-tail (*Anurida*), which is able to retain enough air in its thick hairy coat to last it for four or five days under water. A wingless bronze-coloured beetle, *Aepus*, which runs about over the stones and weeds at low water, is specially adapted for long periods of immersion. It has two air sacs and, in addition, the air contained among its covering of hairs.

GREAT numbers of birds frequent our shores, some resident all the year round, others, the migrants, gathering from far distances and visiting us at their nesting seasons. The Farne Islands, Bass Rock, St. Kilda, Ailsa Craig and the Scilly Islands are among the most famous of the breeding haunts. Here the sea birds congregate, nesting in bewildering numbers on every available ledge and cranny of the cliffs, or on the shingle at the foot of the rocks, often so tightly packed together that movement seems all but impossible. Here myriads of the Auk tribe pass the summer months, occupied with family cares. From these centres they scour the seas around for the fishes or floating plankton on which they feed, scurrying over the surface with rapid beats of their short wings, or diving under in chase of their prey. The common guillemot and razorbill make no nest of any kind, but lay a single egg on the bare rock, and hold it lengthwise across their feet during incubation. The puffin chooses a warm underground burrow for its egg, either excavating one for itself with its little red feet or taking possession of a rabbit's hole. The sea parrot, as the puffin is often called, is one of the most interesting of the shore birds, its comical appearance and habits marking it out from all the others. The large, brightly coloured, parrot-like beak banded in blue, yellow and red, is only a sheath assumed during the breeding season. With the passing of summer and the return of the puffin to its nomadic existence on the ocean, the sheath is cast and the true bill is seen, black and smaller.

THE sea-gulls are with us all the year round, haunting the stretches of shore uncovered by the tide, or gathering in flocks in the harbours and estuaries, circling and screaming in the fight for food. Their graceful soaring flight and wailing cries are well known, even far inland. They are marauders all, levying toll on the weak and defenceless, but the worst and largest of them is the great black-backed gull, a powerful bird with a wing spread of nearly six feet. His breeding places are strewn with the remains of his victims—guillemots, puffins, shearwaters, and even other gulls. The black cormorant, with its white patches on throat and flanks during the breeding season, and the green cormorant or shag, are as well known on our coasts as the gulls. Whether fishing, or sitting upright on the rocks drying their feathers, or flapping heavily back to their nests with fish for their young, they are easily recognized by the long, slender neck and bulky, bottle-shaped body.

Many other birds may be seen on the shore, either nesting or foraging for food, the oyster-catchers with their black and white plumage and red legs and bill, diligently hunting for winkles and barnacles, redshanks wading in the mudflats, catching small crustaceans and molluscs; ringed plovers, curlews, sandpipers, terns or sea-swallows, with their graceful dipping flight, fishing on the wing, and the little rock pipit building its nest not far from high-water mark.

This glimpse of the shore with its teeming life, its beauty and colour, would not be complete without a passing mention of its largest and most elusive inhabitants, the great grey seal and the common seal. They must be sought on the wildest parts of our coasts, where on the rocks at the base of rugged cliffs they may find safety for their young.

Chapter XXIX

The Wild Mammals of the British Isles

By Lewis Spence

Author of " An Introduction to Mythology "

Wild life in the British Isles has dwindled almost to vanishing point in many localities, and our native feral types are few and dwarfish when compared with those of the Continent, where the wolf and the wild boar survive. Still, it is an intriguing and goblin fellowship which continues to haunt our little wildernesses. With the exception of " the red deer and the roe," British wildings are diminutive in scale, as befits an insular economy, and harmless enough to man. Reynard is the pierrot of the lupine race, the wild cat a fairy tiger, the badger a striped harlequin for whose reprieve thousands of hands, both childish and elderly, are raised in appeal. Even the polecat has his defenders and his poets, and the weasel his legends, and surely the most charming folklore in the world clusters around the island zoology, cherished by all save, perhaps, a handful of disenchanted gamekeepers or shepherds who have their own reasons for drawing long faces when Brock or the Gentleman in Red are mentioned in their hearing.

" The noblest among British wild animals," as the red deer (*Cervus elaphus*) has been called, is also the most important both from the point of view of the naturalist and the sportsman. Had his existence in the north not been most earnestly fostered for purposes of sport, he would assuredly have become extinct generations ago, as, contrary to popular belief, he does not thrive on the bleak uplands, but prefers the lower levels and sheltered glens and woodlands. His ultimate fastnesses are the Highlands of Scotland, Cumberland, and Exmoor. I am afraid artists have depicted him as more stately and more bulky than he really is, for the average stag weighs about eighteen stones, and the hind considerably less.

In Scotland the red deer feeds principally on the heather and in winter, like the reindeer, scratches up the snow with his hoofs to get at the lichens and mosses beneath. But, above all, he prefers the soft grass by the burnside—or wheat and turnips, if he can come at them in the croft of the smallholder. He has also an intense craving for salt, which he will travel miles to glut, and in winter frequently makes his way to the seashore, where he eagerly devours immense quantities of seaweed.

During spring he is busy growing antlers and putting on fat. With the advent of October, the mating season, he goes forth in all his might to do battle with his fellows for the favours of the hinds, a furious and formidable fighting-machine indeed, trampling the earth as he goes, and roaring incessantly until he encounters another stag which has succeeded in gathering a female following. The calves are born at any time between May and July, and remain with the hinds till the late autumn.

The stag usually casts his antlers in February, although in the Highlands they may fall as early as Christmas. A stag with three points crowning each horn is known as a " royal," and the average span between the antlers is, perhaps, forty inches. He casts his winter coat about the same time as his horns, while the hind carries hers until well into May.

AN OTTER STARTLED

Next to the badger, the otter is the largest wild carnivorous animal left in Britain. From snout to tip of tail it measures about forty inches. Thus it is about the same length as the badger, though it is lighter in weight.

The roedeer (*Capreolus capraea*), a forest variety of the cervine race, chiefly occupies those woodland districts in Scotland which have been vacated by the red deer, and is also to be found in Cumberland and the New Forest. Its cunning is proverbial among sportsmen, and the crack of a rifle is certain to send it galloping to some trackless shelter where probably no hunter has yet succeeded in following it. Unlike the red deer, it is monogamous and mates in June. Naturally, as a citizen of the woods, it is partial to foliage, and has a surprising reach which enables it to stretch to branches considerably above the ground.

The bucks are apt to be irritable in the mating season and may even attack the human disturber of their haunts. In May the roe grows a light russet coat, but towards October this shades into a

W. S. Berridge

LARGEST OF THE BRITISH MAMMALS

Roedeer (bottom) are found in the New Forest and Cumberland still wild, and in Scotland. The latter country is the chief home of the wild red deer (centre), though he is also found on Exmoor. The fallow deer (top) is the usual deer of the private parks.

heavy brown. The antlers of the roe, however, never approach the majesty of those of the red deer and seldom measure more than eight or nine inches in height. In the wooded parts of the Highlands one grows familiar with the short, sharp bark of this graceful little deer, which is nearly always in sight of the peaceful visitor to his demesne.

The fallow deer (*Cervus dama*) is smaller than the red deer, and is of a pale red colour, spotted with white beneath. There is a marked distinction in the form of the antlers, those of the upper branches being flattened and expanded. During the breeding season the fallow deer runs in mixed herds, and is then very destructive to growing timber. The fawns are born in May or June.

I have often wondered who knows more about the fox (*Canis vulpes*), the people who hunt him, or those who do not. Nobody loves him, save, perhaps, the master of foxhounds, the naturalist, and the poet, and those for reasons far enough apart. In the mountainous parts of Scotland he is a very different animal from the harried mange-stricken beast of the English shires, where a nerve-wracking life of continual hazard induces disease and premature exhaustion. See the Highland fox in his glory—" The Red Dog " as they call him in some parts of the north—and you appreciate the difference between Rob Roy and a pickpocket.

Clever as most of us believe him, we yet do not give him sufficient credit for an intelligence approaching the mysterious. As a mimic he can hold his own with the parrot or the mocking-bird, can imitate the bleat of a lamb or the squeak of a rabbit, can smell steel traps yards away and knows how to dissipate his tell-tale scent by losing it in the tarry, oily odour of a railroad track. In the shires he is the hunted thing par excellence and not the otter himself can better imitate a bundle of rags drifting down a stream, nor can the weasel more deftly fit himself into a background of bracken and leaves in natural and very effective camouflage.

His peculiarly pungent and unmistakable scent is his undoing, and he knows it. The glands at the root of his tail are to him like the antlers of the stag, things of perilous betrayal. Unlike the witches, he loves running water, which alone can break the spell of his unfragrant track. But escape to him is often as disastrous as death, for with broken heart and shattered lungs, he may lie in a damp drain unable to move for days, contracting the fatal red mange, which leads slowly to an agonising death. This, not infrequently, is the sequel to his thirty-miles-an-hour marathon for life. That magnificent brush of his, which he uses as a species of rudder to balance his turnings and dartings when hunting on his own account, is a dreadful hindrance indeed when it is his turn to be hunted.

Born in luckless April, his dam puts him through an early course of mousing. The cubs are assiduously attended to by their father, who often goes far afield for his provender, and does sentry-go at the

THE OTTER IN HIS HAUNTS BY BROOK AND SEDGE

Although the otter is such a fine performer at under-water swimming, it has at first no desire to get to the water. Indeed, otter cubs are very frightened of the water and have to be taught to feel at home in it by the parents. This seems to prove that the otter's ancestors were not originally aquatic, but that succeeding generations gradually adopted this form of existence. The otter's most annoying habit is the one of taking just one bite out of a fine salmon and leaving it. But it likes eels even better.

RED REYNARD AND A LITTER OF FOX CUBS

Hunting being carried on far more intensively in England than in Scotland, it follows that the Scottish foxes are finer, less harried specimens than those of the English "shires." The litter of cubs seen above was found in the district near Perth by a gamekeeper, and was sold to one of the Scottish hunts for breeding purposes. This sort of treatment has been responsible for the fox's survival in the hunting districts where farmers would otherwise have exterminated it. But in the wilder parts of Scotland the fox still flourishes naturally.

Oliver G. Pike

FOX CUB LEAVES HIS LAIR IN THE WOODS

Best known of Britain's wild animals is the fox, which owes its preservation to fox hunting. For if this national sport had not needed the fox that animal would long ago have been exterminated by traps and poison as a pest Foxes are born about the month of April, and there are usually four or five to the litter. In September, when the huntsman's work of entering young hounds begins, the fox cubs get their first experience, in what is called cubbing, of the institution has which preserved their race.

W. S. Berridge

WILD CAT, BADGER, PINE MARTEN AND WEASEL OF BRITAIN'S WILD

Probably the pure-bred wild cat no longer exists in Britain, since it has mingled its blood so frequently with that of the domestic breed which has gone wild. Cumberland and Scotland are the homes of the wild cat (bottom left), which can be distinguished from the ordinary cat that has taken to the woods by its larger size. The badger (bottom right) has for generations been senselessly hunted towards extinction. It is one of the shyest and most difficult animals to see, however, and is a marvellous digger. The pine marten (top left) is still occasionally seen in Wales, the Lake District, and Scotland. It is about two feet long and a fine tree climber. The weasel (top right) is the fiercest animal in Britain and a great slayer of rats and field mice.

mouth of the den. It is, indeed, such excursions, made in the anxiety of parenthood, which earn Reynard so detestable a reputation as a poacher. But he is a model sire. If you try to dig out a family earth you will not find the cubs in its main corridors, for they are almost invariably tucked away each in a little side-passage of his own. Cubs have no scent until the age of four months, and exhibit little of the skulking ferocity of their species. Indeed, I have heard that they are occasionally seen playing with rabbits!

Even the least sentimental will agree that the badger (*Meles vulgaris*) vanishes all too quickly, and that not merely through the trap-door of his earthy retreat, but into that deeper limbo where disappear the species which become extinct. It has been abundantly proved that he does practically no damage to game, and it is encouraging to find that, instead of hunting down this little bruin of Britain with terriers which he does not want to fight, landowners are actually advertising for him as an "embellishment" to their estates.

Brock is a forest denizen, and loves fir and pine woods and the sandy soil beneath them, which suits his tunnelling propensities. But he has almost vanished from the Highlands, and his principal habitats are Wales and the New Forest, that great southern asylum of Britain's feral life. His bodily markings, composed as they are of silver and shadow, prove him to be by nature nocturnal. There is none in the wild so cautious as he, and he is as seldom espied in the open as a centenarian in the Strand. He skulks along by the side of hedges, and along the gutters of fields, for his short legs and lumbering, bear-like gait make it impossible for him to move with expedition, and not infrequently he cleverly connects these runways with a side door from his earth.

The average length of the badger is about forty inches, inclusive of tail, and he weighs from thirty to thirty-five pounds. His provender consists of snails, slugs and beetles for the most part, frogs and worms, eked out on the vegetable side with roots and berries in their season.

As an excavator the badger can, for his bulk, easily beat all rivals, and indeed vie with the steam-shovel. Normally, however, he is sloth personified, sleeping through the hours of sunshine and coming to the surface only once in three or four days to gorge himself. If hunted over sandy soil, he will frequently dig in where he stands rather than run. His warren, which he occupies for a few months only, is marvellously planned, and as intricate as the labyrinth of the Minotaur. It is always freshly bedded, and in time he builds up a regular "kitchen-midden," as an antiquary would describe it, at the entrance to his burrow, consisting of disused litter and other rubbish. He has a wonderful system of communication with his fellows in "scratching-posts"—tree-trunks or rocks on which he leaves the marks of his claws, and in this manner, probably, secures his mate, the place of "registration" becoming also a rendezvous. As a fighter there is scarcely his equal in nature and probably no single terrier is capable of tackling a full-grown dog badger with any chance of success.

W. S. Berridge

HARE AND WILD RABBIT

The wild rabbit (bottom) would soon outnumber all the other countryside populations, but that the father rabbit has a habit of eating his own young and that rabbits have so many enemies. The hare (top) prefers open country and is solitary except at mating time.

In all likelihood no pure specimen of the British wild cat (*Felis catus*) now exists. One frequently notices the capture of these animals recorded in the newspapers, but the breed has become so mingled with the domestic species that it is only the comparative size of the wild cats so called which leads to the supposition that they are of the pure and pristine strain. Nevertheless, the domestic cat, when it takes

W. S. Berridge

W. S. Berridge

W. S. Berridge

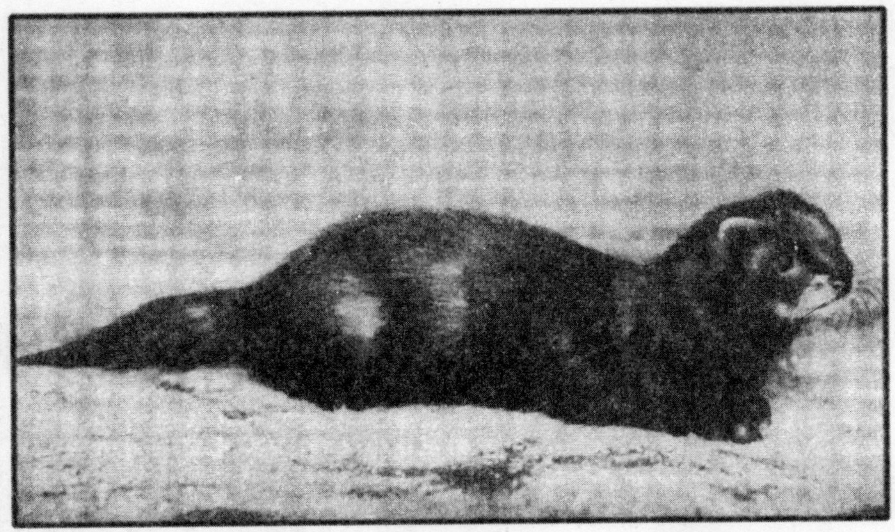

DESTROYERS OF ANIMAL AND VEGETABLE LIFE IN HEDGEROW AND WOOD

Making its home in banks or the hollows in trees, the stoat (bottom left) is hated by the gamekeeper for its destruction of game. The male attains a length of about ten inches, and the female is a little shorter. The hunting is mostly done at night. The polecat (bottom right) which is now extremely scarce, measures about sixteen inches long, tail included, and is renowned for its revolting odour. One of the beauties of the woods is the red squirrel (top left), but it is very destructive to saplings. This is partly compensated for by its habit of burying nuts for storage purposes. Those it forgets become trees. The grey squirrel (top right) is an American importation, and has largely ousted the more handsome native from the home counties.

to a wild existence, very speedily approximates to the appearance of the feral species and grows out of all proportion to its domestic relative. What we now call the wild cat strain probably comprises the remnants of the original *Felis catus* crossed with descendants of the domestic animal which have run wild. I believe that the domestic cat has nearly as much wild blood in him as the so-called wild cat.

APART from its greater size—a wild cat usually measures from three feet five inches to three feet ten inches from nose to tip of brush—the tail is more bushy and distinctly ringed than in the tame species, the head is wider and the ears are much farther apart and stand out so that sometimes they seem almost to flap over the cheeks. The colour is usually tawny. The wild cat is a frequenter of the woodland, and his normal quarry is the squirrel, which he stalks with all the patience of his tribe. But, though he has a penchant for hare and rabbit, he prefers grouse or pheasant to any other flesh. This notwithstanding, he is exceedingly dangerous to lambs and even to young deer. He does not feast immediately after a kill, but carries his prey into the woods, where he devours it tiger-fashion, mauling it about at his ferocious ease.

Although he mates singly, he is a bad parent, and his one annual litter depends almost entirely upon the offices of the mother. Like Reynard, no one wants him, and were it not for his rarity and his picturesqueness the wild could well do without him. In his present impure strain he is confined only to Scotland and Cumberland, and were it not for the accessions he receives from the ranks of the tame species with which he interbreeds, he would speedily become extinct.

WEASELS (*Putorius vulgaris*), stoats or ermines (*Putorius erminius*), and polecats (*Mustela putorius*) are all of one and the same family, the lower assassins and thugs of our woodland society. The weasel attacks any form of life in which warm blood runs, granted it be not too big or powerful, and no man-eating tiger displays half the desperate courage or blood-thirstiness of this demoniac little panther of the British countryside. Yet on the whole, the stoat is much more destructive among game, while the weasel confines himself more to rats, mice and water-voles. Even the bravest male rat, a fighter born, dreads him, and a well-plucked terrier has been known to run from him after experiencing the results of the first rough-and-tumble.

The weasel avoids the open, and in true cloak-and-dagger fashion skulks along walls and ditches, stalking his prey, actually terrifying it by his show of ferocity, moving after it by jerks, punctuated by sudden stops, relentless in his stalking as the timber wolf. His hearing is phenomenal, and his ability to identify himself with his surroundings is equally extraordinary. But strangest of all are the tricks with which he frequently beguiles his victims, throwing somersaults and executing such contortions that domestic fowls and game-birds, consumed with curiosity, draw near—to be devoured, or at least speedily strangled, by the murderous little acrobat.

Weasels and stoats are migratory, and sometimes travel in small packs. Occasionally they gather in regular armies, hundreds strong, when they have been found to be dangerous to human life itself, as many a Scottish shepherd knows. In couples they hunt together like well-trained hounds. But they are easy to trap, as they run along ditches and do not fear the scent of steel.

Yet they have their uses. They keep down the rat pest, and as their own food is chiefly composed of " rats and mice and such small deer " they are partly to be apologised for. The weasel's warren is widespread, but his numbers are strictly limited by the fact that he engages in death-duels so frequently with his own kind—and the ermine in his yellow, wintry coat is certainly valuable commercially.

THE polecat, or foumart, grows more and more rare within the four seas of Britain. Of a dark brown colour in summer, he shades off to a lighter hue in winter, and his head is usually ringed with grey or white. He is a most destructive killing machine, larger than the weasel or the stoat, measuring usually about sixteen inches from nose to tail. Indeed, when one recalls his odour, he has nothing but his rarity to recommend him. He has a peculiar taste for frogs (when he cannot procure game), and has a trick of paralysing them by biting them through the nerves of the head so that he may store them in his larder alive. He usually nests in a disused rabbit-burrow. The young are born in May, and remain with the parents till almost full grown. The polecat hunts exclusively above ground and not, like the weasel, along the corridors or earths and burrows of the pine-woods of his affection. But, like some antiquaries, he has a peculiar taste for ruined buildings standing on the moorland wastes, and frequently rears his family among their crumbling stones.

The pine marten (*Mustela martes*), once common enough in the woodland, has paid the penalty of a handsome skin, and is scarce, except in Scotland, Wales, and the Lake District. He closely resembles a polecat, but his legs are longer, and his head broader and tail more bushy. The rich, dark brown body extends on the average for a couple of feet. He is an arboreal beast and an inveterate egg-sucker, although he has a penchant for ground fruits. His nest is formed of grass among rocks, or in a hollow tree.

The otter (*Lutra vulgaris*) is really an animal of the weasel species which has taken to the water, or rather to amphibian habits. He measures on an average about forty inches from snout to tip of tail, and weighs round about twenty pounds. Many rather terrible tales are broadcasted about his ferocity, both to man and beast, but the bare truth seems to be that he is a mere Paul Pry, insatiably curious or, perhaps, that like the puma, he has a leaning to human society. He is really as playful as a kitten and by no means destructive in the wanton sense.

Indeed, he maintains the numbers of trout by killing off eels and older trout which are apt to devour the growing fish. He certainly has a wretched habit of devouring only the "middle cut" from a prime salmon, but, given eels, he will leave salmon alone.

The speed with which the otter can swim under water is amazing. He is swifter than the sleekest salmon. As a cub, he dreads the water and has to be instructed in swimming by his parents, a proof that his habits were not originally aquatic. He works up the estuaries of rivers from their confluence with the sea, clear to the headwaters, and has his own definite landing-places. In winter he can unerringly pick out a trout from a frozen brook where the pools remain clear of ice. During a heavy frost he will rob hen-roosts or attack a rabbit-warren, but only if driven to it by hunger. Otters usually live in a bank burrow with an entrance under water, and a pair produces only one litter of two or three every year. The young remain blind for about three months, during which time the father mounts sentry at the entrance of the burrow.

No mammal, perhaps, thrives so well on the life of the hunted as the brown hare (*Lepus europaeus*). Naturally he is a good deal of a hermit, except in the mating season, and even as a leveret prefers his own society to that of his fellows, leaving his dam at the age of fourteen days. Like most rodents, he adheres to

Brown rat

Mole

Water vole

Black rat

House mouse

Harvest mouse

SOME OF BRITAIN'S SMALLER MAMMALS THAT LEAD FURTIVE LIVES

Of the house mouse nothing good can be said. It is a spreader of dirt and a carrier of disease. Its relative, the harvest mouse, is, on the other hand, quite a pleasant little creature, and is very engaging to watch as it hangs swaying from a wheat-ear, clinging by its tail. It is about two inches long. The old English black rat has in most places become displaced by the larger brown rat, whose depredations cost the country £15,000,000 every year. The mole is valued for its skin and lives largely on worms. Photographs by W. S. Berridge.

his own particular runways, often with disastrous effect to himself. It is his peculiar ability to see behind him, a trait induced probably through generations of flight, and this it is which enables him to double and dodge his pursuers so neatly, although it not infrequently ends in his undoing, as he cannot well see what is happening ahead.

In March the hare mates, and during that season the males combat, much as do the stags, for the does, clashing together in mid-air and lashing at each other with their forefeet. The young are born in the middle of April, and the mother resorts to stratagem to break her scent when returning to the form where they lie, making tremendous leaps for this purpose. Were it not that nature has contrived checks to its progress the rabbit (*Lepus cuniculus*) would quickly outstrip all other populations, wild or human. But the taste of the buck is for the flesh of his own infants, and bunny, at all stages of his career, has so many foes that the wonder is he survives at all, only his remarkable fecundity giving him the pull he has over other species. He opens his eyes a few days after birth, and follows his mother from the burrow to nibble the short grass. She soon loses interest in her young, although for a week or so she may protect them from the bucks, which chase and chivvy them. Later, they go farther afield, and if prolonged rain does not induce a deathly chill, in time leave their

Long-tailed field mouse

Bank vole

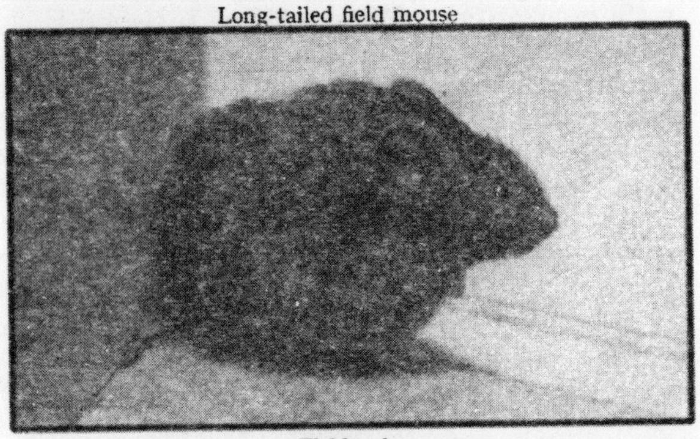

Field vole

Young field voles

Shrew

Dormouse

SHREW, MICE AND VOLES, THE PREY OF MANY CREATURES

A flexible, pointed snout distinguishes the common shrew, which eats no less than four times its own weight of insects in thirty-six hours. The dormouse is quite as sleepy in fact as Lewis Carroll made it in Alice in Wonderland, and is often taken for dead. The field vole is a distant relative of the mouse and a curse to agriculture, eating up the newly-planted seed. The bank vole, keeps mostly to wild roots for its food, while the long-tailed field mouse is a robber of kitchen gardens. Photographs by A. H. Willford and W. S. Berridge.

nest in a shallow field-burrow and go to join forces with the communal warren.

THE rabbit is always on the look-out for danger, and, when he senses it, tattoos on the ground with his hind legs in warning to his fellows, which can hear it roods away. In the Highlands flood or spate is his worst enemy, and he is constantly being washed out of his burrow or suddenly drowned in it. Also, the diseased house rat communicates his ailments to rabbits with disastrous frequency.

It is most necessary to keep rabbits down in sheep country, as they devour the grass, and a sheep will not eat where a rabbit has been. Rabbits begin to breed at about three or four months, and the rate at which they multiply is rivalled only by the rat's. They seldom pair for any length of time.

The squirrel (*Scioros vulgaris*) has only himself to blame if in many British districts he is on the verge of extermination, for nothing is so destructive to the woodland. He will speedily kill off a sapling, and even reduce a whole plantation to ruin, if not severely taken in hand. He is an inquisitive little beast, but has his retiring moments. Of all the wildings he is the food-hoarder par excellence, and can tell a sound nut from a bad one by its weight, burying the good nuts one by one in separate places, and recovering every one in the time of his need. He is thus a natural planter of forests, as those nuts he forgets become trees. He dislikes rivalry, and will fiercely contest his territory with an interloper. In Scotland he is forced to hibernate during a severe winter.

The squirrel usually nests in a tree about a dozen feet or so from the ground. The nest is sphere-shaped and is entered from the side, but squirrel is fastidious, and may build a number before he is satisfied. He is monogamous, and it would seem that he cleaves to his mate for life, although there are exceptions to this, as in human society. The squirrel produces only one litter a year, from three to six young, which set up for themselves, usually at the early age of two months. In size he is on the average from thirteen to fourteen inches, including tail, and changes his russet coat in November.

THE hedgehog (*Erinaceus europaeus*) is one of the oldest among British mammals, dating as he does from an early prehistoric period. He is by no means a vegetarian, making his diet from mice, slugs, beetles and insects, some not very savoury, and hunting them by scent like a diminutive hound. He is quick on his feet too, notwithstanding the popular belief that he is a slowcoach, and occasionally follows gutters like the badger, although he is not in the habit of using runways. He has small method in his hunting, chasing his prey from point to point with elaborate carelessness, and devouring it piecemeal as he seeks fresh victims. Snared rabbits are "pie" to the "hotchi-witchi," as the Gipsies call him, and his habit of reclining in warrens frequently means a holocaust among the nestling rabbits. Indeed, hedgehogs have not infrequently decimated a rabbit population in the breeding season. He is also very destructive to game-birds, eating both eggs and fledglings. The rat avoids him like the plague. His spines protect him from falls as well as from enemies, and he can roll down a respectable declivity without risk. Polecats are his worst enemies. By autumn the hedgehog puts on so much flesh that he is forced to hibernate early, and he subsists on his fat during his winter nap, usually taken in a rabbit-warren. The average weight is round about a couple of pounds.

The mole (*Talpa europaea*) which is commercially valuable as the possessor of an enviable coat, is equipped with spade-like feet, naked, pink and powerful. With these splayed shovels and the aid of a gimlet-like proboscis he tunnels underground, and his progress can often actually be noted, so near the surface does he frequently work, poking up the loose earth with his snout, and raising mole-hills. He is by preference a worm-eater, but has also a partiality for slugs and snails. One historian of nature has imagined a mole as large as a bear—a devastating creature indeed, ravenous and insatiable. His tunnel leads to a hole roofed with hard earth and lined with dry grass, from which diverge various bolts and emergency exits.

VOLUMES could be written about the brown rat (*Mus decumanus*), but here one can but touch on his main peculiarities. Wherever food is the rat is, and there only. From a migratory horde he splits up into communities just large enough to consume such provender as the site may afford. His instincts are well-nigh human, and his destructiveness proverbial, yet the slaughter of him notwithstanding, his powers of reproduction are so extraordinary that all efforts to keep down the rat millions seem hopelessly ineffectual. At the present time he is holding Great Britain to ransom for about £15,000,000 per annum, and it has been estimated that each rat costs the country 7s. 6d. a year! He brings about fifty of his own species into the world annually, and can live for five or six years.

The water-rat or water-vole (*Arvicola amphibius*) is much smaller than the rat, with short, blunt head and fine blue fur. He lives in colonies, like the beaver, but his families retain a large measure of strict privacy. His habits are aquatic and of the daylight, and he is not nearly so prolific as the brown rat. His dwelling is a burrow in the bank of a stream, sometimes more landward in its situation than seems necessary. He is well up in the scale of intelligence, and is certainly not destructive, living almost entirely on willow pith and grass-roots.

The black rat (*Epimys rattus*) was some years ago believed to be extinct, but this type still exists, even in London itself. He is really Asiatic in origin and reached England at some time in the thirteenth century. He is a good deal smaller and more slender than the brown rat, with glossy blue-black fur, hairless ears and pink feet. But he has had to contest every inch of the island with his far stronger and

HEDGEHOG IN A STATE OF DEFENCE AND WHEN HUNTING

By rolling itself up into a ball so that it presents a bristle of sharp spines on all sides the hedgehog has a most formidable power of passive resistance. But this is not the only use to which it puts this posture, for, by assuming it, the animal can roll down steep places with impunity. It is omnivorous, devouring fruit or beetles or roots or young rabbits with equal enjoyment. It can even cope with, and sometimes kill, a viper. In the winter the hedgehog goes to sleep, often in a rabbit warren, living on its own fat.

fiercer brown cousin, who did not invade Britain till the 18th century and who readily devours him.

The common brown mouse (*Mus musculus*) is by far the most familiar and widely distributed of British mammals, and may almost be said to be a particular parasite of humanity. His natural food is grain, but he is really omnivorous. The harvest mouse (*Micromys minutus*) is the smallest of British mammals with the exception of the lesser shrew, measuring just about two inches. His red-yellow coat shades away to white beneath, and his prehensile tail almost serves him as a fifth foot in climbing wheat stalks. His chief habitat is the South of England. He will eat insects in the summer, and stores up grain for winter. The harvest mouse lives in a ball-shaped nest suspended above the ground from some hardy weed. The long-tailed field mouse (*Apodemus sylvaticus*) is an inveterate robber of the kitchen garden, and is of nocturnal habits, burrowing underground, where it stores nuts and grain against the winter, at which season, however, it frequently steals into houses. It strongly resembles and is easily confused with the house mouse.

The field vole (*Microtus agrestis*) is not closely related to the mouse. It has a short stumpy body with blunt head and nose, and reddish-brown fur. It is highly destructive to vegetables and fruit, and although it burrows underground during the winter its tiny summer nest is usually made beside a tuft of grass. The vole is a plague almost as dreaded as the rat by agriculturists and devours new-planted seed and crops with equal impartiality. The bank vole (*Evotomys glareolus*) haunts the hedgerows and wooded country rather than the fields, and is slightly smaller and of a redder hue. It lives on wild roots rather than vegetables or grain.

The common shrew (*Sorex araneus*) is especially noticeable for his long flexible pointed snout, which makes him look like a dwarf tapir. His food is restricted to small insects, he lives in the fields and is comparatively inoffensive. But he is a dreadful glutton, devouring four times his own weight in thirty-six hours. The lesser shrew (*Sorex minutus*) is hardly to be distinguished from the common variety except in point of size. The water shrew (*Noomys fadiens*) is, however, larger than the common shrew, and its snout is shorter and broader. It is, as the name implies, aquatic in its habits and lives in a burrow on the bank of a brook. The dormouse (*Muscardinus avellanarius*) resembles a tiny squirrel, with its prominent eyes and thickly furred tail. It lives in copses and hedgerows, is nocturnal, and sleeps so soundly by day that it is often mistaken for dead.

W. S. Berridge

THE COMMON SEAL THAT HAUNTS THE LONELIER COASTS OF BRITAIN

One species, the common or harbour seal, is native to the coasts of Britain, though several species, including the great grey seal, are not infrequent visitors. The former is from four to five feet long and of a buff-grey colour, and is found off the coasts of Scotland and Wales and also in the Wash and off the north coast of Norfolk. It is disliked intensely by the fishermen for its fish-eating habits, and in the Wash is especially unpopular. It also ascends salmon rivers, pursuing the fish far into fresh water.

Chapter XXX

Survivors of a Lost World: The Giant Iguanas at Home

By T. H. Gillespie

Director, The Scottish Zoological Park, Edinburgh

THE largest lizards in the world are the monitors, with the great Komodo monitor at the head of their family. There are, however, no monitors in the New World and their place there is, to a great extent, taken by the Iguanas, a family essentially American, since, of all the numerous species composing it, only two or three are found in the Old World, in Fiji and, curiously enough, in a spot so far from America as Madagascar.

The family, being large, is very varied, and it includes many extremes: species which show the utmost beauty of colouring and grace of form contrasted with those which emphasise the drab and the grotesque; some of the smallest lizard forms and some of the largest. Certainly, when compared with the monitors of Komodo, the size of the largest iguanas may not seem very significant; still, all things are relative, and when judged by the standards of a race in which, for the most part, magnitude is measured by inches and ounces rather than by feet and hundredweights, they attain very respectable dimensions.

The impressiveness of the larger iguanas does not, however, depend entirely on mere weight and measurement but on something more subtle; it is, perhaps, their general appearance and the way in which they recall all that one has imagined of the great and terrible reptiles of the remote past—the "dragons" of the primeval world—that make them seem more thrilling than bodily bulk alone might do. They are, in fact, much more "dragon-like" in form than the monitors. In this respect three or four species stand out from the others. Unlike the monitors, which are carnivorous, the larger iguanas have chosen the most undragonly diet of leaves and fruit, though some of them are not averse to varying it at times with any odd insects, eggs, or small animals that may come their way.

In the Galapagos Islands, where the youth of the world seems to have lingered and the dominant animal forms are reptilian, is the home of the first of these iguanas, one of the most remarkable of living lizards. It is known, technically, as *Amblyrhinchus cristatus*, and it has the distinction of being the largest member of its family and the largest of American lizards. It has, moreover, a further and more outstanding character, for it is, so far as is known, the only lizard in the world which has taken to the sea for its living, and spends much of its life and finds all its food there. It is therefore most aptly called the marine iguana.

When one remembers how many land animals have sought their solution of the problem of finding food in a return to the sea it seems the more remarkable that only one of the many hundreds of lizards should have done so. Early observers who had seen marine iguanas swimming out to sea concluded that they were going in pursuit of fish; that was an error, however, for they are entirely vegetable feeders and live solely on seaweeds.

Ewing Galloway

GIANT LIZARD OF THE SEA

Largest of its family, the giant sea iguana of the lonely Galapagos Islands is a fine-looking monster, and of a mild and equable temperament. The specimen seen above was nearly five feet long, about the greatest length that is attained by these huge lizards.

It was Darwin who, in "A Naturalist's Voyage Round the World," first described at length the appearance and habits of the sea iguana, and recently Mr. William Beebe, Director of the New York Zoological Society's Tropical Research Department, has added to the earlier information not only much very vivid and picturesque detail but also a wonderful series of photographs of this lizard at home.

The marine iguana attains a length of upwards of four feet. Mere length is, however, no criterion of

A MULTITUDE OF MARINE IGUANAS ON THE LAVA ROCKS OF GALAPAGOS: Among the lava rocks of the volcanic islands which are their home the marine iguanas seem an inseparable part of the landscape. Their shape and their colour blend completely with their surroundings where the surf of the vast Pacific beats for ever against these islands, which are mountain tops thrust out of the ocean. This wonderful photograph was taken on Narborough Island at the beginning of this century, and is a precious record of a state of things which is ending. No such vast hordes exist now, for the iguanas are slowly dying out They have already outlived their age-long day.

Mr. William Beebe: Copyright

SURVIVALS FROM A PREHISTORIC AGE IN A LOST WORLD OF THE PACIFIC

The mystery of the iguanas of Galapagos is one with the puzzle of the archipelago itself. Were these islands uplifted, one by one, by volcanic forces from the ocean bed: were they originally one island which has become split up; or were they a part of a now submerged portion of South America? The iguanas, in any case, have managed to evade the remorseless process of time which exterminated the giant saurians.

This photograph, with those on page 314, and facing page 320 are from "Galapagos: World's End" by courtesy of the author, Mr. William Beebe of the New York Zoological Society; and of the Publishers, Messrs. G. P. Putnam's Sons a lizard's size ; for example, the tuberculated iguana grows to six feet long, though more than two-thirds of that is tail, and it is slender and not to be compared in bulk with its marine relative which is of heavy, massive build. As might be expected in a lizard which spends much time in the water, the tail is flattened sideways for swimming and the lizards swim with ease and speed by the movement of the tail, after the manner of an eel. The seaweeds which they eat grow in fairly deep water and although, when they can do so, the iguanas get as much of their food as possible when the tide is low, they must often have to go beneath the surface to feed. It is to be expected, therefore, that this lizard can remain under water for a fairly long period without coming up for air, but its capacity in that matter rather exceeds expectation. Darwin mentions that one of the seamen on the "Beagle," wishing to kill one of these lizards that he had captured, and thinking, perhaps, that drowning was the readiest method, tied a heavy weight to it and sank it in deep water. He let it remain there for an hour but when, at the end of that time, he pulled it up the lizard was as lively as ever, a toleration of submergence which one exposed to the risks of the sea might well envy.

While this lizard feeds in the sea, it seeks shelter and sanctuary on the shore, and if it is ashore nothing will induce it, if alarmed, to enter the water. Even when one of them was thrown into the sea it returned at once to the rock from which it was thrown, and this it did repeatedly. Darwin suggested, as the explanation of this curious habit, that the iguana has no enemies whatever on shore, man being too recent to have had any influence on its racial behaviour, but at sea it must often fall a prey to the numerous sharks ; its hereditary instinct is, therefore, to regard the shore as offering safety, no matter whence the alarm may have come. It has, moreover, a very remarkable sense of direction, as Mr. Beebe found when he threw one into the water two miles from land. Although the land must have been quite invisible to the lizard, it swam round the ship and immediately headed straight for the shore.

It is when it is ashore that the marine iguana is most impressive. "As black and rugged as the lava boulders themselves," says Mr. Beebe, "these splendid saurians crept about like great prehistoric monsters. No other living inhabitant of these islands seemed so thoroughly a part of its environment. In colour, in rough contour, in the scales of its head standing up like volcanic cones, in its intimacy with lava and surf, it seemed an organic embodiment of the shores of these desolate islands.

Mr Wm. Beebe, Copyright

FIERCE LAND IGUANA

The land iguanas of Galapagos differ from their sea cousins in colour and character—orange and red brown instead of black, and fierce instead of gentle By day they lie beneath the cactus plants (top), following the shadow as it moves.

Dr. G. Kingsley Noble

WHERE THE RHINOCEROS IGUANA OF HAITI HAS ITS HOME AND LAYS ITS EGGS

A particularly imposing iguana is found on two islands of the West Indies, Haiti and Porto Rico, and nowhere else. It lives in burrows (bottom) which it can drive through limestone sometimes for a distance of forty feet. Here we see a bank of fossil corals tunnelled for a home. The eggs are laid a few feet below the surface of the sand. The top photographs show (left) the site of a clutch and (right) a nest being brought to light. The eggs are rather larger than a chicken's but the shells are leathery.

Ewing Galloway

MARINE IGUANAS COME TO INSPECT MEMBERS OF THE EXPEDITION TO THE GALAPAGOS ISLANDS

When American explorers visited the Galapagos Archipelago to inspect the giant iguanas, described by Darwin in his account of his famous voyage in the " Beagle," some of the iguanas of Albemarle Island turned out to examine the explorers. As we see here a number of younger beasts crawled along the rocks quite close to the strange invader, man. It seems as though the Galapagos Islands, which lie in the Pacific 695 miles west of the Ecuador coast of South America, had been left behind in the history of the world. The strange creatures which inhabit them are strongly reminiscent of the prehistoric monsters whose appearance scientists have reconstructed from their fossil remains in other parts of the world.

It lies on shore sunning itself by day and at night, or when alarmed, takes refuge in crevices or holes in the rocks. If the hole should be too small to accommodate the entire lizard and a hold can be got on its tail, it may be pulled out, but only after a great struggle, for it not only clings to its refuge with its strong claws but also puffs out its body so that the rough scales help to grip the sides of the crevice. One might expect that when the iguana was pulled out it would emerge in a particularly nasty temper, and that having such powerful jaws and claws it would use them with due effect. On the contrary, it is a most gentle and docile "dragon" and cannot be induced, either by sudden fright or by prolonged teasing, to bite.

WHILE the marine iguana is still very numerous, Mr. Beebe states that the vast hordes which might be seen some twenty-five years ago no longer exist, and he is of opinion that they are slowly but certainly decreasing. It is unlikely that this fine lizard will ever be seen in any zoological park or garden in Europe (though it has been exhibited for a short period in New York), for when captured it cannot be persuaded to feed. It can, like many reptiles, fast for a prolonged period without losing strength and Mr. Beebe was able to bring some home alive. "From one thousand miles out in the Pacific to New York, and for two months later, these lizards lived and apparently thrived on salt water and air. No variety of seaweed or terrestrial vegetable tempted them to break their fast." After one hundred days of complete abstinence from food they "appeared as active and as strong as when first taken from among their native lava."

The domain of the sea iguana stops with the shore, and inland, on some of the islands, its place is taken by a land iguana only a little less in length and not dissimilar in shape but quite different in colour and character. Instead of the sober blackish colour of the former the inland species is orange or yellow on the head and forelegs, paler yellow below, and reddish brown on the back, a fairly striking combination. In temper it is described by Beebe as being irritable and fierce, and willing, when captured, to do its best with tooth and claw to regain its freedom.

DARWIN's judgement was kinder; "they try to look very fierce," he says, "but in reality they are not at all so," and he adds that "if held and plagued with a stick it will bite very severely, but I caught many by the tail and they never tried to bite me." Darwin gives an amusing account of this iguana's method of burrowing:

> This animal, when making its burrow, works alternately the opposite sides of its body. One front leg for a short time scratches up the soil and throws it towards the hind foot which is well placed so as to heave it beyond the mouth of the hole. That side of the body being tired, the other takes up the task and so on alternately. I watched one for a long time till half its body was buried; I then walked up and pulled it by the tail; at this it was greatly astonished and shuffled up to see what was the matter; and then stared me in the face as much as to say, 'What made you pull my tail?'

At the time of his visit these iguanas were so numerous that "we could not for some time find a spot free from their burrows on which to pitch our single

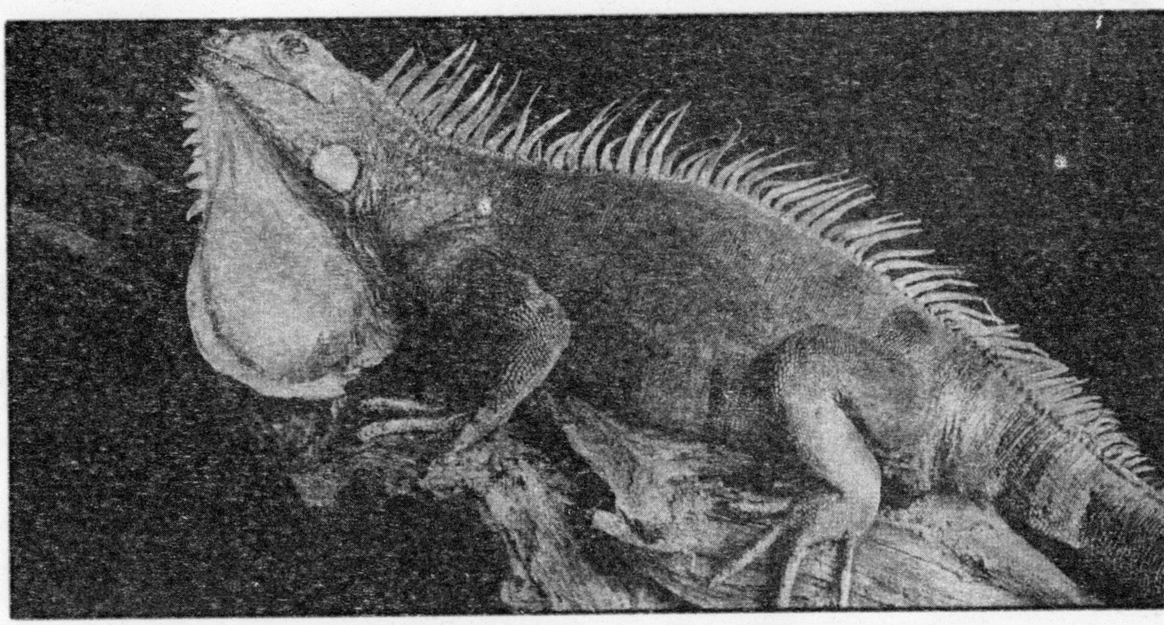

E.N.A.

LIKE SOME PREHISTORIC MONSTER: IGUANA OF CENTRAL AMERICA

This iguana might well be used as an illustration of a dragon for some romance of chivalry and is not unlike some of the gigantic saurians that possessed the earth before man became its master. In reality it is an inhabitant of Central America, living among the trees of the tropical forests usually in proximity to water. It is an expert climber and its diet consists largely of berries and leaves varied by insects. The great dewlap and the spines on the back are characteristic of the species.

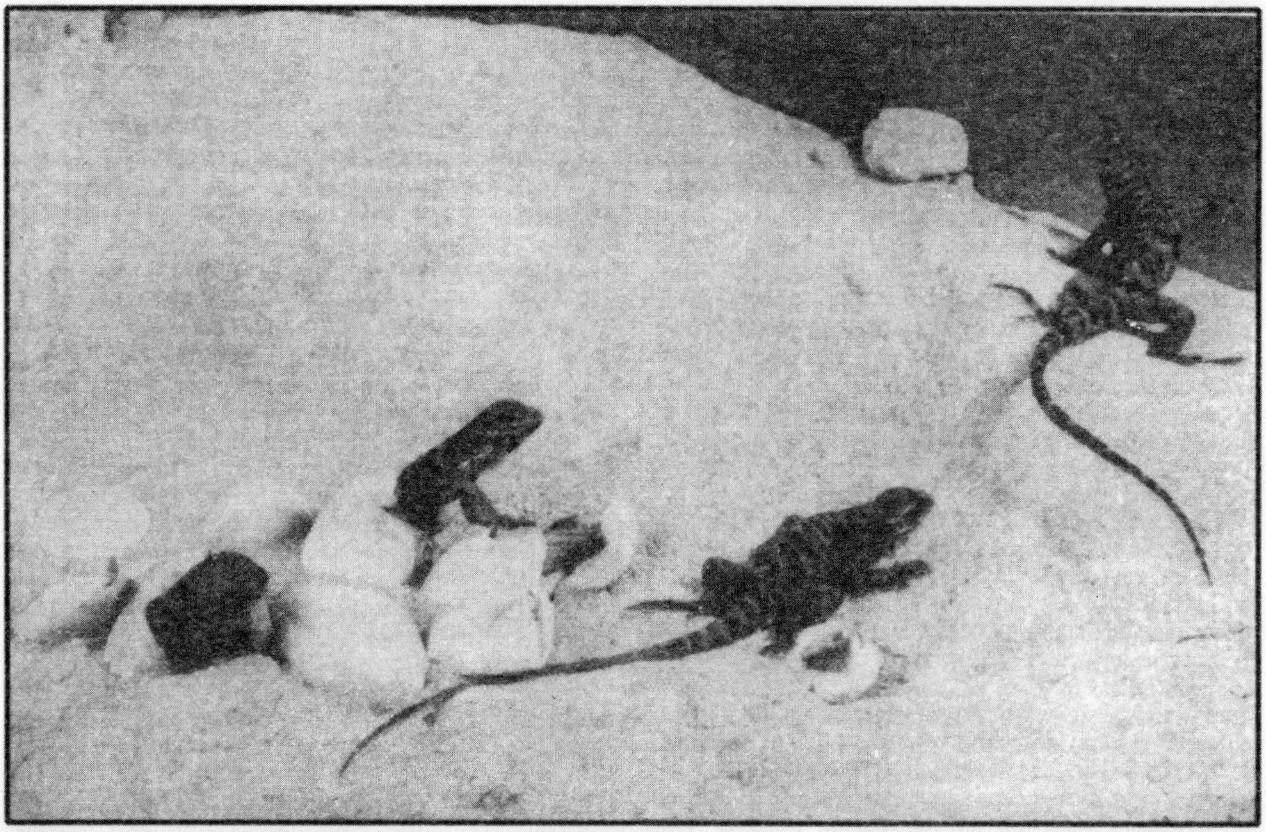

RHINOCEROS IGUANAS AS THEY LIVE BESIDE A LAKE OF HAITI

By the waters of Lake Enriquillo on the island of Haiti live numbers of the rhinoceros iguanas, so named from the horns upon their wicked-looking snouts. When the sun is at its hottest the great lizards come out of their burrows in the coral and the observer may witness a scene such as that shown in the lower illustration. The upper photograph shows some young iguanas hatching out of their eggs in the sand. These photographs and those on pages 315, 319 and 320 are by Dr. G. Kingsley Noble of the American Museum of Natural History.

GAPING JAWS AND CRESTED SPINE OF THE RHINOCEROS IGUANA

These two illustrations are enlarged portions of the lower photograph in the opposite page, showing, at close range, the physique and mien of the full-grown rhinoceros iguana of the West Indies. The lower photograph here enables us to see the wide-gaping jaws of a creature which, unlike the mild-tempered marine iguana of Galapagos, is ready and willing to inflict a terrible bite upon man or animal that attacks it. But unprovoked the iguana is harmless enough The upper photograph depicts one of the creatures just emerging from its burrow.

Dr. G. Kingsley Noble

DOMINICAN SPIKE-TAILED IGUANA

In the island of Santo Domingo there is a salt lake called Enriquillo, and in the middle of it an island. When this island was explored a kind of iguana was found among the cactus bushes there which differed from the rhinoceros iguanas of the mountains about the lake in that it had no horn upon its head, but instead was armed with a strongly spiked tail.

tent." In another matter, too, the Galapagos land iguana differs from its marine brother; it is quite ready to feed in captivity and meets the change from cactus to cabbage in an accommodating spirit, so Mr. Beebe was able to take home a number which lived and thrived in the Reptile House in the New York Zoological Park.

Most showy and most interesting, in the writer's opinion, of all the iguanas is the great horned or rhinoceros iguana (*Cyclura cornuta*) whose home is also confined to two islands, namely, Hayti (or San Domingo) and Porto Rico in the West Indies. This lizard, dark greyish-black in colour, of massive build, with large head and wide jaws, a hanging throat pouch, loose wrinkled skin, and the crest of spines—characteristic of all these iguanas—on its back, seems perfectly modelled to suggest the gigantic reptiles of the past. It receives its popular name from three not very large, blunt "horns" on its nose.

Though it thrives in captivity, this lizard is difficult to obtain. Not only has it a very restricted range but, though fairly numerous in the localities in which it is found, it is not easy to capture it uninjured. With its strong forelegs and claws it is able to burrow deeply, even into the limestone, where burrows as much as forty feet long have been found, and when hunted with dogs (which are specially trained for the purpose) it will not hesitate to turn on these animals.

It is said to be extremely vicious, and when being hunted, or when newly captured, it may well be so, but it can be easily tamed and the single specimen the writer has possessed, a half-grown one, was quite gentle. It would lie contentedly on one's forearm for so long as one cared to bear its not negligible weight, and it seemed to enjoy having the skin of its throat rubbed and scratched. Bananas were its regular and perhaps favourite food, but it would accept a dead mouse promptly; in that it exemplified the recorded habits of its species which is described as being much more carnivorous than most of the large iguanas.

One cannot, of course, judge the behaviour of any wild animal from that of specimens which, in the case of iguanas, have spent weeks in travelling in cramped boxes, with frequent handling, before one sees them, but the writer's experience inclines him strongly to question the appropriateness of such terms as ferocious and vicious in relation to the big iguanas; a reasonable degree of self-defence, which is, after all, a very deep-seated instinct in all kinds of wild animals, being allowed a nervous animal. Those that will live in captivity seem as engaging in disposition as they are interesting in habit and impressive in appearance. Unfortunately, though, many of them have something of the quality of Moore's gazelle!

GREAT MARINE IGUANA OF THE GALAPAGOS ISLANDS

By day the marine iguanas of the Galapagos Islands, which are like a lost world in the Pacific, bask upon the baking rocks of lava by the shore. At night they sleep in some crevice. They wait until the tide is low and then go in search of the seaweeds which are their food; but often they have to swim out to sea to get a meal. Ashore the marine iguanas have for ages had no enemies and they always make for the land when alarmed.

Chapter XXXI

The Fighting Instinct in Animal Life

By A. D. Peacock

Professor of Natural History, University College, Dundee

If the question were asked, "What is Darwin's greatest book?" the answer would be "The Origin of Species"; a naturalist, with scientific licence, might even say briefly "The Origin." But this title is really not enough, for it is too little recognized that the alternative title, The Preservation of Favoured Races in the Struggle for Life, is of the utmost importance in appreciating the master's point of view and line of argument. This article deals with a special and restricted phase of that great hard fact of the struggle in animated nature, not for life, for that has a wide range of meaning, but for the barest necessaries of existence. We are to consider the rôle of force among animals.

The grim instinct of fighting is exercised under four main sets of circumstances, namely, the struggle for individual subsistence, courtship competition, the fight for the family, and the fight for the race. The struggle of the individual centres round the necessity for food and shelter, and in the apostles of brute force they are sought by offensive and predatory methods. These methods may be used by animals against their own kind, as when dogs fight over a bone, or when parent birds drive away their own offspring, or when a lion brings down a deer and is prepared to hold its kill against all comers. Even foothold must be fought for sometimes, and this is well shown on the sea-board among the crowded cliff residents such as razor-bills.

Though it is very far from being a general rule that the mated female spider devours its male partner (see Savoury's The Biology of Spiders) there is no doubt that ferocious cannibalism exists. The common garden spider (*Epeira diademeta*) is one of such habit. Hunger is the mainspring. The eating of the male has nothing to do with the pairing instinct; it is an unfortunate accident, most probably brought about by the inability of the male to escape owing to weakness after pairing. Any other spider near a hungry female, whether mated or not, runs the same risk.

Fighting for shelter may also occur between animals of the same kind, and a good example of this is seen in the hermit crabs (*Eupagurus bernhardus*). Shelter with them is no mere temporary matter, but a vital necessity, for the hind body is a soft, curled, deformed and degenerate part which must be artificially protected within a hard molluscan shell. Growth necessitates a shifting to larger quarters and should a large enough shell be unavailable the homeless crab will attack a more fortunate fellow in its castle.

Ironically enough a wicked pusillanimity, not reaching however to actual mortal fighting, is found not among the beasts of prey but among the vegetarians. The Indian flying-foxes (*Pteropus medius*) live gregariously "as thick as bees," but it is each one for itself as far as food and foothold are concerned. Social harmony seems to reign only during sleep. The fruits collected by each are those of discord; each loves a place in the shadow; and, to get these, their home in the trees is a confusion of noise and violent fighting, the weapons being the teeth and the nasty hooked claw of the thumb.

In the proverbial sayings concerning the "turning of the worm" and "when the sheep rebel," and in the famous but unconscious humour of the French natural historian who naively stated, "This animal is dangerous, it defends itself when attacked," we see a great truth—the fighting instinct is present in most animals and, though it may slumber in the meek, it can be

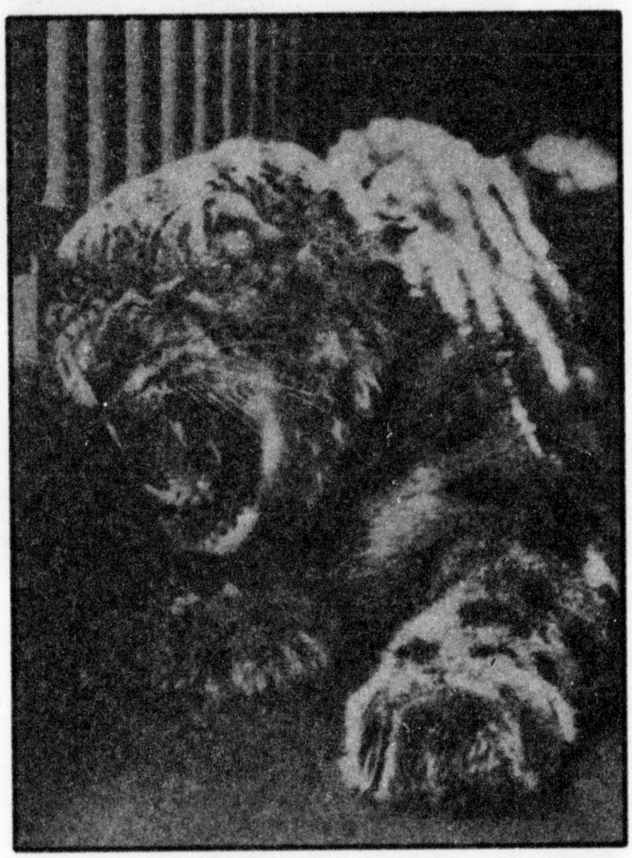

Keystone

SAVAGE SNOW LEOPARD

Leopards are among the fiercest of that fierce family of animals, the great cats, and the snow leopard from Siberia is no exception. When irritated to fighting pitch the animal takes a great deal of stopping and backs its savage snarls with its equally savage claws.

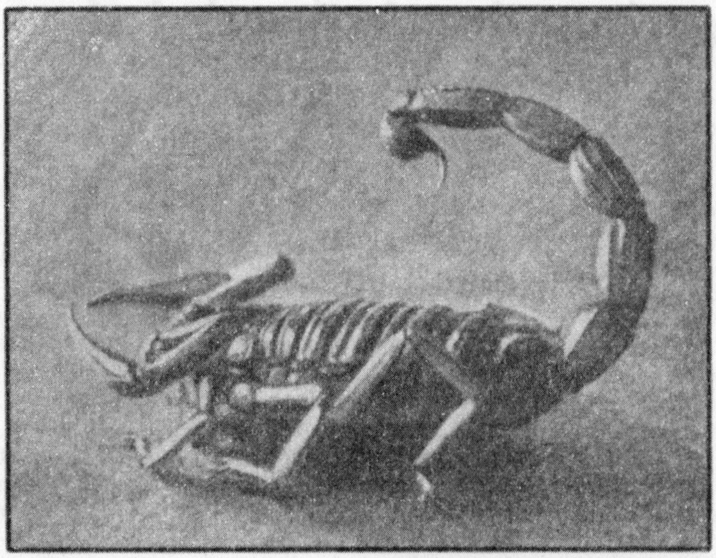

are shed and re-grown. By October the long antlers are hardened and insensitive, the velvet covering that produced and nourished them is shed, the neck swells and is more richly maned, and the stags forsake their solitude with a more gifted voice of wonderful range and timbre that serves at once for an imperious love call to the hinds and a bold challenge to rivals. Each forms a harem, or adopts one already banded, but at the cost of many furious battles. Though the antlers are armament, and engage when the stags meet head to head, they do not decide the issue either by inflicting serious wounds or the " coup de grâce," for the knightly tournament is really one of pushing. Even a bald stag may win. Fatalities are rare, perhaps one per cent, and are usually due to interlocking and hold-fast of antlers, and consequent bodily exhaustion. The fighting instinct being part and parcel of the inspirations of love and jealousy, these conflicts ensue year after year, the weaker being denied the ability to engender offspring after its kind and so lower the efficiency of the race, the stronger giving of its vigorous gifts to the benefit of the generations that are to come.

roused and exercised if the straits are dire enough.

Of a different order, but still compact of the same stuff as the instinct to fight, is the type of " hen-pecking " which determines the order of precedence of fowls in their run, or sparrows and wild ducks in their flocks. Curiously enough, it seems established for fowls that the leader in precedence, who has fought his or her way to the head, is likewise the most intelligent. Whatever there may be of *liberté* or *fraternité* there is little *égalité*. The curious will find much of interest in these matters in Alverdes' "Social Life in the Animal World."

THAT the path of true love is not smooth is nowhere better shown than in the courting days of very many animals, though, strangely enough, most of the animals that indulge in terrific struggles are not of the assertive and pugnacious orders. Rather they are of the shyer, gentler and elegant breeds, which find safety in numbers and are fond of each other's company. Discord comes and lasts only for a particular season of short duration. One of the most famous examples is, of course, the deer.

For the winter months, November to March, the red deer live in herds, both hinds and antlered stags, in perfect amity. But from March to July the stags lead solitary inoffensive lives, what time the antlers

British Instructional Films

FIGHTING FEMALES OF THE MANTIS, AND THE DEADLY SCORPION

The females of the insect called the praying mantis, so soon as mating is accomplished, at once proceed to eat their mates. The females fight furiously, as we see above, for the wretched creature who provides not only the wedding, but the wedding breakfast. The scorpion (top) assumes this posture of defence in a trice and is one of the deadliest insects.

Similar stories can be told of other deer, such as the wapiti and moose, but in their distant relatives, the antelopes, the fights may be to the death.

Of other herding animals—guanacos, vicunas and the feral horses of South America, the zebras and Nubian wild asses of Africa and the kangaroos of Australia—the same general features are seen, namely, the single dominant male, jealous of rivals and willing to fight the herd enemies.

Among European bison the old bulls lead solitary lives and are usually a match for the wolves. But in the rutting season they join the herd and their fighting qualities are used in battling for mates. The ferocity and altruism of the American bison on behalf of the herd are believed now to have been overstated. A curious modification of rutting behaviour is seen in other bovines, such as the South African gnu and the Burmese banteng, where the young bulls league together to drive out the old steers.

Even in aquatic mammals the bulls of the fur seals (*Callorhinus*) fight furiously on the breeding shores to establish and maintain their harems until the friendly sea life once again is resumed.

Turning to the birds we find that the male eagles and capercailzies fight over their mates; but a curious reversion is witnessed in the button quails (*Turnices*) and phalaropes, for their females are the larger, are more gaily feathered and dispute for the males which subsequently rear the brood.

The reptiles likewise have their duels, examples being male crocodiles, Malayan lizards, which change their colour as they fight, and the Carolina iguana (*Anolis carolinensis*) where the loser forfeits his tail and the victor eats it. Omitting the amphibia, which offer little of interest in this regard, and the fishes and other aquatic animals, which are treated specially elsewhere, there is little of remark until we reach the insects, where males of the long-horned grasshoppers, the stag beetles, ground wasps and solitary bees may contend to the death.

Touching the fight for the family we cannot do better than consider briefly one of its phases through the medium of Howard's remarkable book on

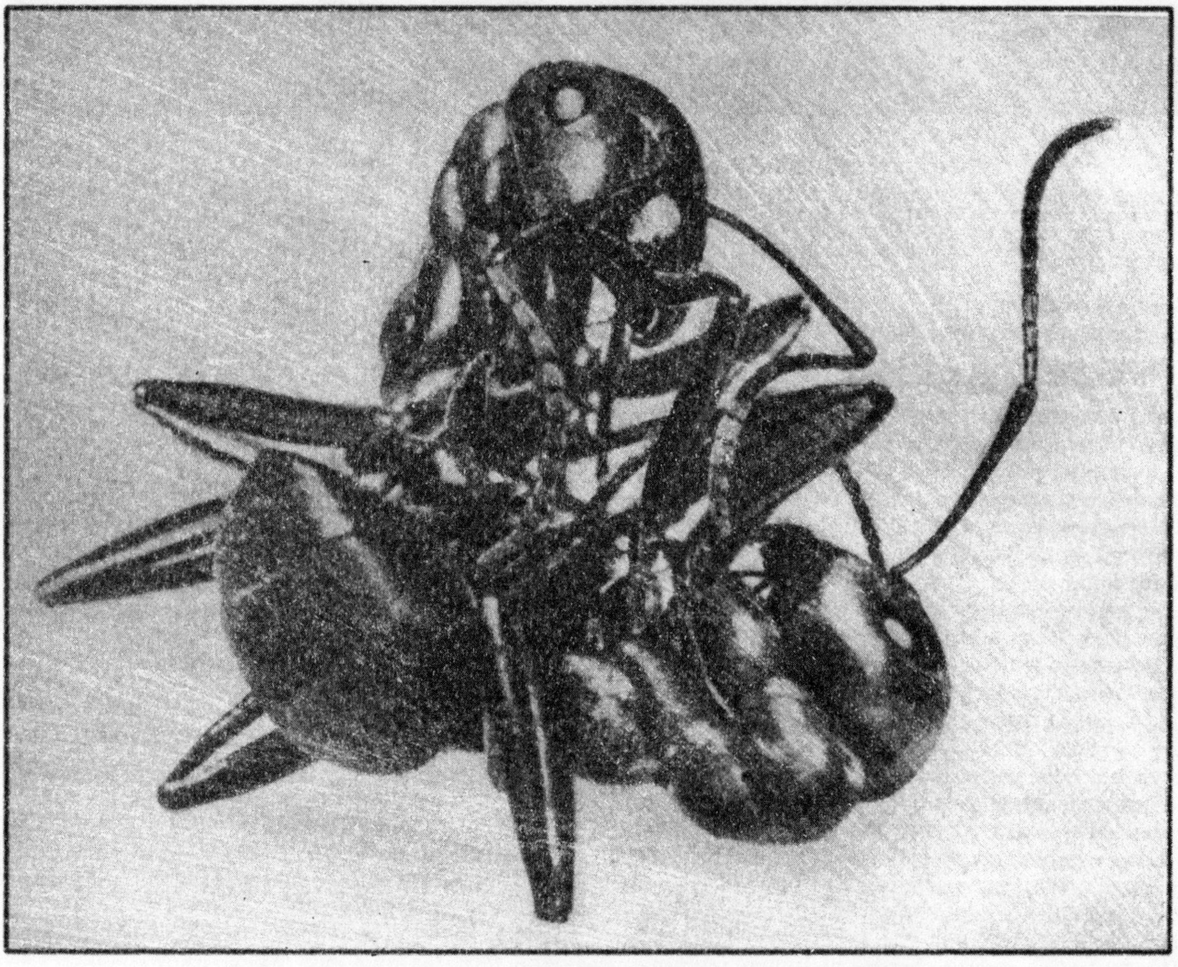

A. E Smith

TO THE DEATH: DESPERATE DUEL BETWEEN TWO WOOD ANTS

Upon walking through a pine wood, one may often see the large mounds of pine needles which form the nests of the wood ants. A close inspection of the ground in the vicinity will often reveal a tremendous activity going on, workers returning with some captured insect, or bringing in more pine needles. But the ants are warriors as well as workers, and a meeting between members of rival communities will lead to a struggle whose only end is death. Here we see (greatly magnified) a couple of these small creatures furiously biting each other.

Neville Kingston

SPIDER CRABS AT DEATH GRIPS UNDER WATER

To test the fighting instinct of the crab it is only necessary to get within reach of its formidable claws. The larger crabs, when stranded in some cranny in the rocks by the departing tide, have also an ugly trick of rising up on their legs from a crouching position, and bearing with their backs against the roof of their retreat, effectually trapping the incautious hand that has alarmed them. This remarkable photograph shows a pair of spider crabs in the act of fighting fiercely under water.

"Territory in Bird Life," a work of unusual merit in the annals of bird-lore and animal behaviour. Its thesis is that, in very many birds, "each male isolates itself at the commencement of the breeding season and exercises dominion over a restricted area of ground." There are internecine struggles between the males of blackbirds, lapwings, cuckoos, pied wagtails, long-tailed tits and jays, and inter-specific battles between peregrine falcon and raven and between the green woodpeckers and the great spotted woodpeckers.

Other workers have shown that moor-hens, coots, swans, wild ducks and wild geese, defend their area and nest against their kind. Not unexpectedly, the quaint penguins add to their quaintness in breeding time by having regular beats around their rectangular stony patches. In those birds of prey, the falcons and eagles, both mates defend their family and their far-flung quartering ground against intruders, and in the case of a South African eagle (*Haliaetus vocifer*) the range extends to a diameter of two miles. Among mammals the same is illustrated by apes and kangaroos, though here it may be that the fighting is on behalf of not only the family but the herd.

The leaders of separate hordes of Indian macaque monkeys fight duels and sometimes thereby provoke a general embroilment. And oriental travellers tell us that "pi-dogs" have their own special low alley haunts, in which a strange dog will be torn to bits. Despite its size we may regard the bee-hive population as one big family and the killing of all strangers at the door as a protective exercise of the fighting instinct. We need not repeat the many prodigies of valour that are performed by mothers in defence of their young—even as the hen defends her chickens—not only against enemies, but, as in the case of beasts of prey, against infanticidal fathers. Fathers, too, may back the protective instinct by fighting, as witness the dog fox in defence of the litter.

The mid-wife toad (*Alytes obstetricans*) also deserves a word. It may more truly be called a "mid-man," for it is the husband that will fight marauders for the string of eggs that encumbers his legs.

A CURIOUS situation arises at nesting-time among the ostriches, where the male arranges the nest and where females are in the majority. Surplus hens, though they may pair, lay their eggs beside those of other birds which have a consort. This leads to fighting between the hens and a tragic smashing of eggs.

But, always excepting man, it is of those Lilliputians the insects that the greatest fighting epics must be written. The stories centre round social types such as the termites and ants which form colonies. In most cases each colony is a single family founded by a mother-queen, and for this reason their fighting behaviour is discussed under the present head. It should be remembered, however, that colonies may

Central Press

FIGHTING INSTINCT AS IT IS EXPRESSED BY THE LAND CRABS

Even in what must be an alarming situation to it, suspension in mid-air, the land crab (bottom) does not cease to grip with powerful claw the clumsy boot that has intruded upon its peace. The fighting land crabs of Gambia (top), the British colony in West Africa, have not earned their name for nothing. When in captivity missing limbs about their place of confinement give evidence of the frequent battle which these fierce creatures wage with each other. Luckily such lost limbs are replaceable.

D. Seth-Smith

E.N.A

SNAKE FIGHTS IN WHICH THE VICTOR DINES ON THE VANQUISHED

In the two fights illustrated here, the end was not merely the defeat and death of the rival, but a meal as well. In the lower photograph is a mussurana snake which has succeeded in coiling itself fatally round a highly-poisonous jararaca. The upper photograph shows a cribo, from South America, which habitually feeds upon other snakes whether poisonous or not, though the cribo itself has no poison equipment. Here it is seen in the final stages of swallowing a highly-venomous viper.

F. Birtles

THRILLING DUELS BETWEEN CROCODILES AND BETWEEN PYTHON AND ALLIGATOR

The lower illustration, one of the most extraordinary photographs of fighting animals ever taken, shows two Johnston crocodiles at the fatal end of a contest. The victor, on the right, has got the snout of the vanquished between its deadly jaws and has almost succeeded in drowning its adversary, whose eyes are already closing in the last unconsciousness. Above is a python crushing an alligator by the Rio Oro in Venezuela. The alligator's body can be seen giving beneath the strain, but the python was so wounded that it died also.

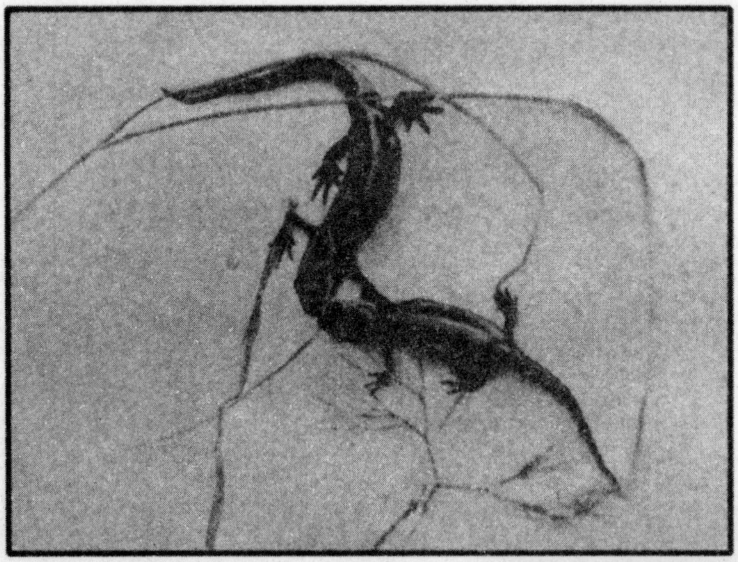

M. H. Crawford

neighbouring formicary of the same species. In one species of "wood ant" (*Formica pratensis*) Forel watched a war over a tree rich in the green-fly which the ants "milk" for their sugary honey-dew. If colonies are about evenly matched the campaign may drag on for days until the truce of a drawn war is mutually assented to through mere exhaustion of numbers. As in most clan fighting, the inhabitants are in worse case than at the start, and the only beneficiaries are a third kind, a small and timid species, which ekes out its living by body-snatching.

One of the greatest epics was the War of Zurich between two colonies of the pavement ant (*Tetramorium caespitum*). The terrain was a grass slope before the university, the front extended more than thirty yards, the campaign lasted over a month and the dead numbered thousands. It was as if humans joined issue over a six-mile front and, indeed, the human parallel was not far to seek, for the Franco-German war raged simultaneously.

Continuing these Froissart chronicles of the ants under the heading of "the fight for the race" we may touch on a British species, the blood-red robber ant (*Formica sanguinea*) which is a slave-raider. Raiding, strictly speaking, is usually a bloodless affair of brute force and not one of fighting, though at times single combats arise between invaders and invaded. The war is by siege and sack. The attackers surround the nest, say, of the dark-

E.N.A

SNAPPING TURTLE AND FIGHTING NEWTS

In the New World the alligator-terrapin or snapping turtle (bottom) looks, and is, fierce. It rather resembles an alligator as far as its tail is concerned, and the head is armed with a formidable beak with which it can inflict a dangerous bite. The upper illustration shows two newts striving for the possession of a worm.

not always be composed entirely of brothers and sisters, so that any offensive or defensive measures may thus be looked upon better as reactions for the good of the race and not merely the family, however large the latter may be. This aspect will be dealt with presently.

In the case of the ants defensive fighting is far from being the only evidence of martial temper. Ignoring for the moment the underlying psychology, we may state that every expression of the old Adam in man is paralleled in the ants — sabre-rattling, gladiatorial combats, alliances, little affairs on the frontiers, civil war, poisoning, slave-raiding, wars of aggression, attrition and extermination and wars of zoological species, orders and classes.

Fabre has been called the Homer of the insects, but in that Swiss doyen of natural history, Auguste Forel, the ants have not only a Homer, but, to adopt the phrase of Professor Wheeler of Harvard, a Socrates. Forel's "The Social World of the Ants" is one of the world's recent great books. Indeed, the social insects are very worthily chronicled to-day and, to mention only two more works, the interested are referred to Donisthorpe's "British Ants" and Wheeler's "Insect Societies." From all three books these brief stories take their source.

It is a grim commentary at this date that among the most warlike of ants are the European. Of these, *Neomyrmica rubida* (it has no common name) is the deadliest, but, just as "it is excellent to have a giant's strength but terrible to use it," this form, despite its stinging powers, is not aggressive.

A war of aggression frequently ensues from a strong colony flouting the territorial rights and riches of a coloured species (*Formica fusca*), but allow the garrison to dribble out, or panic away without the honours of war, and seize the undeveloped brood, "which pillage they with merry march bring home to the tent royal of their empress." Regarding the aftermath, Darwin describes how a *fusca* "was perched motionless with its own pupa in its mouth on the top of a spray of heath, an image of despair over its ravaged home."

But in some ant struggles the defenders are in better case; certain African species, the Cremastogasters, live in the spines of acacias, but should one of the aggressive driver ants (*Anomma*) attempt the entrance hole in the acacia spine the Cremastogasters make a blockade with their abdomens from which they squirt their caustic poison.

The terrible people are the nomadic visiting ants, the Dorylinids. They are a turbulent folk and will go for any insect. Many species are blind, their stings are relatively weak, but their jaws are strong, their courage high and furious, and their numbers legion. Against them the hairs and size of large caterpillars are of no avail, nor the agility of a cricket; neither are domestic animals immune.

Rivalling the ants in social organization, and their hereditary enemies, are the termites, and in their order likewise fighting plays its part. This aspect, entitled "The War between Ants and Termites," is treated by Professor Bugnion in a worthy appendix to Forel's book. There are civil wars, but the great struggle, ages long and never-ending, is with the ants. The ants, undoubtedly, are the aggressors. On the whole, too, they are the victors in fighting and it is believed that the infinite variety of the termite defensive measures, soldier caste, equipment, organization and all, are mainly to counter their particular enemies. However, certain cocoa tree termites (*Eutermes*), under certain conditions, as when lichen-gathering for food, do not decline open combat. If their dispositions for defence are sound and their numbers sufficient they will fight the weaving ants (*Oecophylla*) three times their size, and even beat them, their success being largely attributable to their armament of a head gland that squirts a certain disabling sticky fluid.

By contrast with these insect studies the defensive fighting of other animals sounds tame, but one or two cases deserve mention. After all, there is something very gallant in the union of small song birds to harass a bird of prey, and something rather noble in the defence of the herd against the carnivora, and the rallying of chimpanzees to the aid of a comrade.

Like many other instincts, the fighting instinct may be modified and transformed, and several examples are very interesting. Man has availed himself of the fighting spirit of his lower brothers. We see this in his utilisation of dogs as protectors, but it is also known that apes may act in the same wise. He has also utilised them for "sport," as in the gamecock; but the quaintest illustration of this is in the Chinese cult of the cricket, which equals,

CAMELS WITH NECKS LOCKED IN A FIERCE GRAPPLE

Camels have an unattractive reputation, among those who use them as beasts of burden, as being surly and extremely vicious. Very often bad treatment and overwork accentuate these characteristics, but in general there seems to be no doubt that the camel is a stupid, disgruntled creature which has never taken kindly to the serving of man. The result of all this bad temper comes fully to light when camels quarrel. The bites they can give are capable of doing considerable damage, and the two seen above are locked in a very grim grapple

Major Radcliffe Dugmore

Keystone

MORTAL COMBAT OF THE DEER IN THE RUTTING SEASON

Deer fight very fiercely for the possession of their females during the rutting or mating season. The males, at this time, have just grown their new antlers, and one animal may possess itself of several females when another may arrive and make a bid for their possession (top). Very often these fights have a fatal result, as we see in the lower illustration, where a double tragedy has taken place. Sometimes the antlers get locked together, so that a weakened animal which might otherwise have got away and recovered, dies a lingering death.

Neville Kingston

DOMESTIC STRUGGLES AT THE ZOO AMONG POLAR BEARS AND PELICANS

When there is more than one wife to a family, as in the case of the polar bear (bottom), strife is inevitable sooner or later, and then it is that the husband must step in, or as in this case, swim in, and, so to speak, put his foot down. We see the male bear intervening lustily between his two angry wives. Above is a crested pelican which has taken possession of a convenient perch, and very much resents a move on the part of a common Australian pelican to share it. The attitude of the former suggests what will happen if the latter should persist.

Neville Kingston

HOW SEA LIONS AND KANGAROOS SETTLE THEIR DIFFERENCES

While the sea lions (left) look happy enough at the Zoo in their large swimming pool edged with artificial rocks whence they can indulge in their favourite pastime of diving, yet everything does not always go smoothly even with them. The sea lion is apt to get pugnacious and fretful and his teeth can pay off old scores very well. Kangaroos, too, are excellently equipped for fighting and administer frightful kicks with their hind legs. As though to guard against such kicks these two are standing well away from each other's hind claws and wrestling for position. Indeed **their attitude is strangely like the preliminary grip of a certain historic style of English wrestling.**

IBEX HORNS ENTANGLED IN BATTLE

In this position the ibex twists and pushes, manoeuvring for position with its rival. This species of wild goat is especially remarkable for its fine curving horns, which are used with effect in the mating season. These horns are armed with transverse ridges which give a serrated surface to their already formidable weapons.

if it does not beat, cockfighting. The Chinese have an innate interest and sympathy for insects above all other animals, so much so that the cicada, a symbol of resurrection, the praying mantis, a symbol of bravery, and the butterfly and the dragon-fly are held in highest esteem both artistically and religiously; while the fighting crickets are regarded as incarnations of legendary heroes and have a literature that is all their own.

The fighting instinct in the different pugnacious species of crickets is supposedly attributable to the fact that the insects continually have to guard and maintain their holes against all comers. The points looked for in a fighter are loud chirping, long legs, big head and neck—the fighting parts—and broad bodies and backs. They are called "generals" and "marshals" and are pampered to the full. In training they are nobly fed on special food, including blood-filled mosquitoes, which have gorged on the arm of the fancier, and a tonic soup of a special flower. Before the fight, and to excite ferocity, they may be compelled to fast for some considerable time.

THEIR are heavy, middle, and light-weight contests. In special places, and in special bowls on silken covered tables, the contestants are matched, what time their past form is recited by the referee, styled the "Army Commander" or "Director of the Battle." He excites them by special fine "ticklers" of grass or hair until the issue is joined. The weapons are the biting mouth-parts, which are used with the utmost ferocity, and the battle is to the death. Victory is achieved, not uncommonly, by the "better man" dropping with the whole weight of his body on the back of his fellow gladiator and beheading him. Their fame is scrolled on ivory tablets, frequently in letters of gold, a champion of many victories being a "conquering cricket" (*shou lip*), a champion of champions a "Grand Marshal."

What may be called a twisted instinct is shown in singing birds when they defend the changeling egg or young cuckoo by worrying a full-grown cuckoo that approaches the nest. The beginnings of the dangerous spirit are seen in the *hamadrya* and *gelada* baboons whose respective clans shriek and bellow dislike and defiance at one another. Unnatural conditions too, breed bad feeling and blows; a captive idle baboon may tease a dog, and Professor Yerkes has observed the malicious glee of a young ape inciting his elder companions to fisticuffs by pretending that he had been attacked. In Nature, to use an Irishism, the unnatural conditions induced by the thwarting, on the part of the older animals, of the mating instinct in young male seals and vicunas, lead to constant quarrelling. And, just as in Northumberland and Durham, the Sword Dance really symbolises an ancient heroic fight, so we see a similar transmutation of fighting behaviour in the sports of many animals.

All great students of the order state that many kinds of ants play at fighting, while bird lovers know that ruffs and blackcocks have sham battles which are apparently ferocious but which really serve to rouse mating excitement. It is even stated, and this the specialist may deny, that stag-fighting is really a sport; for the stag, in deliberately seeking out the challenger and thereby risking his whole harem, seems deliberately to go out of his way to battle. One would think, however, that the fighting instinct, no matter how strong, would be subordinate to the instincts of mating and proprietorship.

And the upshot of all this brute belligerency? Is the battle really to those that swing the sword; or shall they perish by it and the meek inherit the earth? For the rival societies of termites and ants—the former mainly non-aggressive in respect of the other—are both successful to-day; so are the peaceful herbivorous herds and their enemies the predatory carnivores. To these questions we shall probably never know the answer, for man in his steady conquest of Nature, to paraphrase the Rubaiyat, is grasping this Scheme of Things entire, shattering it to pieces and remoulding it nearer to the Heart's Desire. Yet even Man in his conquering arrogance may still go to the ant and be wise!

But however powerful the influence of man may become, surely this complex thing which we call, for want of a better term, the fighting instinct, will remain one of the most durable of animal characteristics.

Herbert G. Ponting, F.R.P.S., Copyright

WEDDELL SEALS OF THE ANTARCTIC BASKING ON ICE FLOES OFF ROSS ISLAND

When Scott made his heroic and fatal dash to the South Pole he fixed his winter quarters on Ross Island in January, 1911. It is on the same island that the Weddell seals seen above are basking in the Antarctic sun, which, strange as it may seem, provides a very comforting warmth even when fallen snow is lying thick upon the floes. The animals are enjoying a rest at the foot of an ice cliff of dazzling white and show up conspicuously against their snow background. Presently they will stir and flounder to the water's edge, when, with a dive, they lose all awkwardness and become swift-moving creatures of the sea. **They are named after the explorer Weddell who also gave his name to the bay called the Weddell Sea.**

Chapter XXXII

As the Poles Asunder: Animals of the Arctic and Antarctic

By J. L. Cope

Commander, British Imperial Antarctic Expedition

THE chief differences between the Arctic and the Antarctic Continents lie firstly in the fact that whereas the Antarctic Continent is a land mass (roughly two and a half times the size of Australia) surrounded by water, the Arctic Continent is a mass of water surrounded by land; and secondly that there are no quadrupeds in the Antarctic, the first part of the statement really explaining the second.

In the Southern Polar Continent the mean summer temperature is seldom much above freezing point and vegetation is scarce; the little that does exist is cryptogamic, and comprises fungi, lichens, mosses, and some fresh-water algae, but there are no flowering plants on mainland or island.

In both the Arctic and the Antarctic regions marine life is prolific and there is a similarity between them. This has given rise to what is known as "the problem of bipolarity," that is, the theory that certain species have been enabled to travel from one frigid zone to the other. But against this many zoologists maintain that all such species which resemble each other in the Polar Seas are cosmopolitan and are found in the intervening seas and, generally speaking, the question of bipolarity is entirely unsupported by a study of the fish life and is not accepted by modern zoologists.

In the south, alar life is common both on land and sea, being represented in particular by such varied forms as the skua gull, snowpetrels and the ever attractive penguins.

The penguins are birds that have been specially adapted to lead an aquatic life, and they seek their nourishment entirely in the sea. The food consists of minute shrimp-like animals known as copepoda, which they catch on their tongues by swimming through water in which these crustaceans are dense. Their beaks remain partially open. The tongue of the penguin is barbed, and as the water flows in at the front of the mouth and out at the back on each side, the shrimps are caught in the barbs of the tongue and quickly swallowed.

The young birds are at first looked after entirely by the female, the male parent obtaining all the food for both his wife and children. Often he fills himself so full that the food dribbles out of his mouth as he waddles with great difficulty, owing to his temporary corpulency, back to his nest of stones. He feeds both mother and young by regurgitating portions of his stomach contents into the lower beak, from which his family peck at it.

The largest species of penguin is the emperor penguin, which is found on the most southerly edge of the Great Ice Barrier. Here it breeds in mid-winter. The bird is enabled to do this by important anatomical and physiological specialisations, such as having a special pouch in which to keep egg and young warm during the severe winter, and by accumulating a large amount of blubber on which to feed as, of course, it is unable to get the copepods in the winter, the sea being frozen over.

Every other species of penguin, except the emperor penguin, goes north as the Antarctic winter approaches, partly by swimming and partly by resting on drifting icebergs and floes

The habits of the penguins have been carefully observed and in many cases recorded by the kinematograph, and perhaps their most striking characteristic is their social organization; they are intelligent, and the only "civilized" denizens of the far south.

It has been said that stories concerning penguins are like those of anglers, but the writer can vouch for the truth of this one. In the mating season the male proposes to the female by carrying a stone in his beak and placing it at her feet. If the lady accepts the gentleman's proposal she does so by picking up the stone in her beak and moving it towards her. One day a member of a recent

Herbert G. Ponting, F.R.P.S., Copyright

SKUA GULL CHICK

As a rule the skua gull, which gets its living by preying on young penguins, lays two eggs only. The newly-hatched chick above was taken from an adjacent nest and placed on this pair of eggs for the sake of comparison. Notice the absence of any nest.

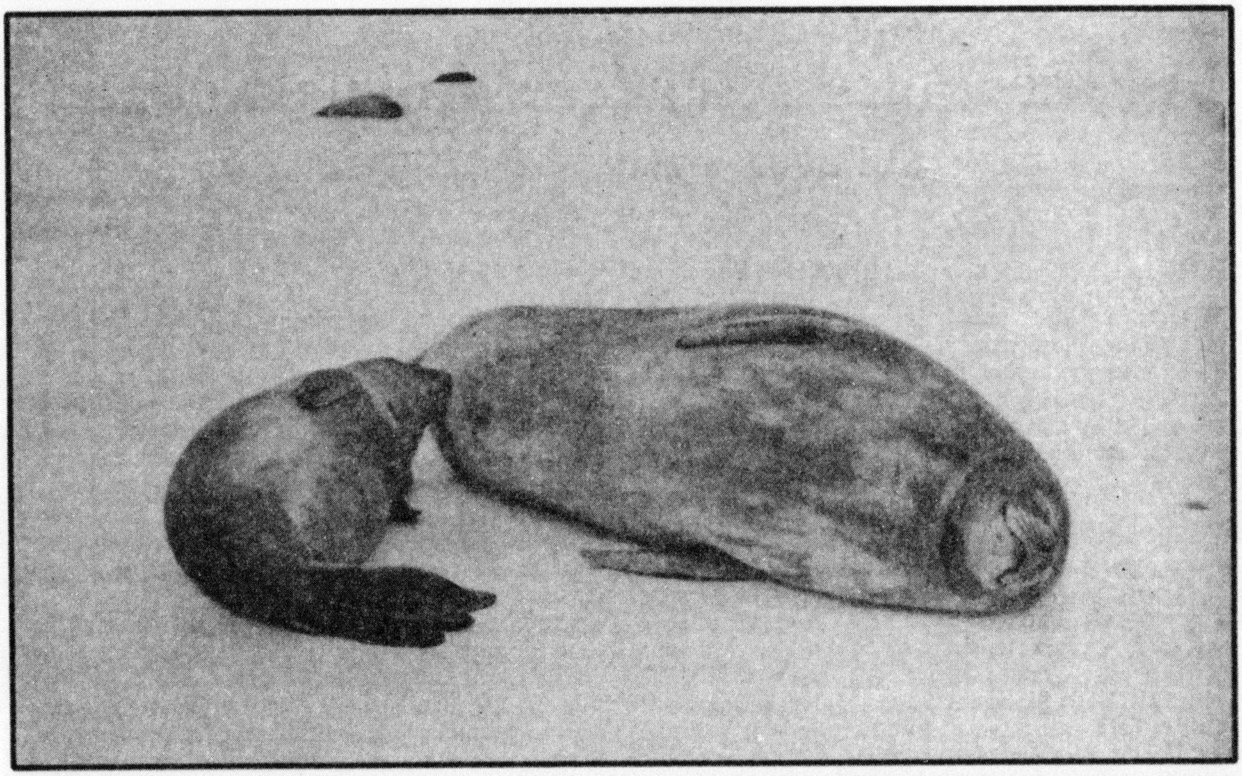

Herbert G. Ponting, F.R.P.S., Copyright

FEMALE SEAL ON THE ICE WITH HER YOUNG ONE

Some idea of the tameness of this particular seal may be gained from the short range at which these photographs were taken. The explorers did not kill or harm the animals unless they wanted food. There was no wholesale slaughtering such as has made seals elsewhere so terrified of man Note how the seal cub is taking its ease on its back and is looking half round at the photographer with a comical air of mild wonder, shared by its equally gentle and unalarmed mother.

WEDDELL SEAL AND THE CONDITIONS UNDER WHICH IT LIVES

While the seal has to seek and find a place where it can mount the edges of the ice cliffs of various heights which form much of the "coast" of the Antarctic, it can depart into the sea very much easier, for it is an expert diver (bottom) In the winter the seal must keep a hole in the frozen sea free from ice so that it may fish Periodically it comes up to breathe (top left). The top right-hand photograph shows a seal from the back, when its flippers have gained a hold, and it is just heaving half out of the water.

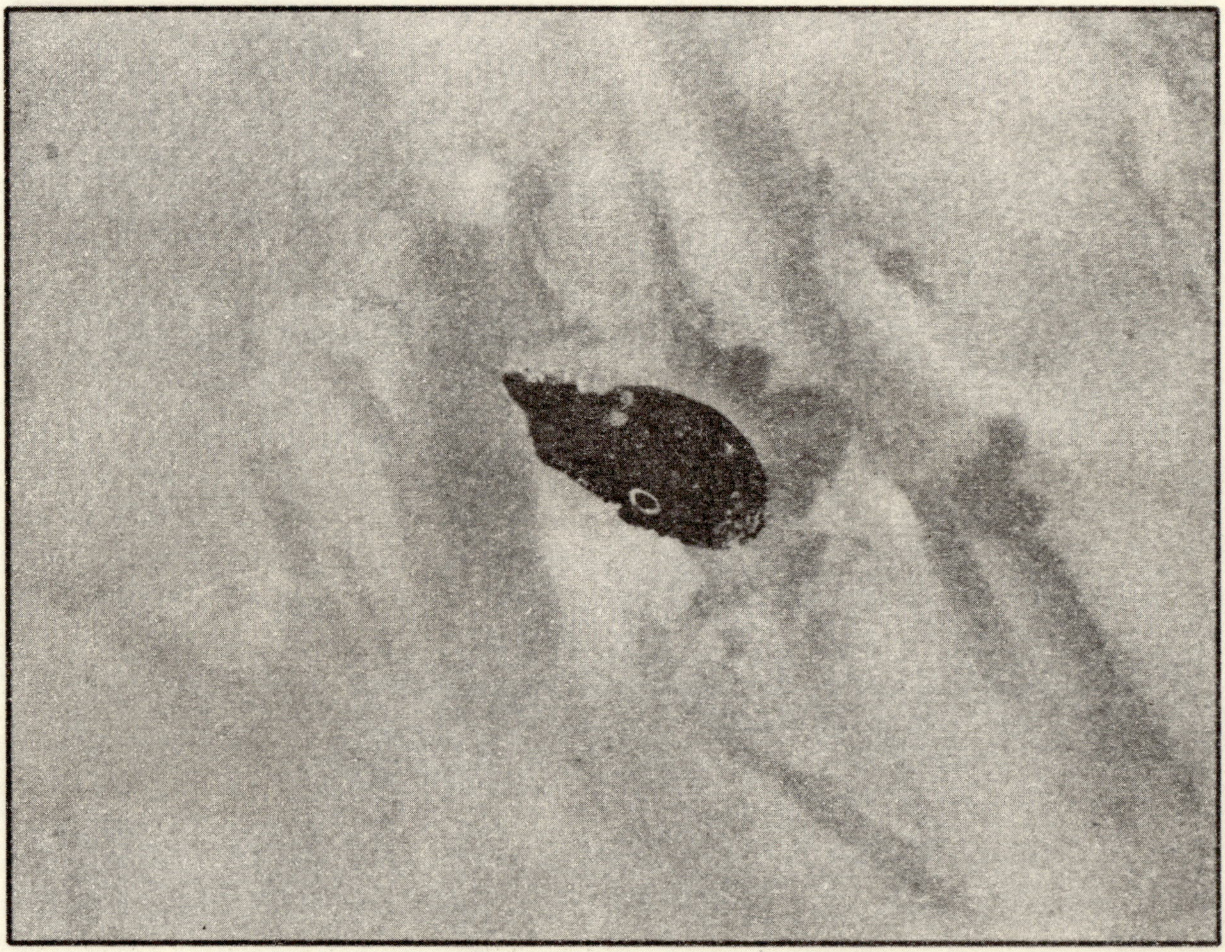

Herbert G. Ponting, F.R.P.S., Copyright

DEVOTION TO DUTY IN THE PENGUIN'S NESTING SEASON

Even a blizzard will not drive the penguin off its nest (bottom), and it will sit valiantly on while the snow gradually mounts higher and higher about it, until finally, as here, only the beak and an eye are left in the air. The eggs are incubated on a pile of stones (top left), and every now and then the eggs are turned (top right) for the sake of airing them, an operation which is frequently repeated, despite the temperature. The Adélie penguin breeds in the Antarctic but goes north in the winter.

Herbert G. Ponting, F.R.P.S., Copyright

ADELIE AND EMPEROR PENGUINS, SOCIAL COLONISTS OF THE FAR SOUTH

Penguins live in communities, and in some other respects also are remarkably like human beings. The wonderful photograph here (bottom) shows a few Adelie penguins resting on the snow with the cone of Mount Erebus, an active volcano over twelve thousand feet high, in the background. The top right-hand photograph shows two Adelies who are mated, and the remaining illustration is of an Emperor penguin, a species which attains a greater size and does not swim north for warmer climate in the winter as the Adelies do.

W. S. Berridge

ONE OF THE KING PENGUINS

Next to the Emperors in size come the King penguins, which, when young, are distinguished by their dark brown coats. A brown-yellow tinge is a feature of throat and breast in the adult, in contrast to the white-fronted Adelies.

Antarctic expedition was sitting on a rock in December, the Antarctic midsummer, writing up some scientific observations, when he felt a penguin pecking at one of his trouser-legs. He tried to shoo the animal away, but the bird was persistent. The man looked from his work down at the penguin, and one can easily realize his embarrassment when he discovered that the reason of the penguin's persistence was that it had placed a stone at his feet!

THE mammalian life in the Antarctic is entirely marine and consists of several species of whales and seals. The whales only inhabit the south polar waters in the summer when they are not frozen over, but the seals remain south all the year round, and during the winter live by blow holes which they keep open in the sea-ice.

Land animals are non-existent in Antarctica for the reason already stated in the opening paragraph of this chapter, but minute wingless insects, degenerate in type, have been found. In the freshwater ponds microscopic life is prolific; here are found the Tardigrada or "water bears," and the rotifers. These animalcules have a wonderful power of resistance to low temperatures and have been thawed out of blocks of ice chipped from the ponds, having been frozen solid certainly for months and it may be, when a pond failed to thaw in a severe summer, for very much longer periods still.

The Antarctic continent in regard to birds and mammals cannot be considered a separate zoological province. Its fauna for the most part consists of certain generic groups of seals which, it is true, are peculiar, but which live as much on the pack-ice as on the continental shores. The species of penguins form a group which is common to the extremities of all three continents of the south, and the other birds mentioned are all found to a greater or less extent elsewhere outside the south polar regions.

When the great southern land mass, known as Antarctica, separated off from the other continental masses by vast stretches of ocean, and gradually became devoid of vegetation, the penguin, as may be easily appreciated, developed aquatic habits which would enable him to pursue his food northwards as the sea froze over in the Antarctic winter. In the north no such events occurred, and this explains the absence of the penguin in the northern polar region. But now, in the water, the penguin, withal his having the appearance of a fine gentleman in evening dress when strutting about over the ice and land, has two serious marine foes in the shape of the killer whale and the sea leopard; while on land, where he is flightless and therefore helpless, the skua gulls rob him of both eggs and young.

BRITISH, French, and Belgian, German and Swedish expeditions have investigated the marine fauna of the Antarctic and since 1900 have added several surprises to the world's knowledge of the fish life of the continental coast and sub-Antarctic islands, such as the relationships of the marine life of South Georgia and Graham Land and the fact that this in its turn bears no resemblance to that of the Magellan-Falklands area. This diversity has occupied a long evolutionary period, and the continent may have lain in the midst of a cold ocean throughout the Tertiary geological period.

Our knowledge of the oceanic life in these parts has been added to especially by the German "Valdivia" Expedition. The abysmal fauna are poor. There are fishes of a dark coloration, prawns of a deep red hue and other bathypelagic organisms. The less deep waters are inhabited by small silvery fishes having large eyes, many small crustaceans, pteropods, and suchlike organisms. In still less depths predaceous fishes with swarms of foraminifera, radiolaria, copepoda, siphonophora and medusae are found. The vertebrate fishes are mostly silvery in appearance with a blue back, while the invertebrate are generally transparent and colourless.

In the surface waters of the ocean microscopic plants, known as microplankton, abound. These plants are nourished by the soluble inorganic substances of the sea water and carbon dioxide, and they form the nutriment of most young marine life, termed animal plankton, such as the small crustaceans and the larvae of fishes. These in their turn form the food of deep-sea fishes, and the smaller of the pelagic fishes become the prey of the larger pelagic life. Thus the distribution of fish life depends greatly on the microplankton and generally speaking these are abundant along coastal regions, but in the open sea are present in greater quantity in the cold regions than in warmer seas.

In dealing with the north polar regions we have, in addition to a more extensive animal life, a very prolific plant life to consider. The flora of the Arctic regions is restricted to the lower lands which are snow-free for a considerable period annually, and it extends to the most northerly land known to man. The growth is lowly, but there are also dwarf shrubs, and it is mostly phanerogamic and cryptogamic. There are some grasses which reach a height of eighteen inches and also some moss-cushions over one foot in depth. Many have brilliantly coloured flowers. Peary Land, lying to the north of Greenland, and other parts are so densely vegetated as to support rodents and ruminants in large numbers. The plants appear regularly every summer in the natural economy of the land, the low temperatures being unable to check the continuance of plant life in the fertile soil.

The Arctic Ocean is well stocked with animal life. *Balaena mysticetus*, the whalebone whale, is now practically extinct by reason of past commercial activities, but in the open waters to the farthest navigable north the white whale and the narwhal are plentiful.

Walrus and seal live on marine life, and the polar bear, Monarch of the Arctic, preys over the whole of the icy vast upon seal and fish. It is curious to note how the walrus and the bear have protective coloration, the one for the sea and the other for the land. The walrus is black, so that he may be less conspicuous in the icy blackness of the cold waters; while the polar bear is clothed in a whiteness that renders him less visible to his prey in the surroundings through which he tracks.

The Arctic fox and wolf are other examples of Arctic carnivores, and the wolf attacks all others save the polar bear and the musk-ox. In the circumpolar

Herbert G. Ponting. F.R.P.S. Copyright

OCTOPUS CAPTURED IN THE ICY SEA OFF CAPE ROYDS

This creature measured more than three feet from tip to tip of its tentacles, and was caught off Cape Royds during the Scott expedition. It was the first octopus known to have been captured in these latitudes. It is frozen stiff as it lies there on the snow, and beside it is the folding measure with which the creature's dimensions were gauged. Polar waters are more prolific of life than any others, but, even so, it is seldom that residents in warmer seas, such as this, travel so far from their homes.

E.N.

From the film "Stella Polaris"

MONARCH OF THE ARCTIC IN HIS KINGDOM OF THE SNOWS

Away from the haunts of men the Polar bear has little to fear in his frozen domain, and preys upon seal or fish unmolested. The coat remains white all the year round, and the long neck and small snake-like head distinguish this from all other species of bear. But when man invades the regions where this great white beast is found he usually does so accompanied by the fierce Eskimo dogs, whose favourite pastime is the hunting of Polar bears (top). Ten dogs are usually a match for the largest and fiercest bear.

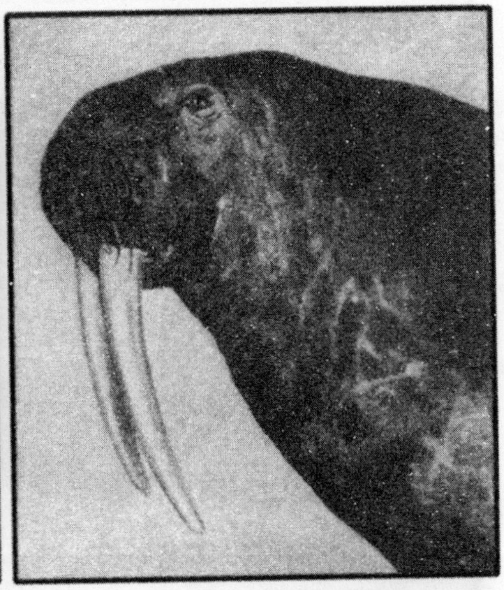

From the film "Stella Polaris"

GREAT SEA MAMMAL OF THE NORTH—THE WALRUS

When full grown a male walrus may weigh 3,000 pounds and measure 12 feet in length, and is a formidable antagonist for even the Polar bear. Ruthless hunting has tended to drive it further and further into the uninhabited North. When young (top left) the fur is light brown, but with maturity the coloration becomes uniformly dark to harmonise with the dark of the cold seas. The tusks (top right) grow a foot long and more in the adult male, and are used for breaking molluscs, the principal food of the walrus, and for fighting.

SEAL CLIMBING A CLIFF AND A HERD OF SEALS ALARMED

From the film "Stella Polaris."

While found in all seas that are not actually tropical, the seal abounds mostly in the Arctic and Antarctic. It is an animal which has cleverly adapted itself to a marine life The tail and hind limbs have become united for swimming purposes in the true seal as opposed to the walrus and sea lion, and are useless on land, where the seal drags itself along by its fore limbs or flippers. It can even climb cliffs thus (bottom). It was the seals' clumsiness and their habit of collecting in great herds (top) that enabled the old sealers to slay such thousands.

W. S. Berridge

MUSK OX AND WOLVERINE, DWELLERS WITHIN THE ARCTIC CIRCLE

Inhabiting country where, even in summer-time the surface of the soil scarcely thaws, the musk-ox takes its name from the flavour of musk with which its flesh is tainted. The head is rather sheep-like in appearance, and the apparent size is much greater than the actual size, since the thickness of its coat, necessary in the Arctic cold, is tremendous. Actually the musk ox is only about two-thirds as large as the American bison. The wolverine or glutton (top) is circumpolar in distribution and measures about three feet in length.

Antarctic as do the penguins, and southward from the Arctic as do the migrant birds ; or the amount of blubber is increased as a food reserve before the winter sets in, as occurs in the emperor penguin of the south and in the polar bear of the north. The warm-blooded polar animals, north and south, are blubber-bearing animals because, in addition to the blubber being a food reserve at such times as in the winter and during the breeding and moulting seasons, when foraging for various and obvious reasons is difficult, it enables the animals to keep warm and resist the intense cold, blubber being a bad conductor of heat. On the coasts of Greenland life does exist and a most peculiar phenomenon is the presence of dense clouds of mosquitoes in the summer as far north as this, just as they

W. S. Berridge

ARCTIC FOX AND THE TIMBER WOLF

Inhabiting almost all the Arctic lands, the Arctic fox (bottom) has a blunter muzzle than other foxes. It feeds largely upon Arctic birds and their eggs. The timber wolf (top) is sometimes held to be merely a local variety of the American grey wolf.

lands of the north wild reindeer exist, but they are not found in Franz Joseph Land, and to-day the musk-ox (*Ovibos moschatus*) is only found in large numbers in parts of Peary Land and the American Arctic Archipelago.

One of the most characteristic of the Arctic vertebrates is the Arctic hare. This animal and the lemming occur most abundantly. Fur-bearing animals, including the well-known ermine, are not so plentiful as once, owing to the demands of Dame Fashion.

Generally the animals are of white coloration and either, like the polar bear, remain so, or, like the hares and lemmings, are brown in summer, matching the surrounding verdure, or white in winter in harmony with the fallen snows.

As in the Antarctic, the alar life of the Arctic regions is a migrant one. In the polar winter the birds go southward and the coastlands teem with their nests ; while in the summer the birds penetrate to the farthest corners of the north.

GREENLAND, in the interior, is an elevated plateau on which, as on many of the large Arctic islands, vegetation and animal life are absent. This is because, owing to the great altitude, there is a permanent snow covering and an extremely severe climate.

Thus food necessary to sustain animal life is wanted here and the intense cold is a further barrier to existence. Elsewhere, as we have seen, the food supply in summer is at least sufficient, although at times existence may be precarious. In the winter animal life either follows its food northwards from the

DOG TEAM TRANSPORT AS USED IN THE ARCTIC

In the far north, and especially in Alaska, the best means of transport is by dog-drawn sledge. The animals used are Eskimo dogs, that are virtually a breed of domesticated wolves which frequent interbreeding with the wild wolf tends to keep wild and hardy. The Eskimo dog rather resembles a large chow with a rough coat, bushy tail, ears held erect, and a sharp-pointed muzzle. Ten such dogs can pull a load of 2,000 lb over a good surface. This photograph from "Four Years in the White North" is copyright, 1918, Harper and Brothers.

are found in much lower and warmer latitudes. Mosquitoes are also abundant in the summer on the marshy tundras of Siberia. The explanation is that the eggs at the end of summer lay in the water in the ground, and become encysted to withstand the freezing winter cold. When they hatch out in the hot summer sun which has then been shining day and night for a considerable period, they do so in such vast numbers that the dense clouds mentioned are formed.

Lastly, in connexion with the Arctic must be mentioned its human inhabitants the Eskimos. In the far north of the continent the conditions of life are extremely severe especially as regards temperature. Their life is a communal one, spent mostly in fishing and hunting. They live by foraging, and a serious menace to this method of existence is the occurrence of ice deserts. But they wage a war against nature which, if eternal, is successful.

The polar regions abound in life but in the south the marine fauna is prolific (probably more so than in the north), while the terrestrial flora and fauna are poor. In the north both marine and terrestrial fauna are abundant and the terrestrial flora, taking all conditions into notice, may almost be described as prolific and certainly as wonderful.

Both northern and southern polar expeditions have found there can always be a supply of fresh food if the foraging is cautious and persistent, but such supplies are obviously much more plentiful in the north; the north is more liveable or as Stefansson has said and shown, it is a "liveable north" and a "friendly Arctic."

Stefansson in his book "The Fruitful Arctic" speaks of the friendly Arctic as "signifying that to those who know how to live there, to those who imitate the habits of the Eskimos themselves and of the many other kinds of mammals who keenly enjoy life there, this region of the long Arctic night and of the bitter cold is not hostile, but friendly." Flowers, mosses, lichens are plentiful and among the grasses even the cotton grass flourishes. There are vast grazing resources and already reindeer are important meat-producing resources in Alaska and in the northern half of Canada, which is one vast pasture or "verdure-clad prairie." In this connexion, reindeer do not have to be fed or stabled, living as they do in and on the open country, and they are, in contradistinction to caribou, which are merely wild reindeer, as domestic as sheep. This was realized, practically, in China as long ago as the fifth century, and in Norway in our own King Alfred's time, and to-day Stefansson has established a large and flourishing industry on Baffin Island.

In "The Liveable North" he says, "The course of civilization has been northward since its dawn. The races of the colder climes have predominated in world power, and man, although a tropical animal, is not

W. S. Berridge

at his best in the tropics. To-day old imaginary difficulties of the North are shown to be fairy tales and inaccuracies and the far north is being conquered as time goes on."

There is a heavier snowfall in Virginia or Germany than in either northern Canada or Alaska. North Polar life, and especially as regards vegetation, depends on the total number of hours of sunlight and not on the number of summer months. In the three months Arctic summer there are as many hours of sunshine as in a tropical summer of five months duration, thus giving northern plants twice as long a growing period. Life, both mental and physical is developed to the highest. The mineral resources of the far north are literally colossal. The climate and civilization of the north will combine to produce "men of unsleeping energy and restless ambition."

Man's knowledge of the Arctic and the consequent development of its resources is vastly greater than that of the Antarctic. Until Antarctic exploration is followed by men of practical as opposed to academical experience this state of things will remain.

Herbert G. Ponting, F.R.P.S. Copyright

SKUA GULL STEALING PENGUIN'S EGGS: YOUNG RAZORBILLS RESTING

On land the worst enemy of the penguin is the skua gull, which seems to have been created especially to help in keeping down the penguin population. The skua not only makes off with the eggs, but swoops down on the young birds also. This photograph (bottom) is from a cinematograph film and shows a skua alighting on a temporarily deserted nest. The penguins make no attempt beyond screaming to defend their young. On the other hand, the gulls do not attack adults The top photograph shows a colony of young razorbills at rest.

Ivory Gull

Antarctic Skua

Snowy Owl

Little Auk

Puffin

Eider-duck

Arctic Skua

BIRDS THAT SWIM AND FLY WITHIN THE POLAR REGIONS

The Arctic has a far greater variety of fauna than the Antarctic. The eider-duck builds its nest of seaweed, and the female, during incubation, gradually lines her nest with the down from her body. About six nests yield a pound of eider-down. Both the eider-duck and the ivory gull are Arctic. Skua gulls are found in both Arctic and Antarctic. The snowy owl is distributed all over the Arctic, but sometimes gets as far south as Scotland. **Puffins and little auks are among the most numerous of Arctic birds. The photographs are by W. S. Berridge.**

W. Saville-Kent

BLEACHED CORAL AND ISOLATED GROWTHS OF QUEENSLAND WATERS

A coral reef is a community-dwelling and a common cemetery in one. Each of the little polyps that are the inhabitants builds itself a protective bulwark made of carbonate of lime extracted from the sea. By the multiplication of these lime skeletons the mass of coral is formed. But the polyps can only thrive in certain temperatures and at certain depths. If the coral mass rises above the level of the sea the polyps die, leaving the coral skeletons (bottom) bleached by the sun. Above are some dead growths on Thursday Island.

Chapter XXXIII

Life in a Submarine World of Colour

By E. G. Boulenger

Director, The Zoological Society's Aquarium

Coral is associated in the minds of most of us with tropical seas of dazzling blue bespangled with romantic fairy-like islands. Whilst it is true that coral reaches its maximum development in tropic and sub-tropic seas, it is not confined to such waters, for immense branching stony corals are dredged from the depths of the North Atlantic, whilst large areas of the water around Iceland are covered with corals that are almost indistinguishable from some of the antler-like forms of the tropical reefs. Even in our own waters corals are not uncommon, though principally of small size and living singly. One of the most popular varieties—the famous red coral—comes from the Mediterranean, where it is fished by drawing tangles of net and rope attached to a wooden frame over the sea bed.

There is still prevalent a general notion that coral is the work of insects, but in reality it is the vacated tenement of a polyp, a creature almost identical with the sea anemone. If an anemone, instead of living stark and unprotected on a rocky basis, built up around itself a rampart of carbonate of lime drawn from the sea water, then we should have a coral. The reefs are built up by countless millions of these " reinforced " anemones, the animals living from a few hours to several weeks, but almost invariably multiplying by laying eggs, budding or " fissure," before they die.

Fissure is the most common method of reproduction. The single polyp divides into two for a distance of rather less than half of its entire length, the result being a sort of Siamese twins, each twin forming around itself a stony bulwark. These twins in their turn subdivide, and so the process continues until the accumulated stony hosts of the polyps raise gigantic masses covering vast areas of the ocean. The newest portion, that is, the most recently-formed section of the coral growth, is naturally exposed to the light and glows with a fairy-like tint. Beneath these dazzling growths are piled the empty homes of polyps that have lived their lives, and the accumulated mass may be brittle to a degree or compressed into granite-like formations that resist the fiercest onslaughts of the waves.

Reefs abound in the Indian Ocean and the warmer waters of the Western Hemisphere. Their size and nature depend on the building material contained in the sea water. It is estimated that in the Pacific a mass of water a million square miles and a thousand fathoms deep contains nearly twenty tons of carbonate of lime. Most tropical seas abound in volcanic islets and submarine mountains that lie just below the surface, and such situations offer ideal anchorage for the nucleus of a coral colony. Nothing in the sea is stable for any lengthy period, for constant uprising or subsidence of the sea floor is taking place. Sometimes a large portion of a continent, its shore heavily fringed with coral growths, slowly subsides, leaving the coral as a barrier reef. Again, the crown of a subaqueous mountain may collapse as the result of volcanic disturbance, and the coral thus left remains as a ring. The resulting lagoon formed by the circular wall silts up and presently acquires a growth of palms and other herbage, and may become a fringing reef encircling a tiny islet.

Such are the vast coral formations which have exercised man's imagination from early times. Hundreds of species of coral may combine to form a reef, a great galaxy of lovely forms, some caricaturing the foliage of both sea and shore, others soaring skywards in miniature towers and battlements, or making big dome-like structures of intricate sculpture twenty feet or more in girth. That portion of the reef nearest the open sea grows apace, the teeming polyps ever sweeping the water with their multi-coloured tentacles in search of the minute organisms that form their menu.

Mere words can convey no intelligent conception of the variety of colour displayed upon a coral reef. Suffice it to say that the corals of the Barrier Reef have been described as assuming every shade of coloration that is to be seen in the air-breathing world. With regard to form, some are huge branching structures suggestive of flattened branches ten feet in diameter, whilst others suggest giant puff balls, organ pipes, and even human skulls. The prevalence of some special form on each reef has largely influenced the nomenclature of the various masses forming the reef, such as Skull Reef, Bush Reef, Stag's Horn Reef, and the like.

Countless other forms of life find ample sanctuary amongst the coral growths hiding in and beneath them, tunnelling through them or living in the calm and sheltered waters between the coral ramparts and the shore. Recent researches have given us glowing hints at the immense variety of marine forms that make a home in our own chilly waters. In the tropical coral seas they reach a maximum development, dazzling the eye and bewildering the imagination. Of recent years the wonderful coral gardens of Bermuda have been photographed and filmed William Beebe, the American naturalist, has even enjoyed promenades amidst their splendours in an ingenious diving helmet weighing sixty pounds whilst a certain artist has placed the submarine orgy of colour upon record by painting under water with specially prepared pigments and canvas

Columbus was the first to make the world realize the vast avenues of unexplored wealth and beauty which lay waiting for all who could face the vicissitudes

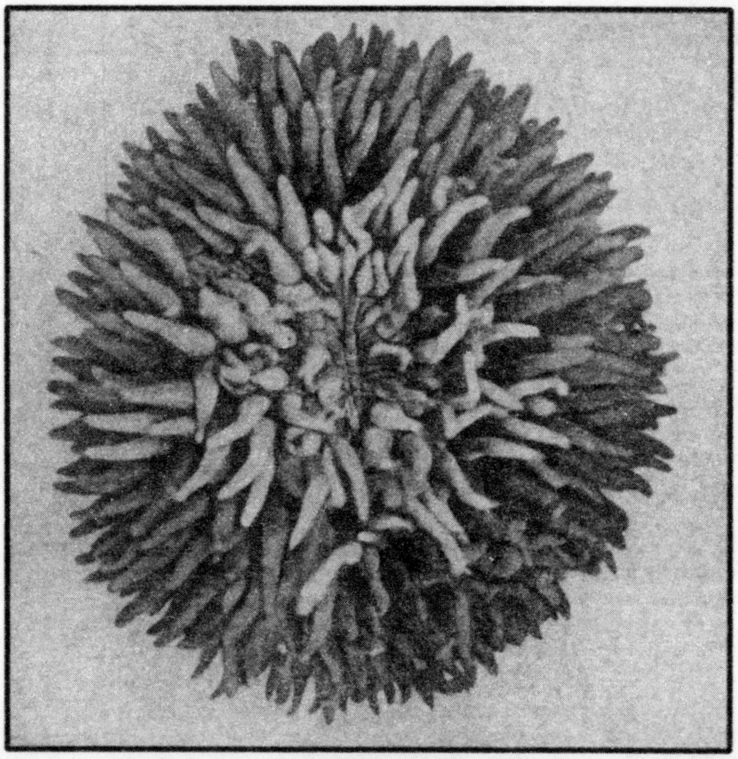

W. Saville-Kent

W. Saville-Kent

CORALS THAT LOOK LIKE FLOWERS

This is how the living coral looks with its tiny inhabitants, the polyps, expanded. The polyps gain their living and build up their skeletons—and these skeletons become massed into a coral reef—by sweeping the sea that flows about them for minute particles The piece of mushroom coral (above) looks like a chrysanthemum while expanded.

and dangers of a long sea voyage. It was not, however, until 1770 that Captain Cook discovered that enormous expanse in the South Seas now known as the Great Barrier Reef of Australia, the largest aggregation of coralline formations in the world. It lies within the territorial jurisdiction of Queensland, extending from Melbourne to well within the tropics, a distance of 1,250 miles. and covering an area of 200,000 square miles. It enjoys a great variety of climatic conditions, tropical and temperate species flourishing within its boundaries. In 1893 it was explored and photographed by Saville-Kent, but even to-day, after over thirty years of continued research by many other workers, it is realized that its vast potentialities have been but very cursorily developed. Oysters, edible and pearl-bearing, shells of every form, coral rock for building material, edible fish, crustaceans, and sea-cucumbers innumerable, these are but a few of the harvests waiting to be systematically developed in the labyrinthine coral pastures of the Great Barrier Reef. Over a thousand species of fish are recorded as making their home there.

It is sometimes asked whether a coral reef can become "played out," either by storm, volcanic eruption, or the steady whittling away of the coral growth for building material. Such a tendency is, to say the least, remote. Despite the ravages of Nature, the ever-multiplying coral cells are continually being augmented and reinforced by calcareous depositions of lime, shells of molluscs, the exo-skeletons of crustaceans, wind-blown coral sand, etc. The coral on the Barrier Reef flourishes only in such waters as reach a temperature of 68° F. from low tide mark to a depth of rather less than twenty fathoms. Judging by statistics covering the last thirty years, there has been little appreciable diminution or expansion of the principal reefs. Losing ground here, gaining a little there, the coral growths keep more or less within the same limits.

Apart from storm, however, there is a constant levy taken of the polyp cells, numerous bivalve and univalve molluscs tunnelling into the solidest formations. A big sea snail (*Caralyaphilla*) becomes embedded in the coral, but to avoid the penalty of its inertia it continually extends the mouth of its shell till a long worm-like tube of carbonate of lime is evolved, its free end always enjoying communication with the open sea. A coral shell the size of a man's fist may present an extension of its doorway nearly a yard long.

Great clam shells also become embedded in the coral fronds and steadily force them apart. These clams often attain huge proportions, specimens three feet long and weighing several hundredweight being quite abundant. All but concealed in the surrounding coral, they lie with the shells slightly ajar, the animals drinking in various organisms through their siphon pipes. The human foot incautiously entering such a mantrap is held in a grip which only axe and crowbar are able to relax, and numerous deaths are recorded as being directly caused by these clams. Pearl divers, especially, frequently come to grief in this manner.

THE pearl and edible oysters of the Barrier Reef frequently settle when young upon the shell of a whelk, and the whelk weighing little over an ounce is presently encumbered with a growth of oysters weighing 10 or 15 lb. Eventually both whelk and its burden settle down into the mud and perish. Pearl oysters were at one time fished by native divers who plunged in naked and remained under water for nearly three minutes. They are now, however, procured by trained divers in up-to-date diving dresses, and as a result some of the beds have been greatly depleted and the culture of artificial or "induced" pearls has become imperative.

Apart from the damage done by the more sedentary sea beasts, coral is also attacked by all kinds of fish, notably by the gaily coloured file fish, and these actually bite off large pieces of the living coral with their front teeth, which literally amount to a pair of well-sharpened chisels. The varied forms of life which we know on our own shores are multiplied a hundredfold in the tropical coral reefs, the genial climate and abundant food supply inducing a maximum of development. Just as the more northern sea animals tend to resemble and take on the hues of the weeds, mud and gravel forming their surroundings, so do the creatures of the reefs tend to harmonise with the vivid forms of the corals, and nowhere is this more evident than amongst the sea anemones. A giant anemone *Discosoma* measures two feet across, its disk swarming with thousands of vividly banded tentacles that present a dazzle pattern of alternating

W. Saville-Kent

ORGAN-PIPE CORAL WITH ITS POLYPS EXPANDED

Polyps, the living inhabitants of the coral, whose skeletons may wreck a tall ship or form a lady's necklace, have short lives, varying from a few hours to a few weeks. They resemble, and are closely related to, the sea anemones; but, instead of relying on stinging powers for protection, they have evolved a way of building a skeleton of lime. The organ-pipe coral which we see here has polyps of emerald-green, and in this illustration they are expanded; that is, they are reaching forth from their pink skeletons for food.

WONDERLAND OF THE CORAL REEF, ABOVE AND BELOW WATER

Fish of the most amazing colours dart and flash among the beautifully tinted coral forests. The lower illustration is of a coral garden on the Barrier Reef off the Queensland coast. The brightest shades of blue, scarlet and green, vivid in the sunlight which pervades the clear sea water, entrance the eye on every hand, fish and coral vying in splendour. When the tide goes down the reef is exposed (top) and much of the brilliance vanishes, the little coral polyps withdrawing within their lime skeletons until the sea covers them again. The photographs by Captain Frank Hurley on this and the opposite page are reproduced from his book "Pearls and Savages," by courtesy of G. P. Putnam's Sons

STRIPED FISH OF THE REEFS AND THE DEATH-GRIPPING GIANT CLAM

Some fish of the brilliant hues which distinguish the tinted swimmers of the coral reefs may be seen in the Aquarium at the London Zoo. The coral reef shows an amazing combination of fish and polyp life which goes to make this submarine world of colour. But there are dangers on the reefs. The upper photograph is of a giant clam. This dreadful thing may attain a length of four feet. At the least touch the serrated jaws shut tight with enough force to snap a man's leg. So held, with a horribly crushed limb, the victim can only be saved by crowbars from a slow death either from exposure on the lonely reef or from drowning when the tide comes in

W. Saville Kent

STRANGE PRICKLY FISH OF THE GREAT BARRIER REEF

The sea-slugs, known to commerce as bêche-de-mer or trepang, are allied to the starfish and, like them, move by means of a great number of tiny tubular organs which end in discs and exert suction on the surface traversed by the creature. The red prickly fish is one of a number of different kinds of bêche-de-mer, and of great commercial value. It is found to grow to a length of four feet, and feeds on minute organisms, called foraminifera, by sweeping a bunch of tentacles over the surface of the reef and stuffing the "catch" into its mouth.

red and golden stripes which harmonise with the surrounding corals. In constant attendance upon these large invertebrates are numerous small fish (*Amphiprion*) which actually take shelter within the stomach of their host and appear to be quite inured to the monster's stinging properties.

Many theories are offered as an explanation of the strange co-partnership. It is possible that the small fish enjoy the monster's protection and are tolerated, since they lure to within reach of its arms fish larger than themselves. The latter are at once caught, paralysed, and engulfed. The little fish invariably bolts for cover into the anemone's interior upon alarm, and a stick thrust into the stomach cavity usually results in dislodging a number of *Amphiprion*, even if none are actually in evidence. It is usual to obtain these fish for aquarium exhibition by employing divers who bring up the anemones, disinterring the fish when safely on board.

A small prawn is also associated with this anemone and, like the fish, is banded cream and orange with touches of blue or black that harmonise with its host. Starfish and sea urchins innumerable glide and scramble amongst the piled terraces of the coral growths, gardens of delight clearly visible to the naked eye through several fathoms of crystal water.

MOST abundant of all are the sea-cucumbers, of which many scores of species are found on the Barrier Reef. The edible sea-cucumber known as trepang or bêche-de-mer is gathered by natives into sacks at low tide. A live bêche-de-mer may stretch to four feet in length, a gorgeously decorated and sluggishly animated sausage. After being boiled for twenty minutes, cleaned, gutted, dried in the sun and subjected to twenty-four hours' further drying in a shed filled with wood smoke, it is still sausage-shaped but shrunken to six or eight inches and of a somewhat charred appearance. In this form it is exported to the markets of the world, even finding its way at length to the Oriental restaurants of England. It is stewed into a soup rich and glutinous and ranks next to the pearl industry as the greatest source of revenue of the coral islanders.

To the naturalist and artist the giant sea-cucumber must appeal no less than to the Oriental gourmet.

Expanded, the creature's cylindrical bulk glows with the richest tints. The body, apart from the hundreds of tube feet on which the animal walks, is beset with thickets of tapering protuberances marvellously spotted, striped, or banded with olive green, mauve and gold to blend with the ramifications of the corals or the chequered pattern of the shells. The head end expands at feeding time—and feeding time is almost continuous—into a crown of delicately cut tentacles that sweep the surrounding water for the minute growths on which the creature feeds. At the same time the tentacles ward off many a foe by their superficial resemblance to the sting-celled plumes of the anemones.

These sea-cucumbers swarm on every portion of the reef. Some hunt the sea floor where they burrow into the sand and coral refuse, others twine amongst the branching stems where they mimic stony fronds. A few species even imitate sea snakes for the sake of protecting themselves, one large specimen being able to stretch to nearly ten feet in length.

In conclusion, the Barrier Reef has stood for thousands of years, and is likely to stand for many thousands more. Man during his short sojourn on earth has decimated the wild mammals, and has gone far to exterminate the birds and even the reptiles. The treasures of the sea, on the other hand, whilst exciting the utmost avarice, are safeguarded by one all-important factor—the sea itself.

One factor alone threatens the existence of this subaqueous fairy land, and that is climate. Such a menace is not likely to be appreciated in the lifetime of the reader, but the possibility nevertheless does exist, for the rocks bear ample testimony by the fossils they contain to the fact that coral reefs must have at one time existed where now is dry land.

Coral can only flourish at certain depths and in certain temperatures. The geologic history of the earth, compared with which the history of man is but as yesterday, shows that ocean and continent have more than once changed places. Of course, any such change would vitally involve ourselves as well as the coral. But that is another story.

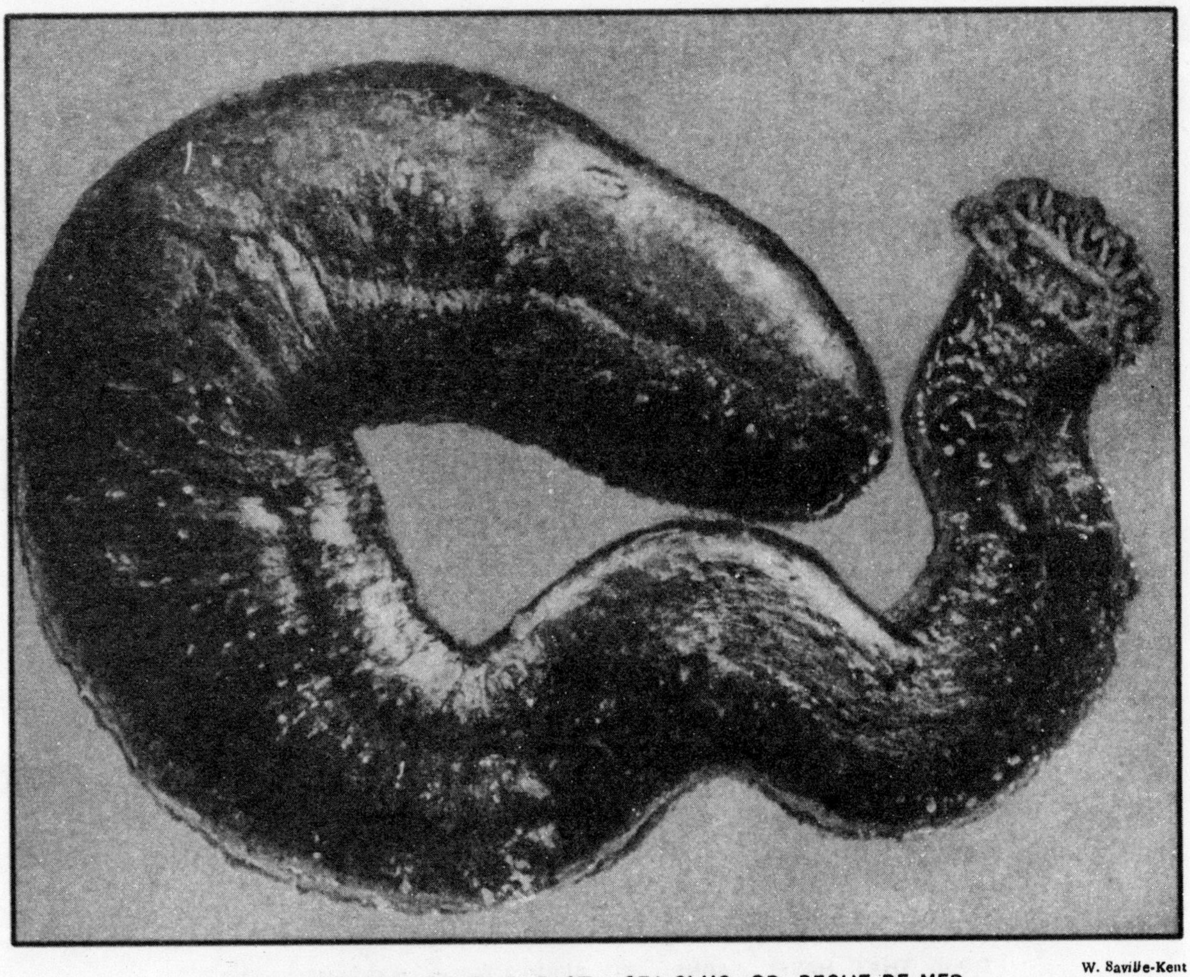

W. Saville-Kent

FOR GOURMETS OF THE EAST: SEA-SLUG OR BECHE-DE-MER

From the earliest times certain forms of sea-slugs have been esteemed great delicacies in Malaya and China. The Portuguese christened the creature bicho-do-mar, worm of the sea, and the French adopted the name and made it bêche-de-mer. In the East it is called trepang. A four-foot specimen, after boiling, drying and smoking, is only about eight inches long; it is then said to make a very pleasing soup. Trepang fishing ranks next to pearl fishing in importance among the coral islanders.

DOGS THAT HAVE LEARNED TO SERVE THEIR MASTERS' NEED

The more intelligent among dogs soon learn to carry their masters' goods, but it is not every one that will go and look for a tennis-racket and get it, as this Alsatian did. No one could be more conscious of being clever than a dog, the animal's whole bearing showing complete self-satisfaction and pride. In the upper picture is a more unusual example of mental activity in dogs. This particular one used to take a mare out of its stable for a walk, solemnly leading it by the bridle, the mare following meekly, nothing doubting.

Chapter XXXIV

Do Animals Reason?

By Frances Pitt

Author of "Animal Mind"

THE first thing in considering the question, "Do animals reason?" is what do we mean by that much abused and much misused word "reason"? Well, I am using it to signify the mental process that results in intelligent behaviour, wherein a being exhibits judgement and purpose and a practical ability to shape its actions to achieve a preconceived and desired end, in contrast to instinctive behaviour, when an animal is driven by blind impulse, arising from an hereditary reaction of the nervous system to a particular stimulus, or series of stimuli, towards an unknown goal.

With regard to animals it is often extraordinarily difficult to know when they are acting from impulse, and when with considered judgement, and observers differ very much in what they attribute to those inherited modes of action we term instinct, and what to an intelligent understanding, but I will give some examples of behaviour that I consider show the working of mind.

Here is the first. I have two tame otters (the otter is an animal of very keen mentality, second, in my opinion, only to the dog in the matter of intelligence) and one of them, the female, Madame Moses by name, was swimming across a pool bearing a mouthful of grass with which to make up her bed, when I called her. On hearing her name, Moses swung round to come to me, then hesitated, turned about, went on, deposited the grass in her sleeping box, and then swam back to me. As a rule she rushes to me the moment she hears my voice, and in this instance the conflict between her desire to come to me at once, and to carry on with her job was most apparent. No one seeing the way she went and deposited the load, and then came back could have doubted that her actions were animated by purpose.

It is the same throughout the long scale of animal life. The careful observer sees even quite lowly creatures performing actions that seem to betoken memory and purpose, as when fish accustomed to be fed at a certain hour at a certain place duly appear at feeding-time; but the higher one ascends the scale, the more obvious do these signs become, until in the apes we find a really enquiring mind.

Professor Köhler made a most thorough and painstaking investigation of the mental ability of the chimpanzee, with some illuminating results. He kept a number of young animals under observation and tried numerous experiments upon them. In one experiment food was placed outside, and some little distance away from, the cage, the ape inside being furnished with several pieces of bamboo rod. Not one of these was long enough to reach the food, but Sultan, one of the apes, found that by putting a thin stick into the hollow end of a bigger bamboo he could make an implement long enough to reach the food, and then proceeded to rake it in. Ever after the ape remembered how to make himself a stick of the desired length, and always did it to reach ungetatable food. Professor Köhler thought his first fitting of the sticks together was accidental rather than thoughtful, but emphasises how quickly the chimpanzee appreciated the importance of his discovery, and that he later made three-length poles to reach to a distance.

These chimpanzees also displayed considerable ability in building, putting boxes one on another so as to make an erection upon which they could climb to reach fruit hung from the roof of the cage; and did a hundred and one smaller things that showed their intelligence, from teasing each other, and human beings, to teasing the fowls. In the latter case, as Köhler explains, the hens were lured near the apes' pen by scattering crumbs of bread through the wire, and when they began to pick the crumbs up an expectant ape poked them through the netting with a stick.

Does not all this show an understanding, an impish mischievous spirit, far removed from the blind impulses of instinct?

HUNGER AND EXPERIENCE

This West Highland white terrier knows that if it eats the sugar before the permission is given, trouble is likely to follow. But whether it is reasoning about the matter as it sits there is a question which is not at all easy to answer

Do Animals Reason?

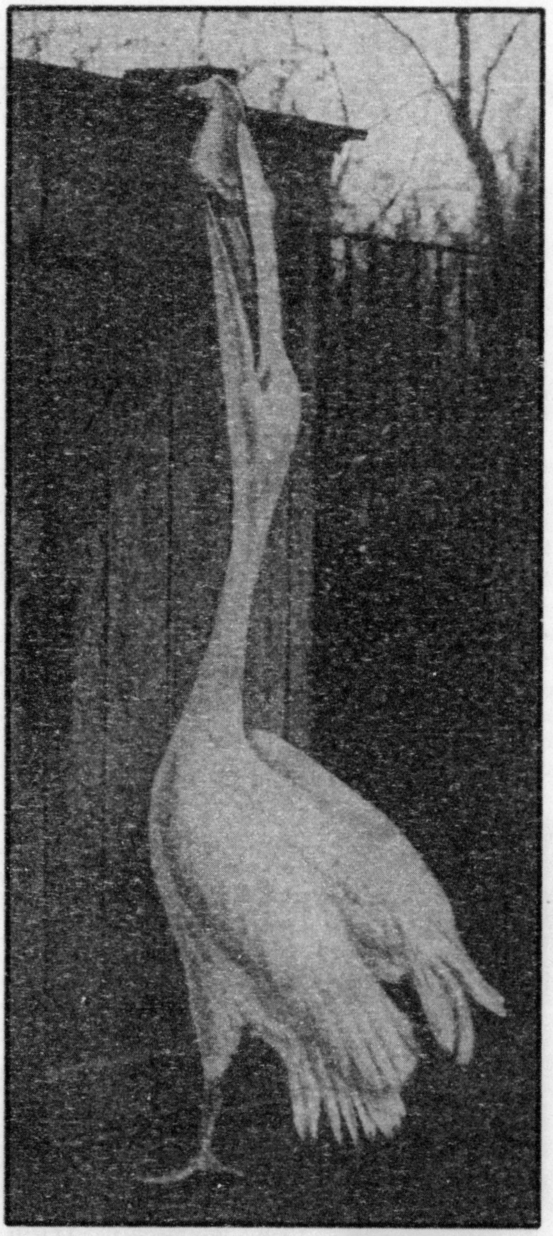

Keystone

THE PELICAN'S STOCKING

At Christmas someone presented a stocking full of delicacies to one of the Zoo pelicans, but, for the sake of testing the bird's intelligence, put it out of ordinary reach. But the wise bird made very good use of a long neck and beak, as we see.

But the anthropoid apes stand so high in the scale of life that some hint of practical judgement is merely what we should expect; what about other animals, the elephant for instance? Here we have a creature long reputed to be of exceptional sagacity, and for once popular story does not belie the animal's intelligence. The care with which it tests each step before crossing boggy, doubtful ground, or venturing upon a planked way, is well known; and I have witnessed retaliation by an elephant which showed its appreciation of a situation. This was in the London Zoological Gardens, and here is the little history as I related it in my book "Animal Mind."

Two soldiers were offering one of the elephants, standing in its stall in the elephant house, a bun. They held the bun out, but when the elephant passed its trunk through the bars and tried to reach it they drew the bun back again, which was repeated several times. The boys—for, despite their uniforms, they were little more—laughed hugely, especially when the elephant turned away as if in disgust. It crossed its stall to where, in the corner, there was a water tap, from which water was slowly dripping. Putting its trunk to this it stood and waited, collecting the trickling drops. The two soldiers were still there, with the bun, when the elephant swung round, walked back to the bars and blew the contents of its trunk over them! The water went into their ears and eyes, and down their necks! The elephant stood swaying its trunk and watching them as they decamped.

If that episode did not show thought and judgement, what can you bring forward as evidence?

In my opinion revenge is the best evidence for memory and of comprehension of cause and effect. Peafowl are not usually credited with being "brainy" birds, yet not long ago I saw a peahen revenge herself most deliberately on a farmyard cock. She was feeding quietly, when the cock, a young and pugnacious bird, came up behind her and knocked her over. She picked herself up, and turned upon him. The cockerel ran, but she ran after him, gave him a good drubbing, and when he ran off, pursued him once more. She chased him and beat him for over an hour, until they were parted, and the cock took the opportunity to slip into hiding. He was a Light Sussex cock, and there were four or five other cocks so like him it was difficult to tell them apart. Yet the next day, Jane, the peahen, unerringly selected the right bird, and proceeded to administer further punishment, which she did most thoroughly!

The raven is, of course, well known to be a bird of exceptional intelligence, yet when experimenting with Old Joe, my pet raven, I hardly expected the retribution which quickly befell me. To test his power of discrimination I took some butter on the tip of my finger and held it out to him. Joe took it with gusto, and scraped every atom from my finger, using his powerful beak with exceeding gentleness. Then I took a piece of soap, of the same size and colour, and offered him that. He looked at it, but did not touch it, though next second I had received such a punishing stab in the finger from his iron bill that I shall never forget it! I can only say I was quite satisfied with his power of discrimination.

Definite evidence of memory extending over any length of time (and memory is the frame on which experience is reared, whence judgement draws its material) is difficult to find. For, though popular anecdotes are many, carefully-observed facts are few; but here *is* concrete and incontrovertible evidence concerning Madame Moses, my otter.

About the otter's enclosure is a high fence, on the top of which I put a white card with a long string dangling from it. I let Moses see me put some food on the card and waited to see what she would do about it. She tried to reach the card, which she could not do, then seized the string with her teeth and tugged it, whereupon the card came down and she got the food. Thereafter she was quick and clever at pulling things down by strings. But from January 20 to August 6, she never saw a card, or anything resembling one. On the latter date, Moses being asleep in her kennel, I put a white card with dangling cord upon the fence, then went and roused the otter, but did nothing to draw her attention to the card. Yet in a moment or two she caught sight of it, trotted to the place, took the string in her mouth, and deliberately pulled the card down. After a period of over six months she instantly recognized the card and remembered how to get it off the fence.

The return of a dog for a buried bone, and of a fox for the prey it has also buried, may be cited as

SWANS RING FOR MEALS

At Bishop's Palace Mere, Wells, there are swans that swim up to a string which rings a bell when they feel meal time coming on. Notice that it is a cygnet that is doing this, the young bird having already learned from its parents.

AT THE STABLE BELL

Horses are by no means the most intelligent of the domestic animals, but this one learned to associate meal times with pulling the cord of a bell outside its stable, and was thus able to attract the attention of the stableman.

proof of memory, which brings us to the difficulty of telling where intelligence ends and instinct begins, or to put it the other way about, where instinct ends and judgement begins. Animal behaviour is a varying blend of inherited aptitude (varying from a definite mechanical response to a stimulus up to a vague inclination to behave in a certain way under certain circumstances) and intelligent adaptation.

For example, the tendency displayed by dog and fox to bury unwanted food is clearly instinctive, and independent of experience. This does not affect the fact that the return to the cache is at the dictates of memory. But referring to the young animal's early efforts, I have seen a hand-reared fox-cub, who had never known what it was to be short of food, take a rabbit's leg to the tray of sand in the corner of the room where she was kept, and bury it, scratching a hole, dropping the bone into it, and pushing the soil back with her nose; I have also seen a small puppy snatch an apple from her playfellow, rush into a corner, and try to bury it in an old sack that lay there, going through all the appropriate actions

WONDERFUL REASONING POWERS OF THE SHEEP-DOG DISPLAYED

At the sheep-dog trials the most impressive examples of canine intelligence are displayed. For the dog must, to a certain extent, act on its own initiative in certain circumstances, besides being marvellously under the control of the shepherd. Below we see some sheep being penned by a dog at the Tring Agricultural Show, and, above, a Border collie marking down a sheep to separate it from the rest. The shepherd says nothing, but only blows a whistle or motions with his hand.

J. W. Henderson

COUNTING AND PICKING OUT NUMBERS

In the upper photograph a dog is confronted by a row of numbered plates turned upside down. The dog turns over the plates until it gets to the particular number which its master has selected. Below is a pony which is said to be able to count up to eight. Whether or not the element of reason is really displayed in these two cases is certainly arguable, but perhaps the sceptics are as liable to err quite as much on one side as the animal lovers do, through affectionate partiality, on the other.

Charles Reid

HEREDITY AND EDUCATION COMBINED: THE RETRIEVER

Retriever pups display a desire to pick up things and carry them, but there is a great difference between these manifestations of heredity and the behaviour of the finished dog when out with the guns. A long and painstaking education develops something already in the animal so that it shall know when a certain action—the picking up of a bird—is right and when the same thing is wrong. This is a retriever with a hare. Long years of careful breeding have, of course, been responsible for the retriever's intelligence.

for interring it in the earth. In each case the impulse was clearly independent of experience, and we can hardly believe that either puppy or cub thought out beforehand what it was going to do.

Yet a great deal of behaviour which is usually described as instinctive is nothing of the sort. Take the case of a song thrush beating a house snail to pieces upon a stone so as to be able to extract the creature's luscious body—how does the thrush know the way to deal with the snail? Does it know instinctively? To test this I hand-reared a young thrush, and when Jack was full grown and able to deal with any sort of food, offered him several snails. He showed no signs of understanding what they were. When they began to crawl about he took notice of them, inspected them closely, and pecked their waving antennae, but when they immediately withdrew he lost interest, and so it went on for a week. Each day I showed him snails, and his inquisitiveness grew. But the disappearance of a snail into its shell mystified him completely. On the sixth day he appeared to lose patience. A snail drew back into its house, he turned the shell over and could not find it, so he picked it up by the lip of the shell, and gave it a swinging thump on the ground, treating it as he would have done any unmanageable food.

The thrush always beats a worm or grub it cannot easily dispose of, and it was clearly this tendency that made Jack hammer the snail on the ground. It rolled from his grasp, but he picked it up again, and jumping on one of the stones I had put ready for him—an experienced thrush stands before his "anvil," not *on* it—thumped the snail repeatedly.

However, he had not yet acquired the art of cracking it, and it was not until the next day that he broke open his first snail, when exasperation led him to beat a snail so hard that it *did* break. After that he knew how to deal with snails, and gradually became as expert at dealing with them as any song-thrush you see smashing a snail upon its roadside "anvil." It is noteworthy that a thrush resorts to a good stone for weeks on end, and a well-used anvil will be surrounded by broken snail shells. Watching my thrush led me to the conclusion that the snail-breaking habit of the thrush was not an inherited instinct, but the result of experience superimposed on the truly instinctive aptitude to beat unmanageable food.

Again, to take a familiar instance of the combination of an hereditary tendency and education, there is the retriever. The breed is distinguished by the pleasure it takes in picking up and carrying things. Quite young puppies have the inclination. It is part of their hereditary make-up, just as the tendency to gallop round a flock of sheep is part of the mental inheritance of the sheep-dog, but there is a very wide gap, only bridged by long and careful education, between the inexperienced puppy and the finished retriever, who sits motionless by his master at a shoot, noting where each bird falls, ready, at the word of command, to go forth, pick it up, and bring it back.

THE finished retriever is a dog of experienced judgement, and it is this profiting by lessons and experience which makes him, likewise the elephant that has learnt its business as a timber carrier, or in any other capacity, such a valued servant of man.

Now, to turn to another aspect of animal behaviour, can we find any cases of co operation which will supply us with evidence of reasoning power? The many stories of rats assisting each other to drag off eggs will at once leap to the mind, but in the absence of well-attested evidence from a competent observer —most of these stories are too much of the "yarn" variety—I prefer to turn to what I have seen myself, when two tame ravens *did* co-operate to tease a cat, one taking her attention by hopping about in front of her, while the other crept up behind and tweaked her tail. When the cat sprang about, with an outraged spit, the first one had her, likewise by the tail! So it went on, a merry game for the ravens, if not for the cat; and one showing a keen understanding on the part of the ravens of how to play into each other's hands, or rather, I should say, beaks.

But the most perfect examples of co-operation are to be found among the lower creatures, among the social insects, with their cast-iron instincts, handed down through countless generations, in which each individual is driven along a preordained path, its nervous system responding to the appropriate stimulus in a manner that would seem to leave no room for individuality, or escape from routine behaviour. Yet even here we *do* find evidence of memory, and even of judgement. The bee, the slave driven by her instincts in most respects, has a memory; she learns her way about the country around her home, and if taken outside her usual radius is quite lost.

F. W. Bond

CHIMPANZEES DELIGHT IN IMITATING HUMAN ACTIONS

Exhaustive tests have been made of the intelligence possessed by chimpanzees, the most adaptable of apes to human surroundings and considered to be the most highly intelligent of the ape family. Sometimes the mere desire to "ape" human beings is mistaken for reason. It is to be wondered if the chimpanzee seen above washing his companion over an enamel basin really thought or cared that the process made his friend cleaner. The action with the sponge is certainly human enough.

Gilliams Service

ELEPHANTS DOING UNUSUAL SERVICE FOR THEIR OWNERS

While elephants are known to do certain things well, their possibilities have not been really thoroughly explored. For instance, some enterprising person at Miami Beach, in Florida, the great American seaside resort, has discovered that a young elephant, which is incapable of heavy work, makes a novel caddie on the golf course, and it neither expresses nor implies comments on the player's game. The upper photograph shows another young elephant sweeping diligently outside its shed. With a broom a mature elephant would be an imposing worker.

A. H. Willford

James

THRUSH AND OYSTER-CATCHER THAT HAVE LEARNED FROM EXPERIENCE

Thrushes have learned that snails are good to eat, and are not to be defeated by the awkward shell. Sometimes a stone is discovered that has been used by one of these birds (bottom) for weeks at a time until the ground is littered with broken shells, smashed as upon an anvil. The snail-cracking habit seems to be the result of experience, added to the instinctive habit, possessed by the thrush, of beating any unmanageable food on the ground. The oyster-catcher (top) is seen using its beak as a prop while it settles down on its eggs.

COCKATOO FINDS HOW TO MANAGE A CUP

Having found that there was something good in the cup that was difficult to reach when the cup was getting empty, this knowing bird at last learned to imitate the keeper. Having grasped the handle in its claws—which are, naturally, very well fitted for such an action—the bird was able to tilt up the cup (bottom) and get the utmost out of a long drink.

It should, however, be noted, that there is some evidence that ants can communicate news to each other, that an ant will go home to the nest to seek help, and, what is more, she will invariably get it.

This seems clear evidence of communication. Here we see signs of more than mechanical response in creatures so different from us as the insects, while up and down the animal scale we see many instances of considered action, varying in degree of judgement, but displaying an amount of gumption—to use a homely word—widely apart from unconsidered response.

WHICH brings us to the question with which we began this essay, "Do animals reason?" My reply is, it depends on how you employ the word. If you use it to denote the power to form ideas, and pile abstract concept on concept, after the manner of a philosopher, then No. But Yes, a thousand times Yes, in the sense of "do animals act thoughtfully and with judgement?" In varying degrees, of course, because as in us instinct is but a shadowy force of which we are hardly aware, so in many animals intention becomes a small power that is swamped by the great impulses of inherited modes of action.

It should be noted that modern psychological research prefers to term the lower forms of rational conduct intelligent, and reserve the word "reason" for working with general ideas or concepts. Now

It is the same with ants, as was demonstrated by Lord Avebury's experiments. Experience, not instinct, is their guide in finding their way to and from the nest, but how far their co-operation in the intricate affairs of the colony is to be attributed to instinct and how far to an understanding more or less intelligent is another matter. Difficult as it is to arrive at any understanding of the mind of mammal and bird, creatures with which we have affinity, how infinitely more difficult is it to arrive at any comprehension of the mysterious remote mind of the insect!

it is practically certain that the only mind capable of dealing with abstract ideas is the human one, hence human vanity can still tickle itself with the notion that reasoning is our prerogative, but I am convinced that in any ordinary everyday acceptance of the term animals do reason. Mind, as I have said elsewhere, permeates all life, varying in degree from the intellect of the philosopher, the mind of the little child, the intelligence of the dog, and the cunning of the raven, down to that unknown thing, the understanding of the insect; yet differing in degree and not in kind.

Chapter XXXV

Great Divers of the Bird World

By Seton Gordon

Author of "Hill Birds of Scotland"

It is early October as I write, and past me, across the headland of Rudha Hunish, in northern Skye, solans fly east in a continuous stream. As they fly swiftly the keen eyes of one of their number descry a fish swimming in the sea far below. There is a quick check to the powerful flight, a sudden dive followed by a plunge, and then the bird disappears in a fountain of spray beneath the surface. And amid such surroundings I begin my essay upon diving birds.

The subject is a wide one, even if its field be limited to the birds of the British Isles.

The diving birds of Britain fall naturally into three categories. First there are the sea bird divers. Amongst these are the solan or gannet, the cormorant, the shag, or green cormorant, the guillemot, the black guillemot, the razorbill, the puffin, the little auk. Secondly are the fresh-water divers. There are but few of them; for example, the dipper and the kingfisher. Thirdly are the diving birds equally at home at sea or in fresh water. The diving ducks of themselves are a goodly company in this category. Then there are the grebes, and the true divers, great northern, black-throated, and red-throated.

Each class of diving birds has its own method of submerging for its food. The solan dives from a height. If he does not drop seaward with sufficient velocity he propels himself downward with powerful wing thrusts, and then closes his wings an instant before he strikes the water. But the diving method of the solan is unique, and most of the divers dive when swimming and not when flying. The cormorant, great northern, black-throated and red-throated divers, the guillemot and razorbill, besides the diving ducks, all dive while swimming on the surface of the water. These birds use the wings immediately they submerge. Watch a guillemot or razorbill as it disappears near the bow of a steamer; you will see it using its wings to aid its descent, and they are driven just as powerfully as when used in flying.

C. J. King

GREEN CORMORANT STRETCHING ITS WING

Where there are cliffs along the British coasts there will be seen the shag, or green cormorant. It is easily recognized by its flight, often within a few feet of the waves. The wings beat rythmically and fairly swiftly, while the long neck is held out straight.

Besides the three categories of divers enumerated are birds which skim the surface of the water and may at times almost submerge themselves in pursuit of a fish. The osprey belongs to this class, as do also the tribe of the terns or sea swallows. Seagulls and petrels do this also, but none of these birds is a diver in the true sense of the word. Nor can the swans, geese, and surface-feeding ducks which "stand upon their heads" when feeding be termed divers, for they do not submerge themselves entirely.

The true divers—and in this instance I refer to the great northern, black-throated and red-throated divers—remain below the water longer than any other of the British diving birds. They cruise deep on the water's surface, as a submarine might do, and when they submerge they send out scarcely a ripple. Compare their skilled methods with those of the cormorant, which half-throws itself out of the water at the commencement of its dive, and leaves a clumsy splash behind it.

Next to the true divers I would place the solan in order of skilfulness. The solan's eyesight is remarkable. It almost alone of all bird divers sights its prey in the air. The others dive first, then seek their fish beneath the wave. The kingfisher approaches the solan in method, but it dives usually from some perch overhanging a stream and not in full flight.

To the auk tribe—all of them diving birds—belong the razorbill, guillemot, little auk, and others. Except during the nesting season these birds live entirely upon the waters. There is no shelter for them from the wildest storm upon North Sea or Atlantic. They must ride out the heaviest seas. Young auks leave the shelter of the parental ledge of rock before they are able to fly. Some of them are hatched upon precipices five hundred feet and more above sea level. In some remarkable way they reach the water, but the actual descent has been very rarely observed. A guillemot was seen to seize its chick and to fly with it over the cliff, holding it in its bill by one

Neville Kingston

HOW THE CORMORANT FISHES

Cormorants usually dive from their swimming position in the sea, but will jump from a rock and thus gain impetus. The swimming is done with the wings, which seem to drive just as powerfully through the water as when the bird is in flight.

stumpy wing. When (as in Mingulay, one of the Outer Hebrides) some of the young guillemots and razorbills are cradled six hundred feet above the ocean, the drop must be indeed a perilous one. The numbers of downy nestlings floating dead at the cliff foot testify to the danger. It is curious that the common guillemot should take its young to sea so early, for the black guillemot, which nests beneath a boulder, with no drop beneath it and the sea, tends its young until they are fully feathered.

The divers of the sea which usually nest near one another are the guillemot, razorbill and puffin. The little auk is a winter visitor only to the seas of the British Isles. The different methods by which these three species carry their catches of fish to their families are always interesting to observe. The guillemot returns with one fish. It is usually a young herring, and is carried half swallowed, with the tip of the tail just emerging from the captor's bill. The razorbill brings back a number of fry. They are smaller than the guillemot's single fish, and are held *across* the bill. The arrangement is remarkable. They are carried in head and tail formation. Thus, if six young herrings are brought, three tails protrude alternately with three heads on either side of the captor's bill. The puffin, like the razorbill, carries its fish across its bill, but there is not the same meticulous care in their arrangement.

The young herring which the guillemot brings its chick is usually so large that the baby has difficulty in swallowing it, and the tail may

remain sticking out of its bill despite its most strenuous efforts. I have seen a young guillemot actually fall asleep thus.

Sea birds, like land birds, migrate, and the guillemot is no exception. As I write, an almost continuous stream of migrating guillemots is passing through the Minch from the north. The birds fly in companies, the low sun striking on their winter plumage so that the travellers flash white. They travel fast, for an increasing northerly wind is aiding them. They have come from afar, for our resident population of guillemots have long since left us. Perhaps they hail from Shetland, or even from Iceland, or the coasts of northern Scandinavia. None of the passing travellers halt in the Sea of the Minch. Their journey's end is unknown and is perhaps the bosom of some distant ocean far to the south.

It is curious that guillemots should be seen on migration in large numbers and yet puffins should rarely, if ever, be seen to pass. And yet puffins do migrate. I remember once being on the shore of the Atlantic not many miles from Bordeaux. The season was spring. A few days before a severe gale had passed over that part of the Atlantic, and now the shore was littered with the bodies of puffins. The birds, evidently on migration, had been overwhelmed by the force of the waves, and had perished in thousands. It seemed to me curious that a spring storm should have been so disastrous to a bird which remains constantly at sea throughout the winter, and I thought it

ston

CORMORANT CATCHING ITS FISH

Once the cormorant has got within striking distance there is little hope for the fish on which the bird has designs. Cormorants in the sea appear to swallow their food under water, though. These wonderful action photographs were taken at the London Zoo.

King & Son

DRYING WINGS: A CORMORANT IN THE SCILLIES

All round the world from Great Britain to New Zealand, the cormorant may be found, some kinds always living by the sea and others keeping to rivers, lakes or swamps. All have dark feathers on their upper parts, giving a black appearance when seen at a distance, though actually the plumage may be dark green or dark blue with a metallic sheen upon it.

possible that the puffins might have been caught by the gale in a part of the sea where, because of strong tides, the waves were short and steep. This made me think that all birds which remain continuously at sea throughout the winter must be careful to choose ocean quarters where the seas are long and regular, and not short and steep. Especially careful, one would think, must the little auk be, for it is the smallest of the sea divers, and does not hold its head very high above the water's surface.

The little auk has its summer home far beyond the Arctic Circle. No one who has climbed to a colony of these small birds on a steep and rocky hillside of Spitsbergen can ever forget the spectacle of innumerable little auks flying in the rays of the midnight sun past him in a continuous stream, while each bird, whistling its loudest, apparently strove to drown the voices of its equally vociferous neighbours. In winter, however, the little auk is a silent bird. It is abroad upon our seas at that season of the year, yet in coastal waters is rarely observed. After some unusually severe winter storm we may read of a little auk being picked up far inland. These birds rarely recover. They are the weaklings; their stronger relatives know that land is as deadly for them as is the ocean for land birds, and avoid it at all costs.

I always associate the little auk in winter with the North Sea rather than the Atlantic. One winter day I was out at the Farne Islands. The wind was freshening, and when off the Crumstone the surf was heavy upon that lonely rock. At sea, in winter, in a small boat the waves seem more eager, and perhaps more menacing, than when watched from a larger craft, and I shall always remember seeing a little auk, a small dauntless figure, flitting above the racing breakers and seeming to embody the spirit of the storm.

All these sea bird divers have few enemies beneath the water. A solan may meet its fate by swallowing a fish that chokes it, but I do not think that it is ever attacked by large fish. Nor are the young of guillemot, razorbill, or puffin preyed upon by sea enemies—that is, in the ordinary course of things. The solan has no enemies in the air. The puffin, guillemot, razorbill, and little auk have at least one relentless foe—the peregrine falcon. Then there are two other enemies which the puffin has to contend with, at its nesting place, and these are the greater black-backed gull and the raven. Both these birds regard the puffin as fair game. A greater black-backed gull will take up its position beside the burrow where a puffin is tending its downy young. It may hear the puffin moving within. At all events, it stands there, quietly and expectantly, and at last, if fortune favours it, out comes the unsuspecting puffin, when it is seized by the powerful gull, disembowelled, and often left to die in misery.

The raven is not so frequently seen to prey upon nesting puffins, but one family of ravens were known to hunt these unfortunate birds systematically, standing together beside a burrow, and expectantly watching for the appearance of the victim, which

W. S. Berridge

ALLAN O' THE SOUTH WIND"

In the west of Scotland the fishermen say that when they hear this bird, the great northern diver, calling, a storm will come up with the south wind bringing mist and rain-squalls. They call it "Allan o' the South Wind" The bird is nearly a yard long.

ARCTIC TERN RISING FROM ITS EGGS UPON THE SAND

Seton Gordon

When fishing, the Arctic tern comes down upon the water with such force that it is sometimes completely hidden for a moment by the spray, and is almost, if not entirely, submerged in the act of taking its fish. The bird breeds in Britain, as far south as the Farne Islands on the east and in the Scilly Isles on the west. The eggs are laid in a depression in the sand that can hardly be called a nest, and it is as well not to approach too near, for the Arctic terns have a habit of banding together to mob an intruder.

Neville Kingston

PENGUIN DIVING FOR ITS PREY AT HIGH SPEED

Penguins are the champion under-water swimmers of the bird world. Their speed beneath the surface is extraordinary, and is due to the fact that their wings are specially made as paddles and do not have to serve the birds for flight as well. They feed on small crustaceans and fish, and are capable of staying submerged for a considerable time.

they promptly despatched. But all this is on land, and it is really surprising how few enemies bird divers of the sea have.

Now let us study for a time birds that are equally at home at sea or in fresh water—birds which feed on the fish of the sea, and the fish of lakes and rivers.

The most interesting of these feathered fishermen are the great northern diver, the black-throated diver, and the red-throated diver. They are all magnificent divers and swimmers. Their bodies are slim, their feathers are tightly pressed to the skin, their legs are set far back; they are very oily. Their young can dive when an hour out of the egg, and not only can they dive but they are able to remain submerged and swim beneath the surface even at that tender age.

The great northern diver is the largest of the three. It is a magnificent bird, powerful and shapely, and in summer plumage it is most handsome. It is able to remain submerged longer than any other diver. When fishing in deep water a great northern diver submerges on an average for a minute and a half, and during that time may travel beneath the water for several hundred yards. When it appears on the surface it is holding (if its fishing has been successful) a fish in its powerful bill for, unlike the solan, it does not swallow its prey beneath the surface. If the fish be a fair-sized flounder the diver may have considerable difficulty in disposing of it. This habit of the diver in swallowing its catch on the surface is unusual. The cormorant and the shag, as often as not, seem to dispose of their fish in the depths of the sea, although if diving for sea trout in a shallow river estuary a cormorant swallows on the surface.

Seton Gordon

RED-THROATED DIVER ON ITS NEST AND A MUSTER OF FUFFINS

All the true divers, great northern, red-throated, and black-throated, swim deep in the water and dive with the least possible disturbance, remaining below the surface longer than any other British bird. The red-throated diver is the smallest of its family. In the *autumn* the red tint is lost for a time. The bird usually breeds by the banks of a tarn and the eggs are often laid right at the water's edge. Puffins (top) are very good divers and swimmers and nest in rock clefts.

Great Divers of the Bird World

James

GANNET, OR SOLAN GOOSE

Most spectacular of the divers is the gannet or solan goose which, while flying, will suddenly close its wings and drop like a stone into the sea with a great splash. The food is chiefly herrings and pilchards. A gannet is often nearly three feet long.

The great northern diver is known to the Gaelic-speaking fishermen of the West as Allan of the South Wind, for when the diver calls they know that within a few hours the wind will back to the south, and bring with it stormy weather with mist and driving rain.

The red-throated diver is the smallest of the three divers. The great northern diver nests no nearer to us than Iceland; the red-throated diver nests in Scotland, but is so widely distributed that it is found in the Arctic, in Spitsbergen, North East Land, Franz Josef Land, and indeed in the far north wherever the foot of man has trod. This diver usually makes its nest beside a very small lochan or tarn hidden away on the moors, and does all its fishing in the sea.

THE black-throated diver—a scarcer bird in Scotland than the red-throated species—on the other hand, fishes on its nesting loch; but it always chooses as its nesting loch a sheet of water large enough to hold fish in abundance. There is one pair of black-throated divers of my acquaintance which nest upon an island where they have as neighbours a colony of herring gulls. One day, when rowing near the divers' island, I saw the divers cruising with their small family far out on the loch. On seeing the boat the old birds submerged and one of the young swam toward the shore. The other continued to float on the water, and was seen by a hungry gull. The gull swooped down, and though I shouted at the top of my voice, continued on its sinister course and was within a foot of the young diver when I succeeded in exciting our collie dog, Dileas, to such an extent that she barked with terrific vigour. That *did* scare the gull, but had the collie barked two seconds later the chick would have served as a tasty tit-bit and its career would have come to an abrupt close.

The great family of diving ducks are, most of them, equally at home upon the sea or on fresh water. Some of them are sea birds in winter and land birds in summer. The long-tailed duck, for example, is a bird of the inland lakes in Iceland (where it nests), but when it leaves Iceland for the coasts of Britain, where it spends the winter months, it desists from its fresh-water habit and is entirely a bird of the salt water from October until April.

Like the long-tailed duck the scaup is a bird of salt water in winter and a bird of fresh water in summer. The eider duck, on the other hand, is a salt-water bird summer and winter, and for this reason is not easy to tame and keep on a lake. There was an old eider drake in Viscount Grey's bird sanctuary at Falloden, and the old fellow was very tame. He spent most of his time courting wild duck. The drakes did not mind his attentions to their mates, for they evidently regarded him as harmless.

The dipper or water ousel is not a diver in the true sense of the term, yet it is equally at home on land or beneath the water. Except in unusually severe weather the dipper avoids salt water; its home is on quick-flowing rivers and hill streams, and I have seen it at the Wells of Dee, just four thousand feet above the sea. The dipper can do what no other bird can do, namely, walk about on the floor of a river pool with several feet of water flowing above it. Walking thus on the bed of the stream it searches amongst the stones for its food, which consists chiefly of aquatic larvae.

The dipper, I suppose, is the only diving bird of Britain which has a song in the true sense of the word. Not only in spring does the water ousel sing. In the depths of winter, standing on some stone in mid-stream, it pours out a flood of sweet music, soft and uninterrupted, as the December light fails.

THE dipper is a very early nester. On Lower Deeside, in Aberdeenshire, I have seen its completed nest on the opening day of the salmon fishing (February 11). One of the dippers which my wife watched from a "hide" was an unusually cheery fellow. He (for one presumes it to have been the male) was always singing, although he had a hungry family to feed. One day, after he had fed his brood, he thrust his head well inside the domed nest on a boulder in mid-stream, and poured out a flood of song. Perhaps he was giving the family a singing lesson! The young dippers must have been deafened by a torrent of sound that made their mossy home ring; they may, I imagine, have felt rather like the English visitor to a certain noble castle in the highlands when not one piper, but seven, marched together into the dining-hall after dinner and, piping shrilly, three times circled the room!

Neville Kingston

SWIFT-DIVING CORMORANT HUNTS ITS PREY BENEATH THE SEA

Chapter XXXVI

Strange Animal Friendships

By Lewis Spence

Author of "An Introduction to Mythology"

STRANGE comradeships between animals, sometimes of the most dissimilar species, seem to show that there are exceptions to the maxim that hostility is the law of nature. Queer compacts are frequently made between domestic animals, and this leads to the assumption that those species which have been "adopted" by man become in a measure "civilized," and relinquish a part of their savage instincts. Be this as it may, affinities between various species were almost proverbial in the ancient world. For example, the strong partiality of the horse for the goat as a stable-companion is alluded to by more than one medieval writer. Herodotus mentions the association between the crocodile and the Egyptian plover, a fact long scoffed at as an absurdity by naturalists, and the fables of Aesop are eloquent of dealings between beasts, some of which may have been founded on direct observation, although, it need scarcely be said, they are for the most part matter of pure allegory.

But every apparent friendship between birds and beasts must not be attributed to mere good-natured tolerance or any excess of amiability, for the lying down of the lion with the lamb is an occurrence quite as uncommon as the hobnobbing of Turk with Armenian. The Montagues and Capulets of Nature do not so readily abandon their vendettas. It is scarcely in a spirit of playful amusement that the crocodile fraternises with the plover. His motives, indeed, are those basely selfish ones which inspire the human to be a trifle obsequious to his dentist, for it is in that capacity that *Pluvianus aegyptius* acts toward his rapacious client. To the gums of the crocodile adhere colonies of ravenous leeches, which cause him considerable discomfort, and these the plover deftly removes with its bill. The arrangement is therefore one of mutual advantage, and this, indeed, is symptomatic of many another apparent intimacy between species the most incongruous.

These convenient alliances have numerous parallels in marine and insect life, as the sequel will show. But more genuine friendships between creatures of widely different species are scarcely to be accounted for otherwise than by "personal" affinity. Such a partnership was that chronicled by the late C. J. Cornish between a donkey, a mare with a couple of foals, and a mastiff, in pastoral Derbyshire. The donkey had learned to open gates, an accomplishment, it seems, not unusual among his tribe, and thus managed to reach his equine friends. Later they were joined by the great house-dog, and, like the animals in Grimms' folktale, all set forth on their adventures, wandering over the countryside until they encountered human interference in the shape of a farm labourer, who drove the horses back to pasture. The donkey, abandoned by his comrades returned home, still accompanied by the mastiff, which, perhaps, had been inspired by the natural motive of his race to safeguard his master's property.

But friendships much more singular have been recorded. Years ago in the Zoological Gardens at Antwerp a wretched little stray dog was thrust into the cage of a lion to serve his majesty as light refreshment. But to the surprise of the keepers, Leo, after sniffing at his destined prey, began to lick him over in the most affectionate manner. Far from being frightened, the dog made every demonstration of satisfaction, and shortly the pair became inseparable, the lion refusing to allow his new acquaintance to be removed from the den. For hours the dog would lie curled up between the lion's paws; it shared his food, and when efforts were made to remove it, set up a doleful yelping, to the accompaniment of the wrathful roarings of its protector.

A case is recorded in which an Australian opossum and a setter became inseparable, lying asleep together on the hearthrug during the day, and playing with one another in the evening. The dog submitted to the opossum washing his face, though it was plain that he resented the operation.

I REMEMBER an inseparable comradeship between a parrot and a fox-terrier, the pets of a relative. The parrot had practically the run of the house, and would flutter up and down stairs, accompanied by the terrier, uttering discordant cries and occasionally questionable language if the dog disappeared for a moment. To watch them wrestling for a walnut, the parrot inserting his beak between the terrier's jaws, was a standing amusement. But the most incongruous instance of animal friendship within my recollection is one between a monkey and a billy-goat. The monkey, the property of a neighbour, had on one occasion been tied, despite its struggles, to the goat's back, to play the part of Mazeppa in "The Wild Horse of Tartary" as part of a childish game. In that prone position it naturally showed every sign of acute annoyance and discomfort, but when placed on the shoulders of the animal in the attitude of a jockey, it not only appreciated the exercise which the truly terrified goat certainly gave it, but when removed, insisted on returning to its seat, frequently visiting the garden, and mounting the goat of its own accord. By degrees its victim grew accustomed to the sport, and tolerated his rider, although a nanny-goat refused the privilege and tossed the monkey badly more than once when it boldly attempted to mount her.

Cornish records a most extraordinary case of friendship between a goose and a crane, both of which belonged to the late Lord Lilford's collection of wildfowl at Lilford Hall, near Oundle. The

BULL TERRIER AND A FAMILY OF KITTENS

Provided that they get to know each other at a sufficiently early age dogs and cats will usually live together in peace. This bull terrier pup appointed itself guardian of a litter of Siamese kittens, and provided his comparatively ample body as a kind of warm couch against which the kittens could lie and be comfortable. The benefit was mutual for the fur coats of the kittens helped to warm the dog. Cats and dogs are proverbial enemies but, nevertheless, friendships such as this often occur, if begun early enough, and continue unbroken.

goose, which was of an Australian species, practically annexed the crane altogether, feeding beside it, and never venturing more than a few yards from it, or allowing it to be out of its sight for a moment. If another crane or a visitor approached it, the goose rushed at the intruder and made as if to bite. For some six months the crane was removed, and when it was returned to the enclosure, the goose at once made every demonstration of joy.

Indeed the goose seems peculiarly prone to friendship. J. C. Hauzeau speaks of a Chinese goose which conceived a quite violent affection for a dog, and which hissed vindictively at any person or animal who offered to interfere with its favourite. When at last its friend was killed by another dog, it pursued the murderer for a long distance, and appeared grief-stricken for days after, moping in a corner of the farmyard, refusing food and all companionship from the rest of its species.

An exceptionally curious instance of animal friendship is that between a cat and a frog, described by W. H. G. Kingston. The servants of a country house had enticed a frog from its hole by giving it food. As winter came on, the frog grew quite tame and was in the habit of making its way to the kitchen fire for the sake of warmth. The usual occupant of the hearth was a favourite old cat, which from the first showed no animosity towards the newcomer. In course of time the frog gained confidence, and actually nestled beneath the cosy fur of puss, which seemed perfectly content with the arrangement. Every evening the frog hopped forth from its hole and nestled like a kitten beneath the soft coat of the cat, which constituted herself its protector, and would not allow it to be disturbed.

"A spaniel," says the Rev. James Wood, "shared his food with an unpopular cock which had been ostracised by the other poultry in a certain farmyard." The bird was not allowed to have a share of what was going, but was driven off and severely maltreated. But the dog became his champion, and stood on guard while he ate a portion of the general meal. At times the bird had even to be fed in the dog's kennel, so bitter was the animosity of the other fowls against him. In the end, however, the cock was found dead in the kennel, as the result of the bad treatment he had received. When discovered, he was "lying closely pressed to his only friend."

Dr. Lauder Lindsay quotes "a local paper of high standing" as vouching for the extraordinary case of a hen hatching out her chickens in a watch-dog's kennel. "The two seemed to understand each other so well that, on her leaving and entering the kennel the dog rises and makes way. . . . Any attempt to abstract the eggs in the absence of the hen meets with the immediate disapprobation of the dog." He also mentions the case of a tame rook, which was very fond of two dogs, one being a bulldog. The rook constantly rode on their backs, and accompanied them on their journeys abroad.

A case is on record of a kitten, born on the roof of an outhouse, which was, by accident, deprived of its mother and brethren. It evaded all attempts to catch it, but just below where it lived a brood of chickens were constantly running about. Growing weary of solitude, the kitten scrambled down and joined the feathered band, which showed no fear of it. In a short time a perfect understanding was established between the kitten and his friends. He assumed the part of leader, and used to conduct them about the grounds, occasionally hiding and darting at them from ambush. One pullet was his especial favourite, and when other broods appeared, the kitten, now grown into a cat, transferred its interest to them, the hen appearing in no way alarmed at having so unusual a nurse for her offspring. A similar instance of comradeship between a cat and a pigeon, whose young had been destroyed by rats, is noticed by Kingston. Feeling instinctively that she would be in safer quarters near puss, the bird sidled up to her, and the pair became inseparable, feeding out of the same dish, and the pigeon brooding over the kittens in the absence of their mother.

Dr. Lauder Lindsay recounts a story of a mastiff and a cat, which, as puppy and kitten, had shown so strong a liking for each other that at last puss took up her quarters in the watch-dog's kennel. She never seemed happy when away from him. She ate her breakfast out of the dog's bowl, and slept in his kennel, with his paws around her. She used to catch mice and young rats and bring them to him, seeming quite pleased when he accepted friendship's offering. When she produced a litter of kittens, the mastiff acted as nurse to them in her absence, and her only surviving offspring in time became as fond of the dog as her mother had been.

The late Rev. J. Watson tells of a strange friendship between a tame tiger kept on board ship on a voyage home from India for a dog, to which it " took " at first sight. The dog, on his part, was not quite so

J. T. Roberts

WELSH COLLIE AND HIS BROWN OWL FRIEND

By some strange process in its mind, this brown owl conceived a liking for the company of a four-footed creature, with which it could not, in the ordinary way, possibly have anything in common. The bird was of the air, and the dog of the ground, and why should the inhabitants of either take any interest in each other, save from the point of view of either eating or being eaten. Yet, unaccountable as it seems, here are the two strangely assorted friends as they were constantly seen together.

Keystone

E.N.A.

CAT WHOSE MOTHER INSTINCT WAS STRONGER THAN THE DESIRE TO KILL

While all the members of the cat family from tiger to domestic tabby are renowned for ferocity, it cannot be denied that cats are excellent mothers. When this strong maternal instinct is thwarted strange things may happen, as we see here. A family of chickens (bottom) and, even more astonishing, young rats (top) may not come amiss to the cat if her kittens have been taken away from her. In the case of the cat in the upper photograph the young rats were actually offered to her, originally, as something to eat.

Neville Kingston

QUEER ZOO FRIENDSHIP AND UNUSUALLY MIXED BATHING

It seems surprising that while animals will very often turn upon a stranger of their own kind, yet they will make friends with a member of an entirely different race. One of the strange friendships formed at the London Zoo was that of an orang-utan and a tree kangaroo (bottom). In the upper photograph we have a scene on the Serpentine in Hyde Park, where two pets, a monkey and a dog, are enjoying themselves together in the water. The monkey, it will be noticed, is on all fours like the dog.

BIRD AND BEAST LIVING TOGETHER IN CLOSE AND HAPPY COMPANIONSHIP

In a certain private collection of animals there used to be a monkey who was attracted by a cockatoo (right) and, braving the beak and claws of this bird, which can be fierce enough when it likes, was happy to find his friendship returned. The two would sit on the bird's swinging perch for hours, contentedly rocking to and fro, the monkey's extra weight being handy in keeping the swing moving. The cat and the starling in the left-hand photograph came together in this way. The cat was owned by a miner who one day found a young starling which had broken its leg. **He put the leg in splints until it was well when, although allowed full liberty, the bird preferred to stay, taking its meals with the cat.**

J. T. Roberts

OWL AND CAT THAT MET IN THEIR YOUTH AND GREW UP TOGETHER

When the influence of man interferes with the normal circumstances of an animal's life, abnormality in some form is often the result. The cat and the owl are both carnivorous creatures which live by hunting and killing, if hungry enough, any living creature sufficiently small to be successfully attacked. But in this case, a young owl which was introduced to a kitten under human influence, settled down contentedly and grew up side by side with it. At first the bird was larger than the kitten (left) but at the end of twelve months the kitten had become a cat and far outgrown its friend in size. But twelve months of friendship, which the camera has recorded, succeeded in keeping the peace even when the cat was big enough to make itself dangerous.

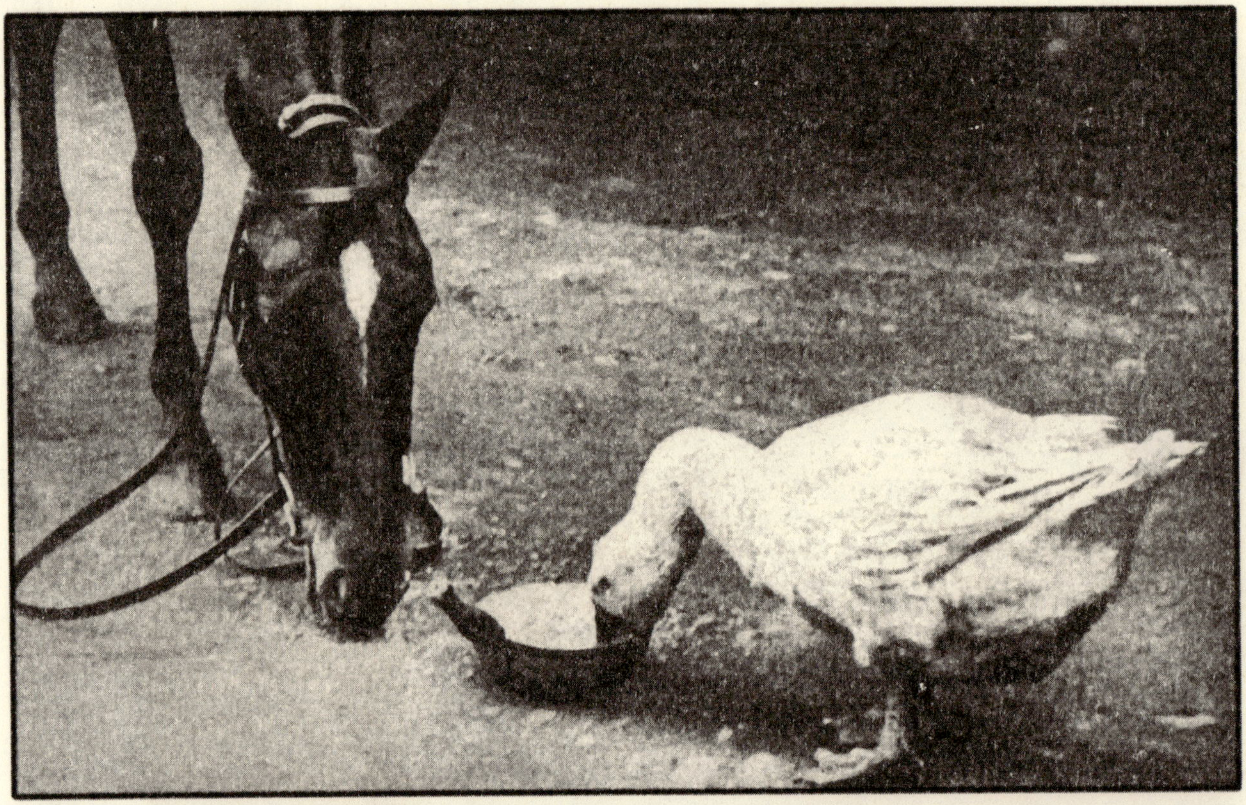

PIGEON AND GOOSE WITH THE COMPANIONS OF THEIR CHOICE

Rats will steal pigeons eggs if they get the chance, and the pigeons recognize their mutual enemies quickly enough. But years of inherited enmity did not prevent this pigeon (bottom) submitting to play the part of horse for a young rat to ride. Geese appear to be very prone to make friendships with other animals, and one particular bird (top), which was kept as a mascot in a polo stable, took a fancy to one of the ponies. The two would accompany each other to the fields and feed together in silent but faithful friendship.

Neville Kingston

TIGER AND LION LIVING TOGETHER AT THE ZOO

Perhaps mutual tolerance would be nearer the truth than friendship as a term to describe the relationship between the tiger and the lion which were put in the same cage at the Zoological Gardens, London. Luck seems to play a great part in such associations between the large carnivora. So small a matter as a wasp sting on the nose might lead to the victim snapping at its companion purely as the result of the shock. Then, if the fight was not stopped in time the lion would probably be vanquished by the more rapidly moving tiger.

anxious to strike up an acquaintanceship, but after a day or two of comradely advances on the part of the tiger, it displayed not the slightest fear of its new messmate, and the twain henceforth became inseparable. Thomas Belt tells of the singular attachment of a young jaguar for the dog which had captured it. It became greatly attached to the dog, living with it in harmony as a companion.

INSTANCES of animal friendship arising through compassion are not rare. A terrier dog was suffering so severely from distemper that it was necessary to confine her to her kennel. A bantam cock, noticing her plight, took pity on the sufferer and squeezing himself through the bars of the kennel, took up his abode along with the stricken terrier, never leaving her save to pick up his daily food. When he did so, the terrier whined and betrayed every symptom of uneasiness. Her condition became worse, and the bantam, for the purpose of keeping her warm, took his place between her forelegs, the poor little invalid making use of her feathered friend as a sort of hot-water bottle. Eventually the terrier succumbed to the disease, when the bantam appeared inconsolable at the loss of his friend, and it was some time before he recovered his usual spirits.

Sir Benjamin Brodie remarks that the want of society is specially felt in the case of domestic or gregarious animals which are accustomed to be constantly surrounded by friends and companions. In their case, solitary confinement is frequently attended by dementia or other forms of mental derangement, just as in man. Mr. Frank Buckland, once editor of "Land and Water," says that horses dislike solitude, and are rendered savage by being kept alone. Love of company is, indeed, strongly marked in the horse. Pierquin cites a case of frenzy in a carriage-horse when his companion was not in harness with him. White and Stirling have shown that the pigmy ape and other animals exhibit mental disturbance when deprived of companionship.

Every now and again in the daily Press odd cases of animal fosterage are alluded to. We read of a hen mothering a brood of ducks, or a cat rearing puppies.

Neville Kingston

RAT FRIENDSHIPS FOR OTHER ANIMALS

A seemingly unfair competition is illustrated in the lower photograph, where a Gambian giant rat is feeding out of the same bowl as a white mouse. The rat is one of two African species possessing cheek pouches, and it attains a length of two feet. A rat the size of a terrier is an unusual pet, and certainly a rather dangerous companion for the diminutive white mouse. The upper photograph shows a tame squirrel which became friendly with a rat with which it shared its meals.

Neville Kingston

GREAT CARNIVORA IN TOLERANT MOODS AT THE ZOO

When one of the great cats condescends to tolerate the weak the result is impressive indeed. At the Zoo a certain cat named Rusti (bottom) took to going into the cage of Rajah, one of the tigers. Why this particular cat was not afraid, and why this particular tiger did not resent such impertinence is hard to explain. Laziness may induce tolerance. Witness the lion (top) that, while dozing, noticed a cock sparrow in its cage and rolled over on its back—that being the movement involving the least trouble—to watch the little bird.

Keystone

GOAT AND RHINOCEROS DWELL TOGETHER: DEER LIVING WITH HARES

Goats have in all ages been regarded as rather mysterious creatures, and it will be remembered that they were always associated with the great god Pan. A young mountain goat (bottom) discovered a playmate in an infant rhinoceros and the two would romp together till exhausted, only it was always the rhinoceros that got exhausted first. Whereupon, the goat would take up its stand upon its friend's back and assume a threatening attitude. Above we see a queer association between deer and hares at a Paris Agricultural Exhibition.

Neville Kingston

GOOD COMPANY: FOX AND KITTEN, LURCHER AND WOLVES

Fox cubs are hard to beat for playfulness, but kittens make good rivals to them. The pair in the lower photograph provided much entertainment for their owners as they played at hide-and-seek or battles to the death. But the rules of mock warfare were never transgressed. An unusual combination of domestic dog and wolves appears in the top photograph. An English lurcher took upon itself the guardianship of some young American prairie wolves. All dogs originally descended from the same ancestors as the untamable wolf.

E.N.A.

DOG AND EAGLE FRIENDS IN HUNGARY

From Hungary comes the remarkable photograph of a dog which made friends with the fiercest of the birds of prey, an eagle. The eagle had a block of wood to perch on and the dog used to lie down beside it and appeared to like the strange company.

and more rarely of the solicitude of a cat for a nest of young rats, or a rabbit for motherless chickens. These, of course, result from the cravings of the natural maternal instinct, and it is doubtful if they survive the stage of helplessness.

A TERRIER which lived at Dunrobin Castle in Sutherlandshire had a family of puppies which were destroyed. She took up with a brood of ducklings, carried them off one by one to her kennel, and would allow no one to remove them. When, later, they made their way instinctively to water and plunged in she showed the greatest concern, evidently fearing that they would be drowned, as her own puppies had been. As they returned to the land, she picked them up one by one and took them back to her kennel. The same terrier, on losing another litter, seized two cockerel chickens, which she " brought up " with the same care as she had bestowed on the ducklings. But their attempts to crow proved a source of such annoyance to her that she was glad to resign her charge in the end.

The firm of Messrs. Hagenbeck, of Hamburg, so long famous for the supply of wild animals to zoological societies and shows, has for many years made a specialty of " happy families " of the largest carnivora in single cages. Lions, tigers, leopards, jaguars and large boarhounds are placed together, but it has been observed that these merely tolerate each other, with the exception of the dogs, which strive to introduce a spirit of camaraderie. Only the other day a serious situation arose in a circus in the North of England, in the arena of which a number of lions and tigers were being put through their paces. A lion snapped in passing at one of his striped companions, which at once joined battle with him, and in a moment the entire pack had lashed itself into a frenzy of savage rage, to the terror of the audience, who, however, were duly protected by iron barriers. Only the menace of burning torches served to separate the ferocious combatants and drive them from the ring.

IT would not do to conclude such an article as this without some reference to animal affinities in folk-lore. In many countries the people have long believed that certain beasts or birds have a strong affinity for each other, and that in some cases they afford mutual protection, a fallacy which in certain instances has been disproved only after long observation. Thus the common notion that crows and seagulls are companionable simply because they are frequently in the habit of gathering together in one field, is based on mere imagination only. The fact is that both species of birds are attracted to fields where seed has been sown by a common rapacity and nothing more, and that they tacitly ignore each other is obvious to anyone who observes them for more than a few minutes.

The old notion that dogs frequently join wolf-packs in countries where the wilder species is common, is equally groundless. No dog would be tolerated in a wolf-pack, and would, indeed, be torn to pieces the moment he showed himself. The oft-told tale that the South American puma has an affinity for mankind, and occasionally follows him out of a desire for companionship, has certainly more to commend it, and seems to be founded on fact.

That badgers and foxes frequently occupy the same earth is well known, but that anything in the nature of companionship occurs between the species is more than doubtful. Mutual toleration there may be, but nothing more. The same may be said of the owl, and the American prairie dog, which share burrows.

The conclusion to which we are bound to arrive at is that animal friendships are based on mutual aid, and that only occasionally do individuals of different species grow companionable out of a freakish liking for one another, which is probably aroused by contiguity and long association. But that these latter cases more commonly occur between domestic animals is obvious, instances of comradeship between wild species being almost unknown, unless based on the law of mutual assistance and convenience: and even then only in circumstances which would have to be described as exceptional.

Chapter XXXVII

The Skill of the Spider

By Susan Finnegan

of the Natural History Museum, South Kensington

Many stories and superstitions have gathered around the history of spiders, and one of the earliest occurs in Greek mythology. Arachne, the daughter of Idmon of Colophon in Lydia, a dyer in purple, acquired great skill in weaving; her patterns were so beautiful and her work so faultless that at length she ventured to challenge the goddess Athena. Athena was displeased at what she considered the presumption of a mortal, and took as the subject of her work her quarrel with Poseidon, intending it as a warning to such as dared to pit themselves against the immortals. Arachne chose the metamorphosis of the gods and illustrated their adventures. When Athena discovered that there was no blemish to be found in the work that Arachne had done, she took it up in rage and tore it to shreds. Arachne in despair hanged herself, but the goddess in seeing this had compassion and loosened the rope so that it formed a cobweb and Arachne changed herself into a spider, continuing to spin.

This story refers to the superior skill of Asia over Greece in the art of weaving. It also focuses attention on a habit that is fundamental in the life of all spiders — the production of silk and the art of weaving. It is undoubtedly due to this, and the varied uses to which the silk can be put, that spiders have secured such a hold in the animal world. They extend over the whole of the globe except in the extreme north and south, and have adapted themselves to all kinds of surroundings and habitats, from deserts to marshy plains, mountains and valleys, freshwater ponds and the space between the tide-marks of the sea-shore.

There is only one constant use to which all kinds of spiders put their silk, and that is the production of a cocoon for their eggs; this is the primary function. The eggs are enclosed by the female in a case of silk which may either be spun loosely around them, forming a flocculent seamless mass, or the cocoon covering may be spun in two parts, the eggs being laid on a sheet of silk previously woven for them and then enclosed by an outer covering which is swathed around; sometimes this has bits of gnawed bark and pellets of mud and clay introduced into it to strengthen the framework.

Although cocoons are constructed by all spiders and webs formed only by some, spider silk is more popularly associated with the web. This is natural, since the aim of the spider is to conceal the cocoon, rendering it as far as possible invisible to insects that would prey upon the eggs, while on the other hand, the web as a snare is often exposed and therefore more easily observed and reported upon.

There are many different forms of webs, the sheet-web of the common house spider, *Tegenaria derhamii*, which forms such ugly, dusty cobwebs in the corners of unused rooms and outhouses; the beautiful wheel-like web of the garden spider, *Epeira diademata*, and the silken tubes of the trap-door spider. The evolution of these forms is interesting. From a simple, more or less horizontal, sheet of threads the common house spider constructs his web, providing it with a small tubular hole to serve as a retreat; *Angalena labyrinthica*, the labyrinth spider of the countryside, has also an extensive horizontal sheet built among gorse or rough grass, but the tube in this instance is more complete, actually forming a tunnel through which the spider can escape into the vegetation below. But the *Lycosidae*, or wolf spiders, to which the true

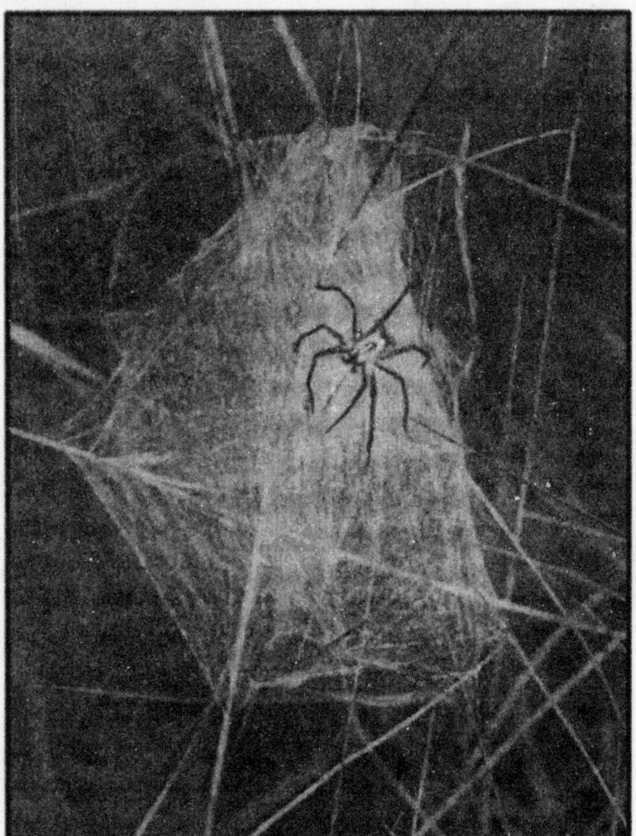

M. H. Crawford

SPIDER'S NURSERY

Secure in a silk cocoon which she has woven, the mother spider deposits her eggs, storing the whole contrivance in some safe place. Sometimes small pieces of mud or bark are used to strengthen and stabilise the framework of this wonderfully constructed "nursery."

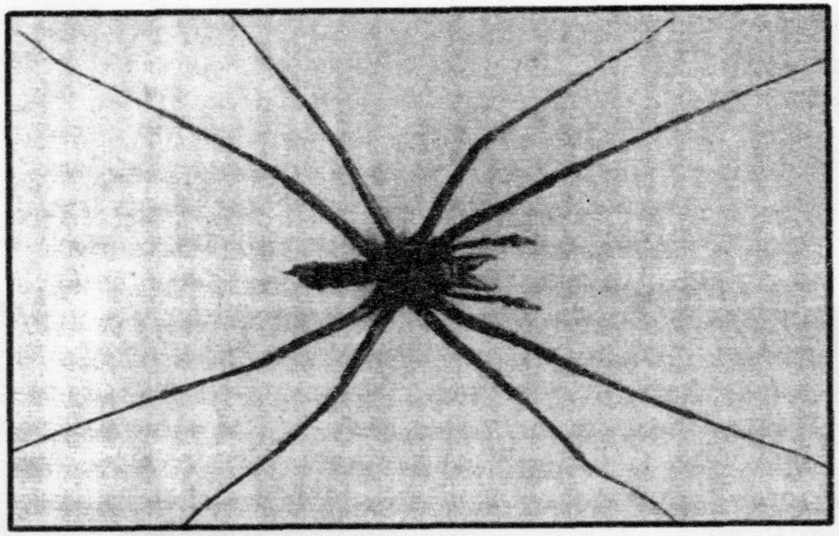

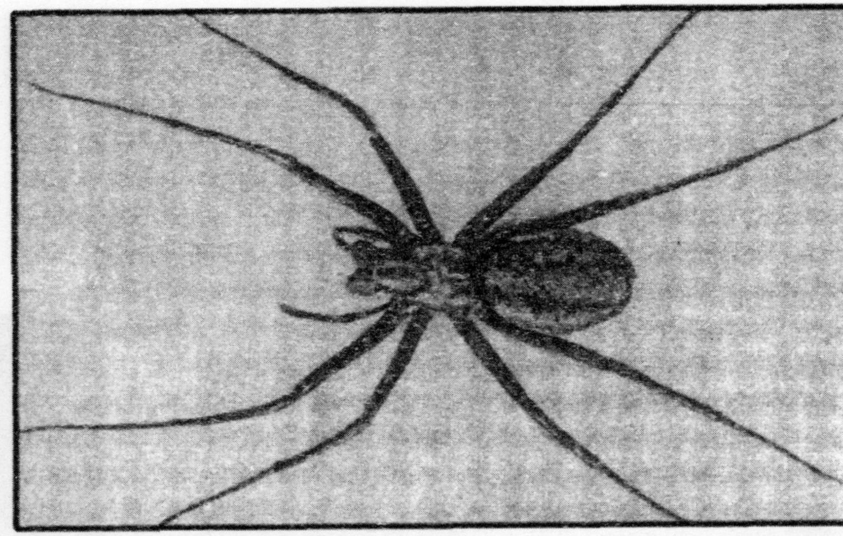

F. Martin Duncan

John T. Roberts

A. E. Smith

BEST KNOWN OF WEB SPINNERS: GARDEN AND HOUSE SPIDERS AT HOME

Both lower photographs show the round plump-bodied garden spider of Britain, which sometimes catches one's face with its threads, hung invariably between bushes or among low branches. The upper photographs are (left) of the male and (right) of the female house spider, which is responsible for the housewife's bane, the dust-collecting cobwebs. The male, we notice, has longer legs than the female, and he needs them to escape being eaten by his "intended," when he goes wooing. The female, on the other hand, is the larger of the two. It is interesting to recall that the female house spider, dipped in butter and swallowed whole, was held to be a certain cure for the ague in the Fen country, when that complaint was common in those parts.

tarantula belongs, and a very different group, the Mygalomorphs, which are great tropical spiders, both have their retreat underground.

The tunnel which they burrow in the earth is lined with silk to prevent the infall of loose soil or mould, while the aperture may either have a portion of the tube extended through it to the outside or may be closed by a hinged door which can be opened only from the inside, but is securely closed on the outer side. This is often coated with débris to match the surroundings so closely that it is almost impossible to detect the existence of the trap.

But there is another line of development; instead of the tube we may get mechanical skill employed to a very high degree in the construction of a sheet of threads in such a manner as to form the delicate wheel-like web of an orb-weaver like *Epeira diademata*, the common garden spider. This perfect orbicular web is built by the spider stretching a horizontal thread across to two neighbouring objects, and allowing itself to drop down from one end of the line to a point of attachment below. It then climbs up, crosses the horizontal line and drops down on the other side, laying down three lines of the quadrangle in this manner; to complete the fourth line it climbs up the one just secured, crosses the horizontal line once again, drops down the other perpendicular line and draws the thread across, making the quadrangular framework. Next the corners are joined and the radii laid down with great exactness.

The spider then returns to the centre of the web, and moving outwards to the circumference in a spiral it lays down a temporary scaffold of concentric lines. From the circumference it retraces its way to the centre, this time laying down a viscous thread with great deliberation; this spiral crosses each radius approximately at right angles. The thread is broken off at a short distance from the hub and the spider disposes of the temporary scaffolding by rolling it up and eating it. Finally the notched zone is added, which consists of a few turns of spiral, the thread of which leaves each radius slightly below the point of original attachment. Passing back from the centre of the web to the underside of an adjoining leaf, or some other situation chosen by the animal for concealment, there is a single thread, the trap-line, which communicates directly with the spider. By this means the spider has passage to the web, or if menaced by some danger it can drop easily to the ground, still retaining its attachment.

The web has great elasticity, which resides not only in the silk itself, but is increased in some species by the removal of the centre, which has the effect of easing the strain on any one particular spot. Wind can be a source of considerable annoyance, and the means taken by the owner to overcome this difficulty is to drop to the ground and after appropriating a very small stone or some suitable piece of debris, actually to secure it to the end of the thread to serve as a weight.

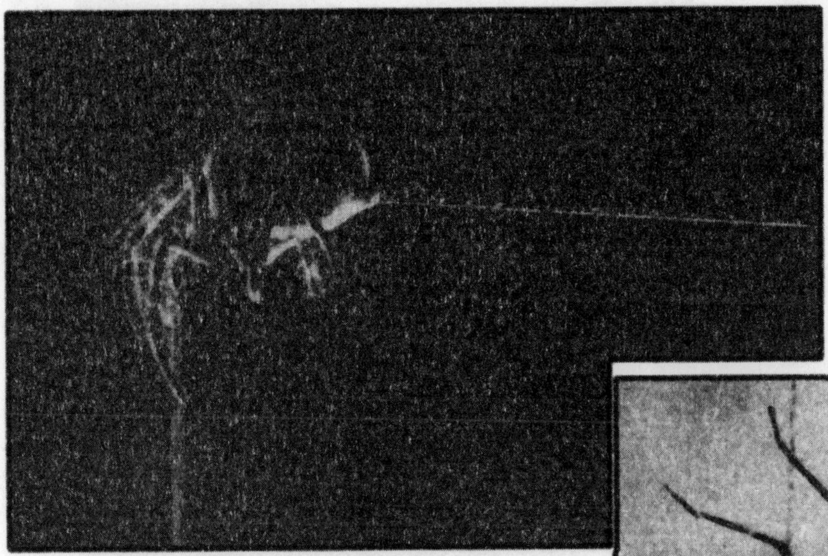

J. T. Roberts

SPIDER MOULTING AND SPIDER SPINNING

Here (top) is a garden spider paying out the silk from its spinnerets. Notice that the line, as seen against the light, is covered with sticky globules. When the house spider moults (bottom) it has to disentangle its old skin from the web as we see here.

Spiders have another use for their silk which not only is of immense value to themselves but also has resulted in much speculation among people from a very early time. About the month of September or the early part of October, the young spider climbs up a stalk of grass or takes its position on the top of a

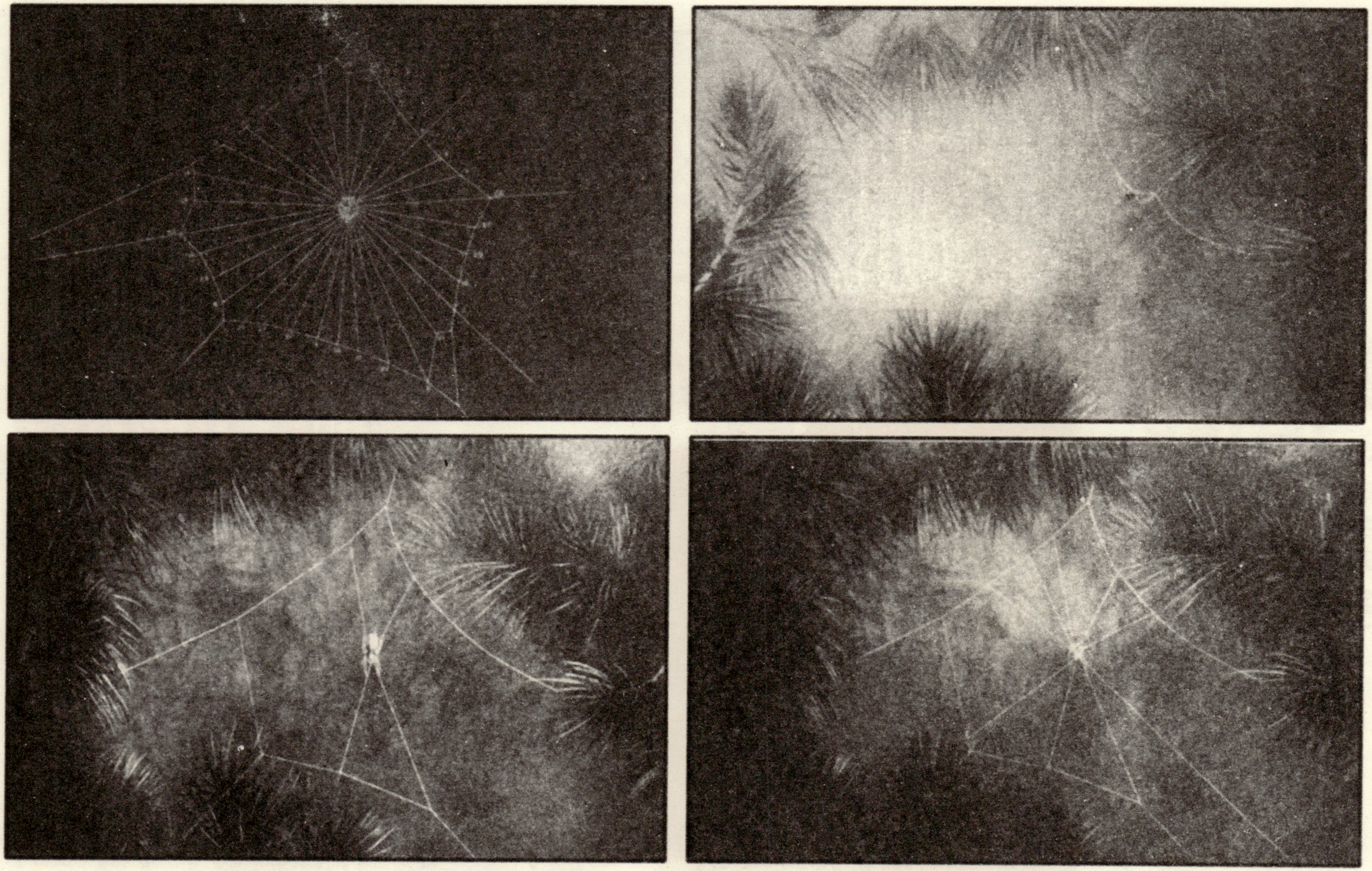

James

PHOTOGRAPHS AND DIAGRAM OF THE EARLY STAGES IN THE CONSTRUCTION OF A SPIDER'S WEB

The spinning of a spider's web is no matter of an orderly procession round and round a circle with the threads laid down in rotation. The numbered diagram (top left) shows the order in which the threads were actually laid down in a web which came under scientific observation. The spider starts by emitting from its body the liquid which, solidifying immediately on contact with the air, at once adheres to the leaf or branch which the spider has chosen for the beginning of the operation. It then either crawls to another point or lets out a light thread which is caught by air currents and so wafts the spider to some other suitable support. Thus the initial line of the web is stretched between two points. Then it crawls back along this initial line (top right), making a stronger cable.

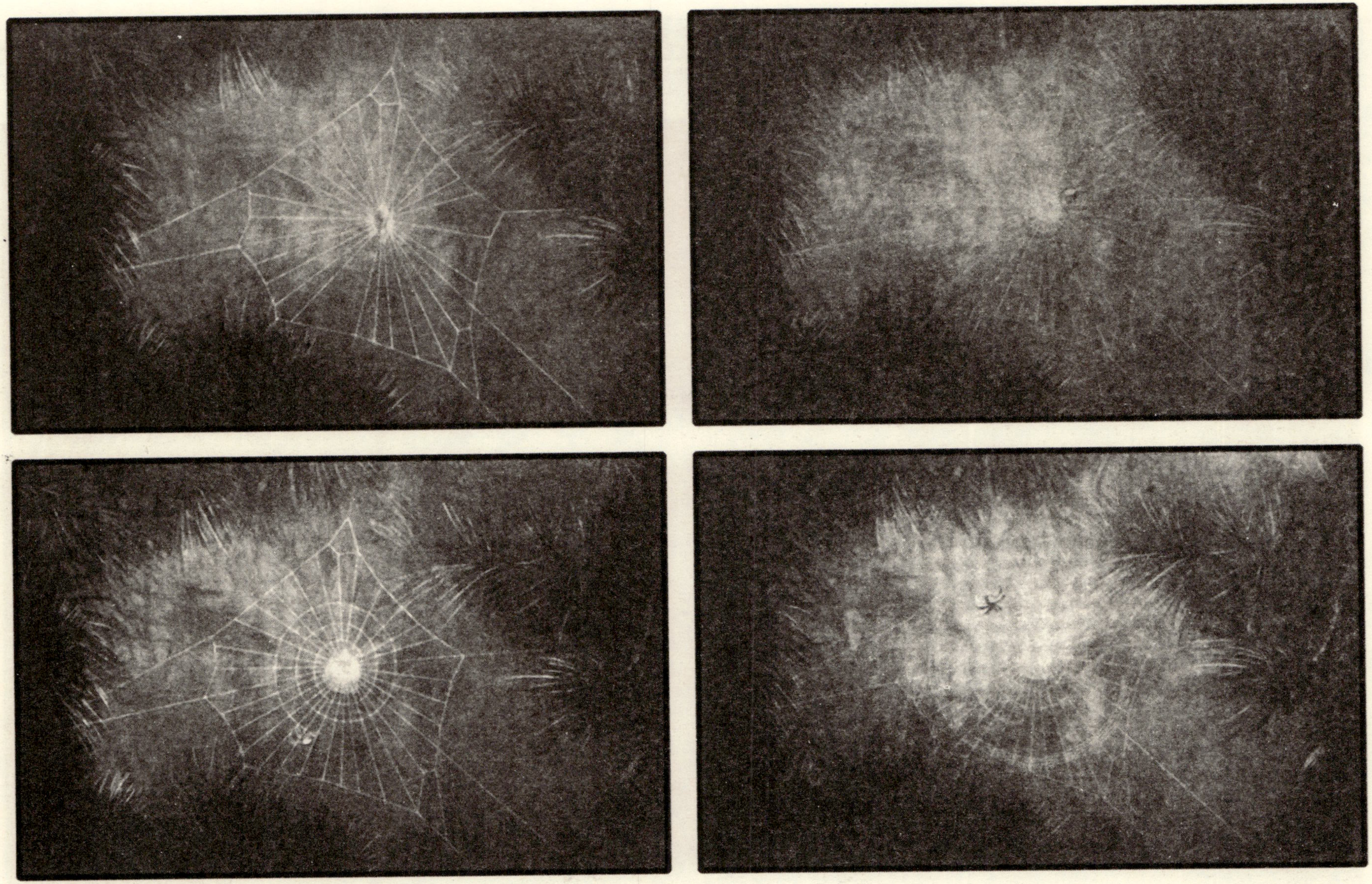

James

LAYING DOWN THE RADII AND BEGINNING THE SPIRAL OF THE WEB

So soon as the first line is made the spider drops others, one from each end, and either joins these two to form a triangle or continues the process until the framework is a trapezium or a polygon and, having tested the strength of each line, has the framework complete. If necessary, additional supports are run off to convenient points of attachment. Then, starting from some point on the frame, the spider starts to walk round, paying out a line which it carefully holds clear of the frame. When it has reached a point opposite to the start of its walk the spider hauls this new line taut. Thus the framework is bisected by a diametrical thread. The mid-point of this then becomes the starting-point for a number of radii or "spokes" from the centre to the framework.

James

WEB ALMOST COMPLETE WITH ITS DEADLY VISCID SPIRALS

When the radii or " spokes " have been completed the spider goes to the centre and plucks at each line to test it. Then a spiral is spun about the centre to steady the whole web, and the transverse threads are laid down. These, when first emitted by the spider seem the same as the rest of the web, but soon begin to assume a stouter appearance. This is due to the fact that the transverse threads are coated with a viscid or sticky substance, so that any insect striking the web will adhere to it. It appears that the spider excretes some special antidote to the sticky properties of the transverse lines or " viscid spiral " of the web so that it does not get caught in its own trap.

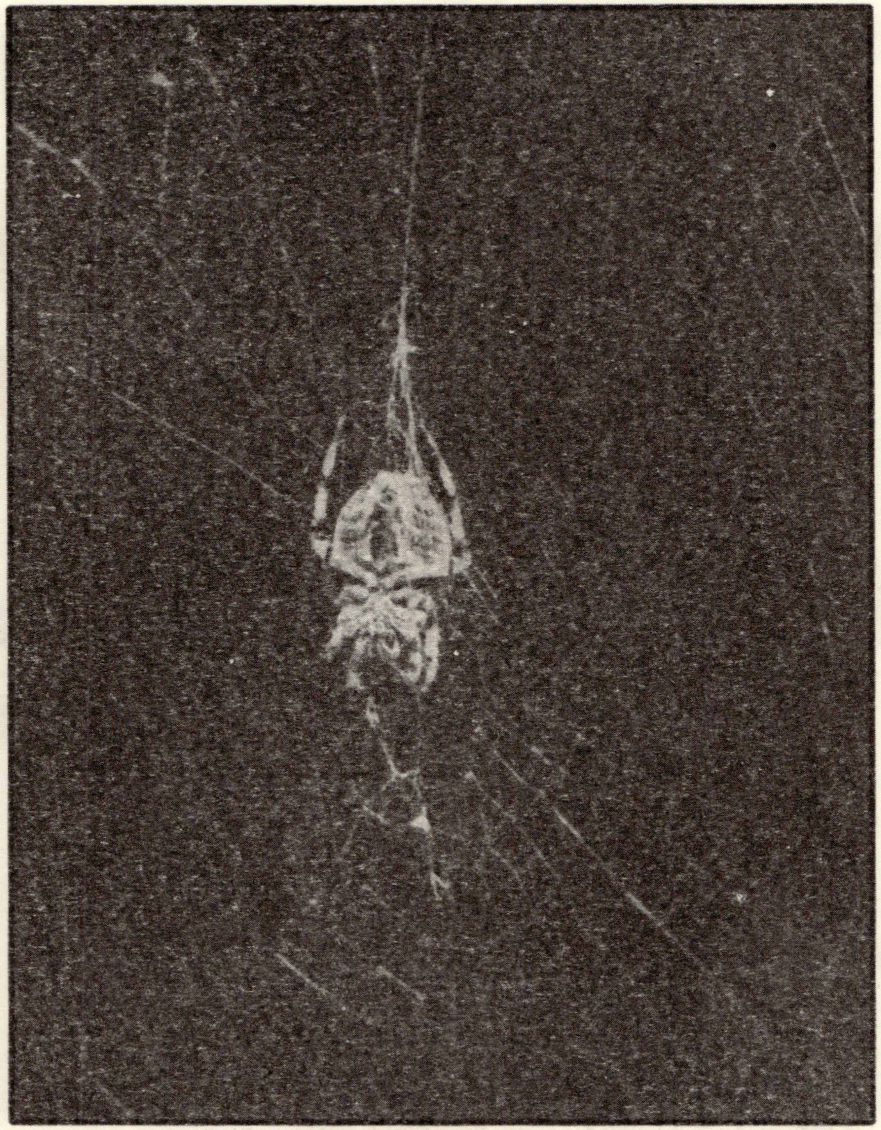

F. Martin Duncan

WEB CAUGHT BY MORNING DEW AND BEING REPAIRED AFTER DAMAGE

Our attention is most strongly drawn to a web in the early morning when the dew upon it catches the sunlight (left) forming a shining silver net. It must be remembered that the spider has to allow for all this extra weight of moisture, and, indeed, the silk of which the web is made possesses the most extraordinary elasticity and strength. Not only has dew to be provided against, but wind also. The spider, wise from experience, often cuts away the central nucleus of its web in order that the wind resistance may be lessened where the pressure is strongest. The right hand photograph shows a spider in this central part, very busily employed in making rapid repairs after damage by some mischance.

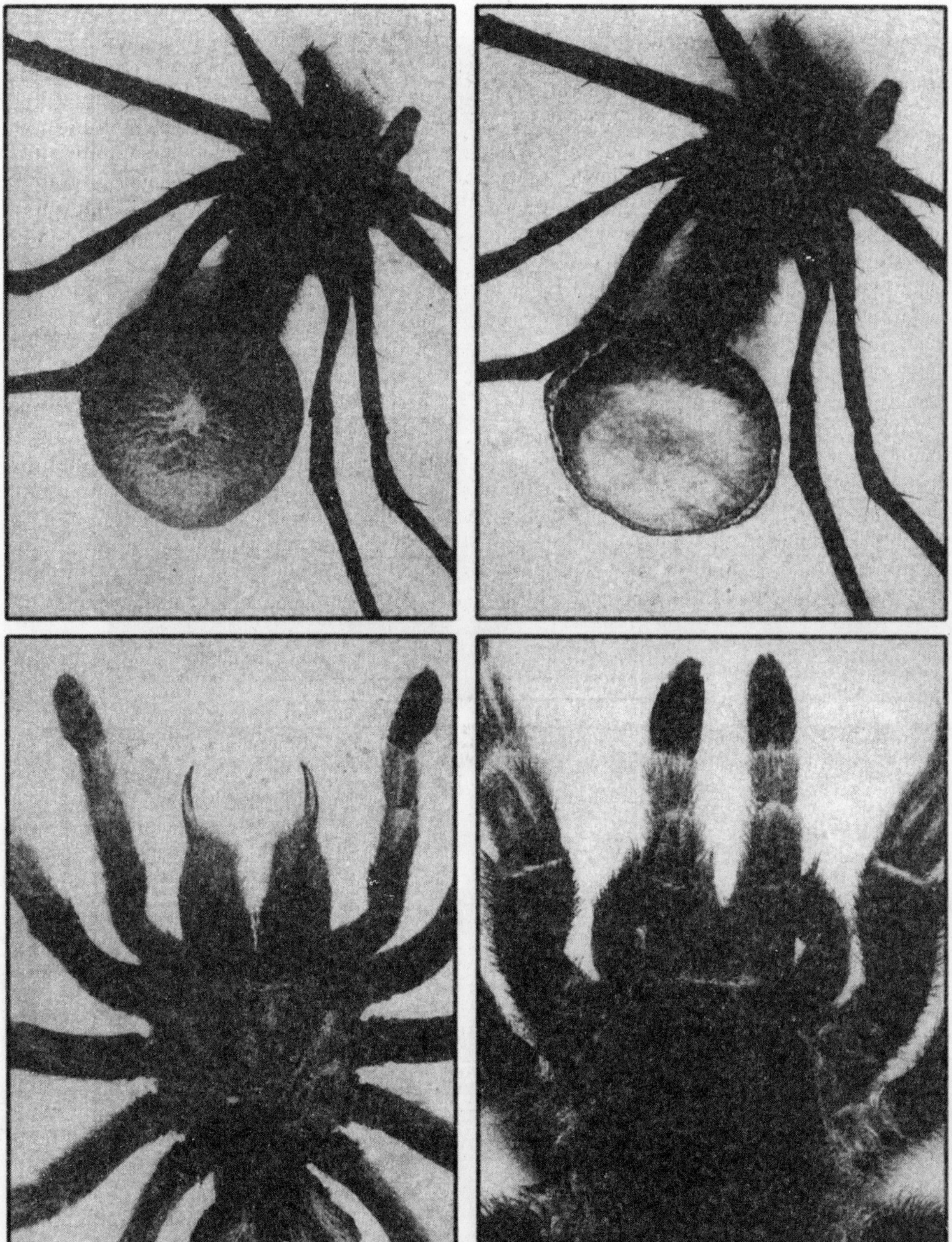

F. Martin Duncan

HEADS, FANGS AND COCOONS OF THE VERSATILE RACE OF SPIDERS

Mygale spiders are large in size and found in the tropics. The Californian mygale (bottom left) has downward curving jaws which enable the creature to strike home with its poison fangs when it jumps upon its prey. The Brazilian mygale (bottom right) is known as the bird-eating spider as its poison can kill a small bird in a minute or two. These mygales do not trap their prey, but pounce on it on the ground or in trees. The huntsman spider of tropical and sub-tropical regions is born in a cocoon carried by the female. The upper photographs show (left) the underside of the cocoon and (right) the upper side and its beautifully fitting lid.

fence; it then jerks its abdomen up into a vertical position, at the same time emitting a streamer of silk filaments from the spinnerets (or spinning organs). These are caught by the wind and drawn out into threads of considerable length; if the current of air is favourable and the thread trustworthy, the young spider sets afloat in the air; by this means it may be carried many miles, even by moderate winds.

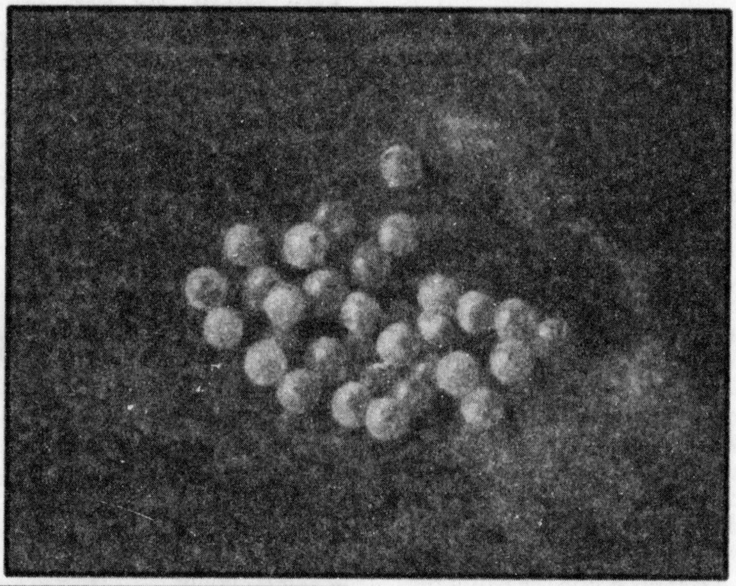

This habit is of value to them as means of dispersal and is probably one of the most important factors in securing their present wide distribution. It has stimulated speculation very naturally among those who have observed the large sheets of gossamer carried by the wind and at length deposited on fields and hedges, or on the rigging of ships far out at sea. Many attempts are made by these animals before suitable conditions guarantee the safety of the undertaking, and so vast quantities of gossamer are set floating in the air.

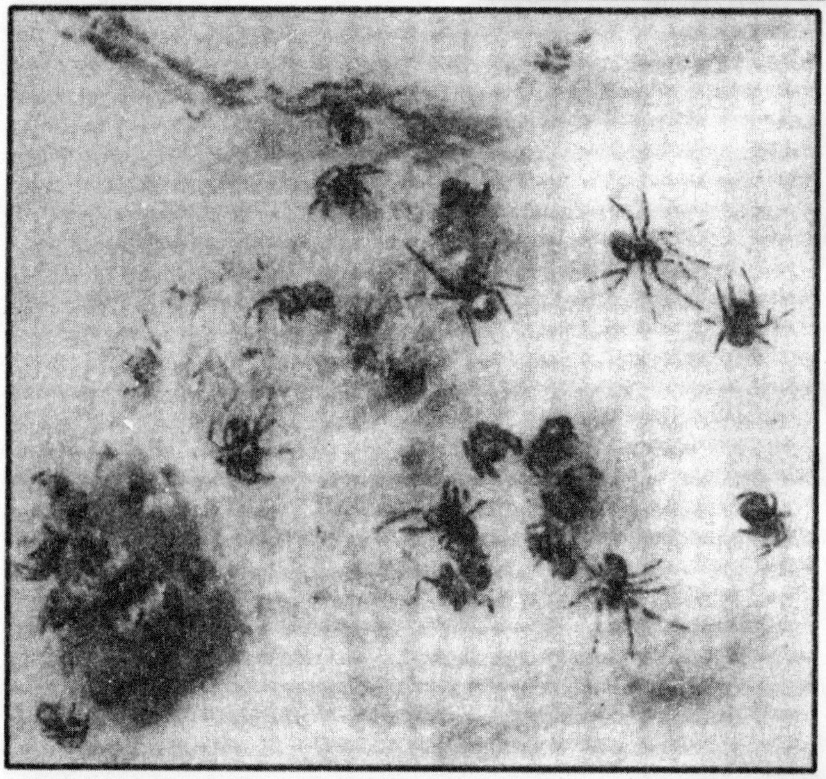

J. T. Roberts

YOUNG SPIDERS AND EGGS IN THEIR COCOON

When the time for laying her eggs approaches, the female spider spins a silk cocoon and attaches her eggs to it (top). Within this nest the young spiders hatch out, while in certain species the mother spider remains inside with them. The first moult which the young spiders experience takes place within the nest, and then they bite their way out to freedom.

The nature of gossamer has puzzled many generations of observers; the word itself in the early form "Gar-summer" is supposed to indicate summer hoar, as opposed to winter hoar, and the frosty or dewy appearance presented by gossamer on the ground fostered this belief. Spenser's description in the Faerie Queene is often quoted in this connexion:

> More subtle web Arachne cannot spin;
> Nor the fine nets, which oft we woven see,
> Of scorched dew, do not in th'ayre more lightly flee.

And it is easy to understand how the idea of "scorched dew" presented itself to the poet's mind if we realize the effect of dew on sheets of gossamer on the ground, the dew later evaporating in the sun's rays, but the gossamer remaining as "scorched dew" to bear the heat of the day.

The elasticity of spider's silk, its gossamer fineness, have been proved to us by the creature itself, and its possible commercial value has often been considered. Travellers coming back from distant islands and the East have recorded its use among some of the peoples in articles of apparel, but one of the earliest accurate accounts of definite attempts being made on a commercial scale was by M. Bon, in 1709. He communicated to the Royal Academy of Montpelier that he had successfully manufactured a new material from silk obtained from spider cocoons and presented them with several pairs of elegant stockings and gloves. The Academy investigated the question thoroughly, but found that as a commercial undertaking on a wide scale spider silk would be unprofitable, for not only are a very large number of spiders necessary for the production of any quantity of the material, but the cannibal tendencies of the animals themselves make it impossible to put it on a good commercial basis.

The various devices adopted by spiders in building their webs indicate the different methods employed by them in capturing their prey, for their skill as hunters is no less than their skill as architects. The Lycosids and Mygalomorphs excavating their burrows in the ground demonstrate two independent lines of action. Where there is an external inflated portion of the silk tube that lines the burrow, the policy favoured by the hunter is to wait till an insect alights on this, then the spider rushes out, grabs it from within and draws it into the burrow, where, after making a meal of its catch, it mends the torn portion of the tube if necessary. Where, however, there is a definite trap-door to the tube, the spider goes about securing its prey in a more predatory manner. Cautiously it lifts the flap of the burrow and peeps out, and when an insect comes within sight and grasp, it springs out, catches it and drags it in, the elastic hinge of the trap-door closing the flap securely behind them.

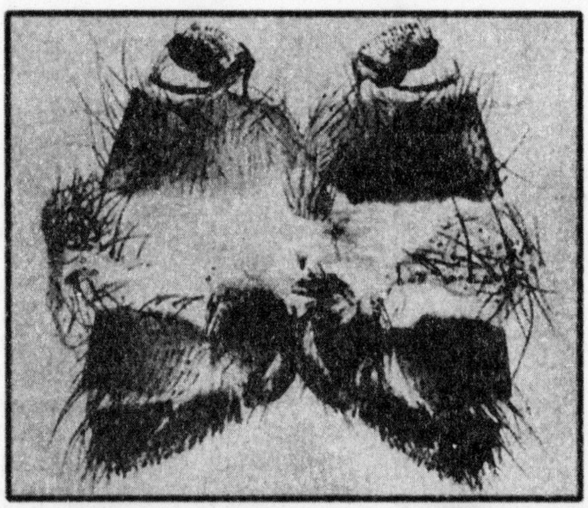

H. S. Cheavin

SILK FACTORIES OF SPIDERS

At the hinder end of the abdomen in spiders are the spinnerets, *complicated organs covered by a number of minute tube endings* which emit the secretions which make the silk. (Bottom) house spider's spinnerets; (top) garden spider's.

F. Martin Duncan

H. S. Cheavin

SPIDERS' WONDERFUL FEET

The house spider (bottom) has the toothed claws of its feet more curved over than the garden spider (top). The foot of the latter is covered with hairs to form a kind of comb for drawing out and holding the silk when web making.

Spiders that build their snares in the open do not conform to one line of action, either; *Tegenaria derhamii*, the common house spider, lurks in the tubular portion of her sheet of silk and the vibration of a piece of straw skilfully applied on the web, brings her running out to secure the prey. *Epeira diademata*, with her complex orbicular snare, can dart with certainty from her place of concealment to the exact spot where an insect has entangled itself; the vibration travelling along the trap-line brings the spider rushing to the hub where the vibration of the particular radius is perceived and the exact position of the insect located. The great tropical Nephilids, with their immense, strong webs, have as their prey animals often much larger than themselves, many observers recording small birds and even snakes *hopelessly trapped.* One story which would seem to indicate that web-weavers do not always wait for

F. W. Bond

HAIRY BIRD-EATING SPIDER AND THE ONCE-DREADED TARANTULA

The lower photograph shows a bird-eating spider of South America. The extreme hairiness of the creature is due to the fact that it has just moulted its skin. Soon after this change it loses much of its hair. Above we see the famous tarantula, named after the city of Taranto in Italy, where it is common. It belongs to the family of the wolf spiders. In medieval times and until recent years hysteria was supposed to be caused by the bite of this spider. A special dance called the tarantella was invented to cure people of the supposed effects

H. Bastin

HOUSE SPIDER DEALING WITH A BLUE-BOTTLE CAUGHT IN ITS WEB

When an insect becomes entangled in a spider's web, news of the arrival is conveyed to the owner by the vibrations along the line which connects the web with the spider's retreat. This retreat is usually concealed as much as possible. The spider comes out to inspect its latest victim, and if it is too large and powerful, a wasp, for example, soon cuts it free before the whole web is ruined Otherwise, it pounces on the luckless insect, in this case a blue-bottle (left), and disables it with its fangs. It then proceeds to suck the juices of its captive (right) until only a shrivelled skin is left. It is possible to imitate this premonitory trembling of the web with a piece of grass. The spider will soon appear if the movement is not too violent.

fortune to favour them, but occasionally try to assist it, is that of a small spider, unfortunately not accurately determined, passing filaments of silk threads around the tail of a mouse which had stationed itself below the web. All the struggles of the mouse were of no avail as it was very slowly and gradually hoisted up by the spider till finally its whole body was lifted from the floor and drawn up some inches off the ground.

As was mentioned earlier, all spiders do not weave webs, and these stalk their prey, as a cat does a mouse. *Epiblemum scenicum,* the zebra spider of this country, may often be seen on a sunny day running along a fence with cat-like movements. When the insect is sighted it stalks it carefully, keeping its great shining eyes fixed on it and running with hesitating movements; finally it leaps and drives its mandibles deep into the victim. Before this leap the precaution is taken of providing a means of swift return by attaching a silk thread to the point from which the jump is made.

What of their skill in evading the hunters when they themselves are the destined victims? There are, in particular, three ways of avoiding pursuit: they can seek a habitat unfrequented by their natural enemies; they can escape observation either by close resemblance to their environment, or by mimicry; and finally they can render themselves distasteful to their enemies.

Spiders have adapted themselves to many varied habitats. They are to be found in desert wastes, in marshlands, in fertile valleys and at high altitudes on the barren mountainside, and they may even be found, like *Agyroneta acquatica*, spinning their nests under water. This animal has overcome the difficulties of living in the unusual element by taking down with it as it plunges, a film of air; the air is retained by the hairs of the body and released by the spider when it reaches its home, by passing a leg over the hairs and practically combing it out into the thimble-shaped web until that is full of air, and fit for the spider to take up its residence in. The few marine spiders that we know living between the tide-marks of the seashore retire into a crevice which they have rendered watertight until the tide has ebbed and they are free once again for a few hours.

F. Martin Duncan

FORMIDABLE JAWS OF THE ZEBRA SPIDER

Of the jumping spiders the commonest British species is the zebra spider. It is handsomely striped and may be seen running along fences or garden walls. It stalks its prey like a cat and finally leaps upon the luckless insect, driving home the terrible jaws illustrated above. Before making the fatal and final leap the spider takes the precaution of attaching a silk line to the "take off" of the jump, so that a swift return can be made, if such should be necessary.

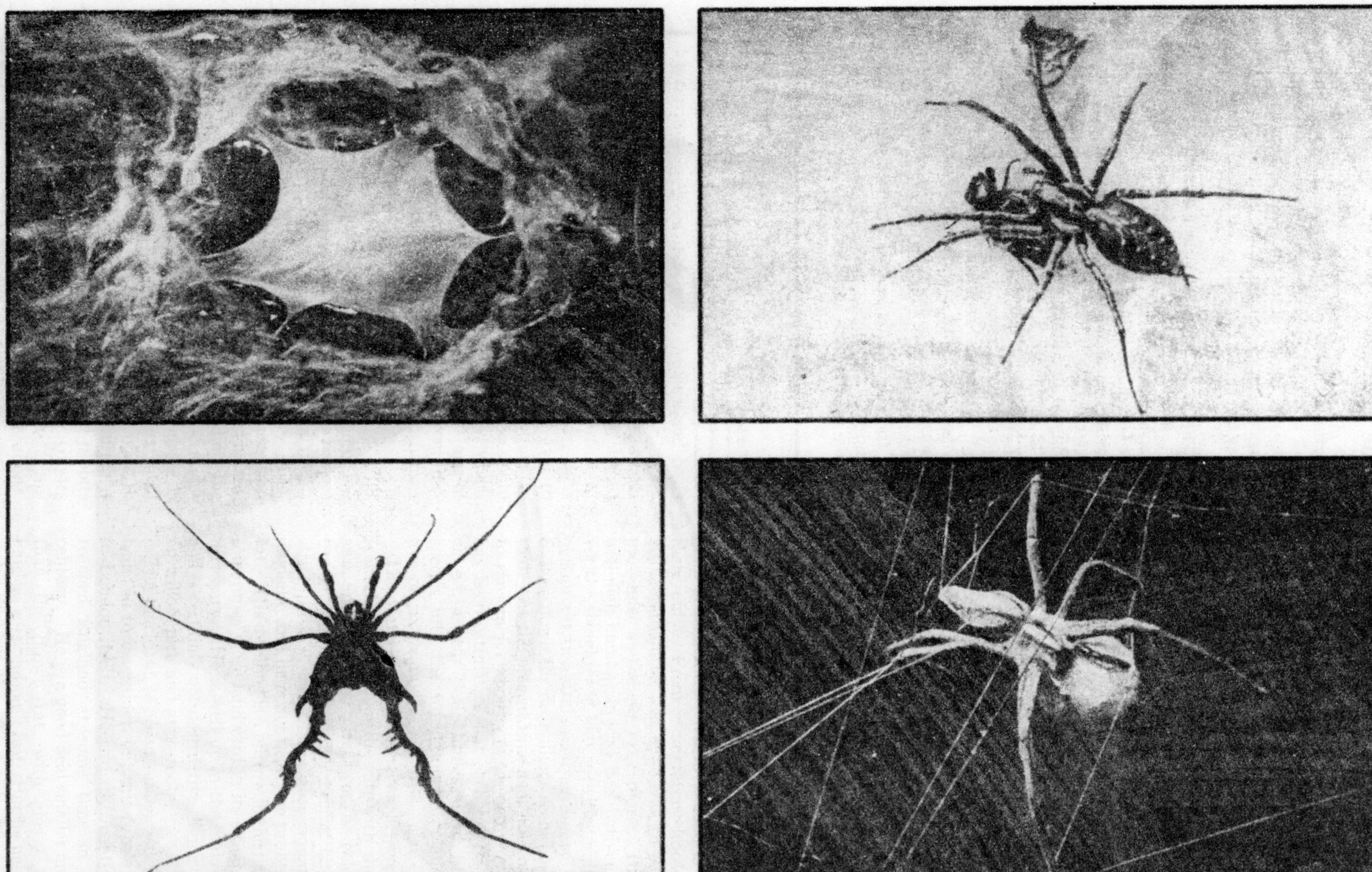

J. T. Roberts

SOUTH AMERICAN HARVEST SPIDER, WOLF SPIDER, AND A HEATH SPIDER SLAYING A FLY

Grotesque and fierce-looking, the South American harvest spider (bottom left) has its hind legs armed with spurs. The wolf spider (bottom right) chases its prey and leaps upon it, and the female, as we see here, carries her cocoon of eggs about with her. Some members of the family make a hole in the ground, where they lurk, while others have no home at all, but creep under some leaf or stone if they need shelter. The upper photographs show how the heath spider spins a cocoon to hold its eggs (left), and (right) the fierce destroyer which has leaped upon a fly. The fly is on its back, helpless, with its wings caught by the entangling, clinging web, and the spider is giving the death stroke with its fangs.

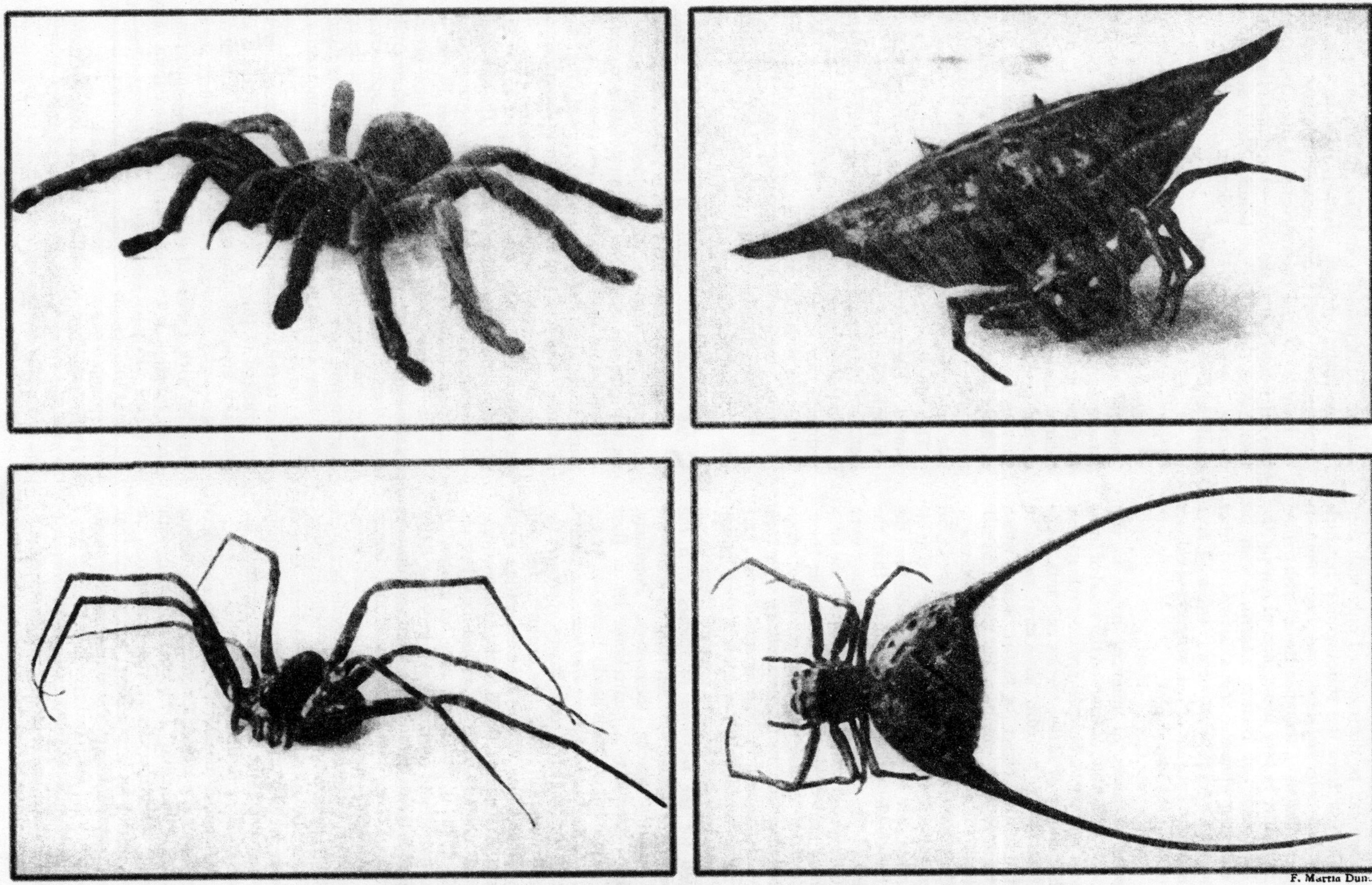

F. Martin Duncan

NEAR VIEWS OF FOUR STRANGE SPIDERS OF THE NEW AND OLD WORLDS

Huntsman spiders are remarkable for their aeronautic powers, travelling great distances by letting out strands of silk and allowing the air currents to carry them along. This habit, and the Trade winds, seem to account for them having circumnavigated the globe, so far as the Tropics are concerned. Here we have a female (bottom left) grasping her cocoon. The Tropics of both Old and New Worlds have the strange gasteracantha (bottom right). The Californian mygale (top left) hunts its prey and is armed with a pair of particularly deadly-looking jaws. The remaining specimen (top right) comes from the Far East and has adopted protective mimicry, for its body resembles the seed of some spiny plant

The Skill of the Spider

Many spiders can be distinguished only with considerable difficulty from the surroundings in which they move ; *Dolomedes fimbriatus*, one of our common marsh spiders, has on its abdomen two whitish yellow stripes that render it very inconspicuous among the rushes. The colour of certain *Thomisids* can be observed changing when the animal is removed from a pink flower where a pink colour was assumed, to a yellow flower with splashes of red, when these colours take the place of the former pink.

NUMEROUS instances of mimicry occur in this group ; of flowers, of knots on the wood of trees, and of twigs and sticks, but perhaps most remarkable of all is the mimicry of snails, beetles and ants. The enemies that spiders probably have most reason to fear are the solitary digger, or mason, wasps, which prey on them in large numbers, but do not attack ants ; therefore it would be of the first importance to these spiders that the wasps should be deceived. So very accurately do the spiders mimic ants, that it requires much care to distinguish the model from the original, but the deception is carried further than the appearance of the animals, as the spiders have even adopted the motions and busy movements of the ants.

Sometimes spiders are passive in rendering themselves distasteful to their enemies, examples of which may be found among the *Gasteracanthids*, with their hard spiny abdomens ; but the venomous species are armed with so formidable a weapon in their poison that few creatures deliberately provoke them.

So much for the relations of spiders with the outside world ; it would be interesting to study the relations existing among themselves. Popularly, spiders are regarded as a quarrelsome lot in their domestic relations, but this is hardly borne out by the evidence. In the case of *Epeira diademata*, and many others, it is true that the male has to approach the female with temerity. When he comes to her web he gently strokes one of the threads, setting up a vibration which acts as a signal to the occupant, who regards him gloomily while he makes his advances. Ultimately, if he is patient, he may be allowed to approach, but should he lack this virtue the larger heavier female bears down upon him and devours him. On the other hand, the male and female *Agalena labyrinthica* are often to be found living together in perfect amity. Many Salticids however, provide their mates with amusement before venturing too near, by executing most intricate dances before them, waving the plumes that adorn them and displaying their brilliant colours during the dance very much as birds do.

Lastly, we should consider the relation of spiders to other groups in the animal kingdom. They belong to the division known as *Arthropoda* (animals with jointed legs), which includes so vast a congregation of insects, arachnids, crustaceans, and so on, that in numbers they would outrival all the other animals in creation.

Within this division, spiders, together with scorpions, mites, ticks and harvestmen, form the class Arachnida, and are distinguished from other Arthropoda by having four pairs of legs. Spiders may in turn be distinguished from their nearer relations which are included in the class Arachnida, by having the two chief divisions of the body—the cephalothorax in front, and the abdomen behind—separated by a narrow " waist," and the abdomen (except in one small family) unsegmented.

THE cephalothorax from the dorsal aspect is generally seen to have a median depression with lines radiating from it to the sides, indicating the attachment of internal muscles ; the part anterior to these lines is the head region or " caput " often clearly marked off from the thoracic region. This portion bears the eyes, usually eight in number, but varying in size and arrangement. Ventrally, the cephalothorax is protected by the " sternum," a large plate variable in shape and notched on either side for the reception of the legs.

There are four pairs of walking legs, typically seven-jointed. The cephalothorax also bears the pedipalpi, six-jointed leg-like feelers, anterior to the legs ; the last joint of the palp in the male is modified, and has a rounded bulbous appearance. Anterior to the pedipalpi are the chelicerae, or mandibles (not homologous with the mandibles of insects), consisting of a stout basal portion and a strong fang. The duct of the poison-glands has its opening near the tip of this formidable fang.

SOME spiders are capable of producing humming or hissing sounds, and this is performed by the friction of two rough surfaces, which, when modified for this purpose are known as "stridulating organs."

The abdomen may be globular, pea-shaped, or very much attenuated, and may have additions in the form of spines, scuta and protuberances; it is unsegmented except in the small family *Liphistiidae*, from the Oriental region. On the anterior portion of the abdomen transverse slit-like openings (the spiracles) can be seen. These are the openings to the respiratory organs, the lung-books, which may either be two or four in number ; in addition to the lung-hooks, tracheae are almost universally present, and generally have their opening just in front of the spinnerets.

Most characteristic of all are the spinning organs or spinnerets, on which the tubes of the spinning glands open ; they are normally six in number and usually placed beneath the abdomen near its apex and anterior to the anal tubercle. Generally the spinnerets are arranged in three pairs. Sometimes there is an accessory structure, the cribellum, which is a sieve-like plate, and associated with this the fourth leg is provided with a series of stiff hairs, the calamistrum, whose function is to draw out the thread from the cribellum into a hackled band. *Amaurobius similis*, found on old pieces of timber in outhouses, has a web composed of such a hackled thread.

It is easy then to realize how so many diverse stories and superstitions have become woven around this extremely interesting group.

Chapter XXXVIII

Animals Man Has Tamed For His Use

By David Seth-Smith

Curator of Mammals and Birds, London Zoo

FROM a very early period man has tamed and made use of the lower animals to provide him with food, clothing, and draught power. His more highly developed brain has enabled him to bend them to his will, and right well have they served his purpose. By his skill in domesticating certain species that were fortunately suited to his purpose he has provided his race with food and raiment that could never have been procured in sufficient supply had he had to rely upon killing the wild animals. Without draught power he would have been unable to till the land and grow his vegetable food.

There existed in prehistoric times a very large bovine animal in Europe known as the aurochs, which prehistoric hunters pursued and killed for meat. The calves were sometimes captured and tamed, and when they grew up, it was found that they took to captivity readily, and in their turn produced young, while from the captive cows milk was obtained. Hence began a domestic breed of cattle, while the wild animals became scarcer and scarcer, until they eventually became extinct. It is uncertain at what date the aurochs disappeared from Britain. In Scotland it lingered longer than in the south, while it was still abundant in Caesar's time in the Black Forest of Germany, and there is evidence that it still existed on the continent of Europe in the twelfth century.

There is little doubt that the aurochs was the direct ancestor of at least our largest breeds of domestic cattle. What its colour was is uncertain, though as the so-called park cattle, which are probably the remnants of captured herds of aurochs and have been carefully preserved in several parks in Britain, are mostly white it has been suggested that this was their colour. But as captivity and domestication frequently tend towards albinism, it is more probable that their owners had a liking for white specimens, and destroyed those of other hues.

FALCONER OF BISKRA

One of the most ingenious of man's adaptations of Nature was the training of bird to catch bird in his service. This is an Arab falconer at Biskra with his hawks hooded, one on his wrist and the other on his head. Hawking dates from at least 2,000 B.C.

There would seem to have been little difficulty in the process of domesticating cattle, for it has been accomplished in other species besides the aurochs. In India, China, Africa, and Madagascar, the cattle are distinguished from those of Europe by the presence of a large hump on the withers, and by other structural features, and voice, indicating that they have descended from some species that has long become extinct. In north-eastern India the gayal exists as a domestic species, and in Java the smaller form, known as the banting, has been successfully trained to the regular service of man.

In Tibet we find a species clothed with long hair to suit it for the rigorous climate, the yak. This also has been domesticated by the inhabitants, who use it both for food and clothing, and as a beast of burden.

Although there are many wild species of sheep, the origin of the domestic animals is clothed in some mystery. Domestic sheep, or, at any rate, nearly all of the breeds, naturally possess long tails, which are not found in any of the wild species. The wild animals, moreover, are clothed with hair, whereas their domestic descendants mostly grow wool. But of the existing wild species, those most closely allied to the domestic varieties appear to be the mouflon of Corsica and Sardinia, the urial of north-west India, and the Armenian wild sheep. The varieties or breeds of domestic sheep are very diverse in type, and very numerous, and it is possible that several wild species may have shared in their production. It is possible that the production of wool instead of hair may be an acquired character due to selection.

The domestic varieties of goats are very numerous,

but it is probable that they were originally derived from the wild goat of Persia, though, since the various species of wild goat will readily interbreed, it is possible that crosses with some of these may have been partly responsible for the great diversion in type of the domestic races.

It is impossible to trace the date of the first domestication of the goat, but we know that the ancient Egyptians kept goats, and they were also possessed by the prehistoric inhabitants of the wonderful Swiss lake-cities.

WHILE several species of deer have been kept and bred in semi-captivity in parks, the only species which man has thoroughly domesticated for his use in providing him with food, clothing, and draught power is the reindeer, which inhabits the northern regions of both the eastern and western hemispheres, being known in America as the caribou. It is specially provided by Nature for a life on the snow, the hoofs being large and able to spread to give a good foothold. It is a somewhat heavy and strong animal, and has been made use of in Siberia, Lapland, and part of Norway. It has become indispensable to the life of the Laplander, to whom it serves the purpose of horse, cow, sheep, and goat. Being capable of hauling considerable weights, and possessing a remarkable power of endurance, it is harnessed to a sledge and is able to travel hundreds of miles over the snow. Its flesh and milk are used for food, and its skin for clothing, while a somewhat larger breed in Northern Asia is used also for riding.

The Arabian or one-humped camel became extinct as a wild animal so long ago that its original habitat is a matter of conjecture, though it is generally believed to have come from Arabia. Fossilised remains have, however, been found in the Pliocene rocks at the foot of the Himalayas, which seems to indicate the possibility of India being its original home. Be that as it may, the camel is one of the most valuable of domestic animals, and indispensable as a beast of burden in desert countries both in Africa and Asia. It is peculiarly adapted for a life in the desert in the formation of its feet, enabling it to travel easily on soft sand, in its ability to close its nostrils to exclude the driving sand during sandstorms, in the possession of a reservoir of nourishment contained in its hump, and in a specialised form of stomach in which a store of water can be carried. This useful beast was undoubtedly one of the earliest animals to be domesticated. References to it in the Old Testament are many. The patriarch Job possessed six thousand, and camels formed part of the present which Pharaoh gave to Abraham.

There are several breeds or varieties of the one-humped camel, such as the baggage camel, a sturdy beast capable of carrying heavy loads, and the long-legged and swift-riding camel or dromedary.

The two-humped or Bactrian camel is to be found in the desert regions of Central Asia, between Afghanistan and Turkistan, and in China and Southern Siberia. It is distinguished from the Arabian camel by the presence of two humps, and by its stouter and more clumsy build and shorter legs. It is adapted for carrying heavy loads in rocky country with precipitous ascents. It is more thickly covered with hair to adapt it to a colder climate.

In the Yarkand regions there are many wild Bactrian camels, but there is little doubt that these are descendants of domestic animals that have escaped.

There is no doubt that both the llama and the alpaca are descendants of the wild guanaco, an animal that inhabits the countries from Ecuador and Peru to the plains of Patagonia. Its domestication by the Peruvians extends back to a very remote period, and before the introduction of horses and mules the llama was an indispensable possession to its owners as a beast of burden, as well as for food and clothing. Prior to the Spanish Conquest these animals were kept in enormous numbers, the males being used as beasts of burden, the females being kept for milk and as providers of flesh.

E.N.A.

CARAVAN OF BACTRIAN CAMELS ON ITS WAY THROUGH TURKESTAN

Central Asia is the home of the Bactrian camel, which has two humps. It is specially adapted for work in rocky and mountainous country and is not so good on sand as its one-humped relation, the Arabian camel. The hair is long and the legs short, while the whole build is heavier and more clumsy. Of the animals that man has trained for his service the camel takes a high place, for it has served the trade routes under conditions in which no other creature could possibly have survived for centuries.

E N A

McLeish

EGYPTIAN CAMELS AS THEY HAVE WORKED FOR CENTURIES

Despite the influence of Western ideas, the agricultural methods of some parts of Egypt are still much what they were in Bible times. Here (top) is a mixed team of camel and ox working a primitive-looking chaff-cutter. This mixing of teams for cultivation is still quite common, and it is interesting to recall the old Commandment in Deuteronomy: "Thou shalt not plough with an ox and an ass together." In this case, of ox and camel, the division of labour is evidently fairer than that. Below is a yoke of camels ploughing by the Nile.

DONKEY THAT HAS LEARNED A SPECIAL SERVICE FOR ITS MASTERS

Animals have long been used the world over for drawing water, but this form of pump is rather unusual in England, in fact almost unique. It consists of a great treadmill made entirely—treads, and spokes and spindle—from the solid oak. The quality of the workmanship will be understood when it is known that the wheel was made about 1640. The donkey is trained to go into the wheel and walk, turning the whole contrivance as it goes. A farm at Kenworth, near Dunstable, is the scene of this remarkable labour on the part of an animal.

The alpaca was bred solely for its wool, which is of excellent quality and considerable length. It is kept in large herds in Bolivia and Southern Peru, and is regularly sheared.

There are very many different breeds of domesticated swine, but their origin is shrouded in obscurity. Doubtless they are partly descended from the European wild boar, but some of the Eastern breeds are quite likely to have been derived from the Indian wild pig, and there is no evidence that they are not descended from others of the numerous wild species still existing. That the domestication of swine is of great antiquity is proved by remains found on the sites of the prehistoric lake-dwellings of Switzerland.

In prehistoric times, when the mammoth and the woolly rhinoceros roamed over Great Britain and the continent of Europe, primitive man hunted wild horses for their flesh, and subsequently domesticated them. Some of these men of the Stone Age left in the caves which they occupied crude sketches of these horses, which are seen to have been not unlike the wild horses or tarpans which exist to the present day in Mongolia, though they have long since become extinct in all but a small area of their former range.

Whether all of the present-day breeds of horses are derived from one and the same wild species is uncertain. The swift and elegant Arab horse is so unlike the heavy cart horse that it may perhaps have sprung from an ancestor of a very different race, but we know that remarkable variations can occur under domestication. When we compare the whippet dog with the St. Bernard we see little resemblance between the two, but we know them to have been derived from the same ancestor.

Herds of wild horses exist to-day in America and in Australia, but these are the descendants of domesticated animals that have escaped and reverted to the wild state. The ease with which they are captured and broken to man's service shows that the original wild horse presented no great difficulty in the matter of domestication.

It is probable that the ass was first domesticated by the ancient Egyptians, who knew it long before

Realistic Travels

Ewing Galloway

BEASTS OF BURDEN IN CENTRAL ASIA AND SOUTH AMERICA

In Western Tibet, where the lower photograph was taken, the yak is the chief means of transport. A native of the country, it can survive hardships and conditions which might kill other animals. With only a little hay to eat it can carry a good load. The giddy mountain paths that thread the Andes necessitate the use of pack animals and, here again, the animals native to the country have been pressed into service. The photograph (top) shows a llama pack train outside La Paz, the commercial capital of Bolivia.

K. G. Whigham

WHERE OXEN ARE STILL BEING USED FOR THE PLOUGH IN ENGLAND

Oxen for agricultural labour, while still common on the Continent, are almost unheard of in England. Yet both these photographs were taken in England. The lower one shows a team drawing a hay cart on the estate of Earl Bathurst, while above is a ploughman of Sussex ploughing with three yoke of oxen on the South Downs. It is probably the last team for the purpose left in the country, and the scene might well have been taken from another century.

OXEN IN INDIA AND SOME OF THE WORK THEY DO

Nicely balanced as they are, these great baulks of timber (bottom) seem a tremendous load both for cart and animal as they trundle through one of Bombay's broad streets. The ox is the principal beast of burden in India and is not only used for such menial labour as this. It takes its part on state occasions, as we see in the upper photograph of a zenana or harem carriage belonging to a maharaja. The oxen are humped, and it is to be noticed that the rich draperies that cover them are shaped to fit the humps.

Wide World Photos

HARNESSING THE WAPITI

Of the red deer family the wapiti is the largest and finest. Formerly common in Montana it is now mostly confined to reservations. In the United States it is often confusingly called the elk. An attempt was made in Chicago to start a fashion for "elk" driving (top).

they knew the horse, for it was then as now, a common wild animal in the desert regions of North-Eastern Africa. As a domestic animal, useful both as a draught animal and for its milk, the ass has been introduced into practically every part of the world. In England it was known in the reign of Ethelred, but it did not become common until after the reign of Queen Elizabeth, having probably become extinct and been re-introduced in the meantime.

In most parts of Europe the ass has greatly deteriorated in size under domestication, due to poor feeding, but in the south some very fine breeds have been produced, while in the United States a breed of very large proportions has been established, some specimens reaching a height of sixteen hands.

Of all animals, the elephant is the most easily tamed and trained to perform useful service to man. From time immemorial the Asiatic elephant has been trained to work, the natives of India and Burma showing great aptitude for the handling of these and other wild animals; and it must be remembered that the elephants in captivity are almost all wild-caught animals, not those bred from captive animals, for the elephant does not readily breed in captivity. It is not encouraged to do so, for since these animals are so easily tamed from the wild state when captured as adult or semi-adult animals, it would not pay to breed them in captivity. A few months after capture the elephant is sufficiently docile to be worked.

The natives of Africa have shown little aptitude for the handling of wild animals, which may account for the fact that the African elephant has rarely been tamed. It is probably less suited to work than its Eastern relative, but it has been proved to be quite capable of domestication.

There is much evidence to show that the dog was one of the earliest animals to be domesticated. Men of the Iron and Bronze Ages possessed several distinct breeds, and Darwin remarks that "At a period between four and five thousand years ago various breeds, namely pariah dogs, greyhounds, common hounds, mastiffs, house-dogs, lapdogs and turnspits existed, more or less closely resembling our present breeds." It is not surprising, therefore, that the species from which the domestic dog has descended should remain a matter of conjecture. We should incline to

F. W. Bond

MIGHTY ELEPHANT USED IN ENGLAND FOR GIANT'S TASKS

Log lifting by elephants is familiar enough in the teak yards of Malaya, but seldom seen in England. Our upper photograph shows a Zoo elephant coping with a large piece of tree trunk while the keeper, mounted on the animal, is directing operations. Below is a pair of circus elephants engaged in cultivating a field on the farm belonging to the proprietor of the circus. He makes his elephants earn part of their keep by a little land work on his Surrey estate during the winter.

Keystone

OSTRICH, GREATEST OF BIRDS, BROUGHT INTO MAN'S SERVICE IN THE REALMS OF PLEASURE

While much horrible and revolting cruelty has been practised on birds whose feathers are desirable as ornaments, the ostrich is docked of its feathers without pain or fear. Here (left) is a scene on an ostrich farm at South Pasadena, in California, where a considerable number of birds are reared. The operation of plucking is in progress. The bird is hoodwinked at the start so that it shall not be restive, and the feathers are cut off at the quills, not pulled out, which would involve pain and injury. In Czecho-Slovakia the ostrich has been pressed into the service of amusement by the organization of ostrich racing (right). This is the winning bird with its jockey at an ostrich race-meeting.

TAKING PART IN THE ATTRACTIONS OF THE ZOO: OSTRICH AND ITS CART

All the fun at the Zoo is not kept behind the bars. Various animals have been taught to play their part in aiding in the upkeep of the Zoological Gardens by earning some extra money as providers of "rides" for the children. The ostrich makes a novel steed to draw the children's chariot and is one of the most popular of the various attractions of that sort provided by the Gardens. Incidentally, the ostrich is one of the swiftest runners of the animal world, but at the Zoo its pace is stately.

the belief that the common wolf of Europe was the ancestor of the dog, and that the extreme variation of types that has long existed is the result of selection during a long period, but since many of the wild species of wolves and dogs will interbreed and produce fertile offspring, the fact that domestic dogs of various breeds are fertile when crossed is no infallible proof that one wild species alone was their ancestor.

The domestic cat was kept by the ancient Egyptians, and it seems probable that it was derived from the Caffre cat, the common wild cat of Egypt, but whether the present-day domestic cats of Europe, which have been distributed to all parts of the world, are all descended from the Caffre or Egyptian cat is open to question. There seem to be two distinct types of domestic cat, one of which closely resembles both the Egyptian cat and the European wild cat, and doubtless, it owes its descent to both of these species, but the other type resembles no wild species existing at the present day, and may be the descendant of some extinct species. The so-called Persian, Siamese, Russian and Manx cats are merely varieties which, so far as we know, have been derived from the same stock as the others, but have been specialised by careful breeding and selection on the part of man.

Among rodents, there are several that have been domesticated; the brown rat and the house mouse have proved themselves capable of existing in a tamed state as readily as in the wild, and have produced many colour varieties, but these two species have been kept rather as pets than as utility animals.

The rabbit has for long been domesticated for food and its fur, while the domestication of the cavy, or guinea-pig, probably dates back to the time of the Incas of Peru. It was introduced into Europe by the Dutch during the sixteenth century, shortly after the discovery of America.

The ferret is merely a domesticated polecat, an animal that is found throughout the greater part of Europe, but is now rare in most parts of the British Isles. It is a bloodthirsty animal, killing and devouring any creature that it can overcome. Very long ago it was found that the young could be tamed, and, when adult, would breed in captivity, and that the tamed animals were extremely useful for bolting rabbits and rats from their burrows. Precisely

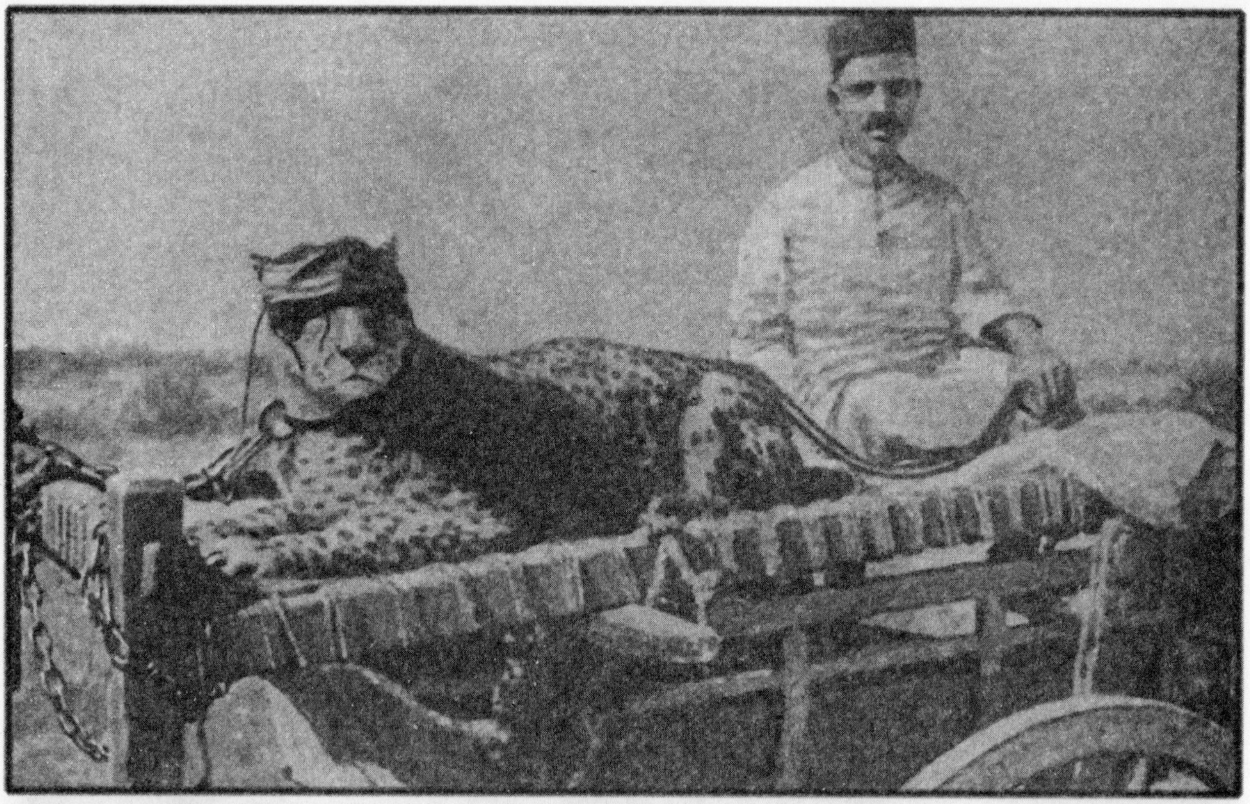

WORLD FAMOUS ST BERNARD DOGS AND INDIAN HUNTING LEOPARD E. N. A.

For generations the monks of the hospice at the head of the Great St. Bernard Pass have trained the famous breed of mastiff (bottom), called the St. Bernard, to find travellers lost in the snow. The St. Bernard is the largest domesticated dog known in Great Britain and is possessed of remarkably keen intelligence. Among its special characteristics are the very large feet. In India the cheetah has long been trained for hunting, and is known as the hunting leopard. This one is being driven to a " meet."

Keystone

FISHERMEN OF JAPAN WHO USE LIVE CORMORANTS INSTEAD OF HOOKS AND BAIT

A most ingenious method of catching fish is practised in Japan. The fishermen set forth in their boat (top), which has an iron basket in the bows. The fishing grounds are reached at night and a fire is lighted in the basket. This attracts the fish and the cormorants dive into the water and seize them. The birds are attached by lines to the boat and are hauled in and made to give up the fish. Thus there is no question of waiting for a bite. The lower photograph shows some fishermen with the birds.

E.N.A.

ZEBRAS WORKING IN KENYA COLONY

The fact that the handsome Grevy's zebra of East Africa is immune from the attacks of the dreaded tsetse fly has recommended it to colonists as a substitute for the mule. But though easily broken to harness the zebra has far less power of endurance than the mule and is much more liable to panic. Here we have a team in Kenya where two zebras are harnessed in between pairs of mules.

when the polecat was first domesticated, and thus became the ferret is not known, but we know that it was familiar to the Romans, and that it was employed for rabbit catching in Pliny's time.

Certain of the birds were domesticated by man at a very early period, one of the earliest probably being the common fowl. Domestic fowls have all been derived from the wild red jungle-fowl of India and Burma, and it is probable that the latter country was the one in which the domestication of the species commenced, at a date somewhere around 1400 B.C.

The wild duck, or mallard, was also early domesticated, and from it have descended all of the present-day breeds of domestic ducks, if we except the muscovy, which hails from South America.

Domestic geese have been derived from the grey lag goose, a widely-distributed European species that at one time bred freely in the fen-country of England, though it has long since ceased to do so. It still breeds sparingly in Scotland and in the Hebrides. Its domestication probably dates back to a very early period.

The domestic turkey is derived from a wild species inhabiting Mexico, and its domestication probably dates back to an early period, though its introduction into Europe was accomplished by the Spaniards about 1518, on the discovery of Mexico.

The tame guinea-fowl is descended from a wild species inhabiting West Africa.

THE latest bird to be tamed for utilitarian purposes is the ostrich, the demand for whose plumes led to its being farmed in South Africa and other countries, where it has been bred very extensively for feather production and thus saved from extermination.

Other birds have been tamed for the service of man, such as the falcon for hunting and the cormorant for fishing, but these have now been bred in captivity from generation to generation and thus become thoroughly domesticated.

We have space only to mention certain of the insects that man has found serviceable to his well-being, and brought under his control. The honey bee, which is supposed to be of Asiatic origin, has for ages past been extensively cultivated, and has formed a great industry, while the silkworm is of no less importance. The silk industry is of great antiquity, and originated in China, where it was carefully guarded for many centuries before it reached Japan in the third century. There it grew into a great industry, a knowledge of which eventually spread westward to India and beyond to Europe.

The cochineal insect, a little creature which feeds upon various species of cactus, is a native of Mexico, where its valuable dyeing properties were known long before the arrival of the Spaniards in 1518. These introduced it to Europe. It has since been cultivated in Algiers, the South of Spain, and the Canary Islands.

Closely allied to the cochineal is the lac insect, which has also proved of great service to man by the resinous incrustation it forms on branches of trees, which is of considerable value, both for dyeing purposes and as shellac. The insect is carefully cultivated in the East Indies, Bengal, Pegu, Siam and Assam.

It must be borne in mind that for successful domestication animals must possess certain qualities. They must be useful as food, as fur-bearers, as draught animals, or for some other definite utility purpose, or their culture will not be profitable. It is essential, also, that they be adapted for a captive life, that they breed readily in captivity, and their young mature rapidly. It would appear as if there were few animals left that possess these qualifications, or, at any rate, possess them to so great an extent as those that have already been domesticated. To take the case of the zebra, for instance. There is no difficulty in breaking-in zebras to harness, but when this is done, they have less stamina, and are far more subject to panic than horses. The only object there may be in taming the handsome Grevy's zebra of East Africa is that it is immune to the attacks of the tsetse fly, and for this reason its adoption may be worth while. The taming and breeding of fur-bearing animals, such as silver foxes and skunks, is already practised, and others may perhaps be domesticated to meet the world's demand for furs.

Chapter XXXIX

The Mystery of the Jumping Bean

By John J. Ward

Author of "Insect Biographies With Pen and Camer

THE observing naturalist not infrequently discovers instances where Nature has, as it were, re-used an ingenious idea in some entirely different connexion, merely altering details, but, nevertheless, revealing the plan of the same architect. Such instances offer, perhaps, the greatest possible proof that in Nature's creations there is certainly mind as well as matter.

There is, for example, the jumping bean of Mexico, and the much less familiar jumping disc of the sycamore leaf of the British Isles. Here we have parts of two entirely unrelated members of the plant world animated by caterpillars also far removed in relationship, the former belonging to the order Lepidoptera (butterflies and moths), and the latter to the order Hymenoptera (ants, bees, wasps, sawflies, and so on), yet in each case the principle of their movement and the ground plan of their scheme are almost identical.

The so-called jumping bean is not really a bean at all, but one of three divisions of the fruit of a large species of spurge of the genus Sebastiana, a native plant of Mexico. British spurges of the genus Euphorbia are familiar in most country gardens as weeds, the stems of which when broken yield a milky juice—a rustic cure for warts. If we examine the yellowish-green fruits of these plants with a magnifying lens, we find they consist of three "beans" just like those of the Mexican species, but on a miniature scale. None of them, however, is able to jump. How comes it then that the American species should possess this extraordinary attribute? This is one of the mysteries with which the enquiring mind of the scientific investigator of Nature is continually being confronted.

It is not all the "beans" of the Mexican spurge that will jump, only an occasional one; one that has received an egg from a moth (*Carpocapsa saltitans*) that is nearly related to our British codling moth (*Carpocapsa pomonana*), whose larvae are the cause of worm-eaten apples of the codling species. The egg is placed on the "bean" at an early stage of the fruit's growth, and the caterpillar hatching from it bores its way inside, consuming the developing tissues but avoiding the outer covering skin, which hardens as the fruit matures. When the ripened seeds are ready to fall the caterpillar is full-fed, and it is then securely enclosed in its curious domicile. It is then ready to change to the pupa stage, but does not immediately pupate; indeed, not for several months to come, for it may need to jump on many occasions during that period, and after becoming a chrysalis its jumping powers cease.

Why does the caterpillar within the seed need to jump? The Sebastiana spurge grows in warm, marshy areas, the temperature of which during the growing season exactly meets the needs of the moth larva. When, however, the dry season begins, and the seeds fall in exposed places, there is always the danger of the scorching rays from the sun; hence it is very necessary for the caterpillar to be able to move its residence to more sheltered situations. It is, therefore, always ready to decamp to a more shady area, and should the sunlight eventually reach that place, it once again begins to travel. As the moth necessarily has to appear to deposit its eggs at that season when the young fruits are growing, the caterpillar, to avoid this danger of the heat, has to keep active within its covering shell for seven or eight months. In the early part of the year it changes to the pupa stage, but before doing so it perforates with its mandibles in the roof of its case a circular lid that can easily be pushed aside when it, as a perfect moth, is ready to emerge. Having now learned what the "bean" is, the nature of the creature that controls it, and the stimulus that excites it to activity, there remains for explanation the mystery of its remarkable form of locomotion. For remarkable is the only word that describes this ingenious business which is so simple—when we understand it. We have but to think for a moment to realize that the caterpillar in the closed case is apparently moving in a manner that contradicts the laws of mechanics. It is obvious that the forward thrust of the larva enclosed in its shell would be counteracted by the push backwards of its own weight, yet it continues to travel with regular little jerks, and, still more wonderful, occasionally gives distinct hops, even lifting itself and its case well clear of the surface on which it happens to be resting.

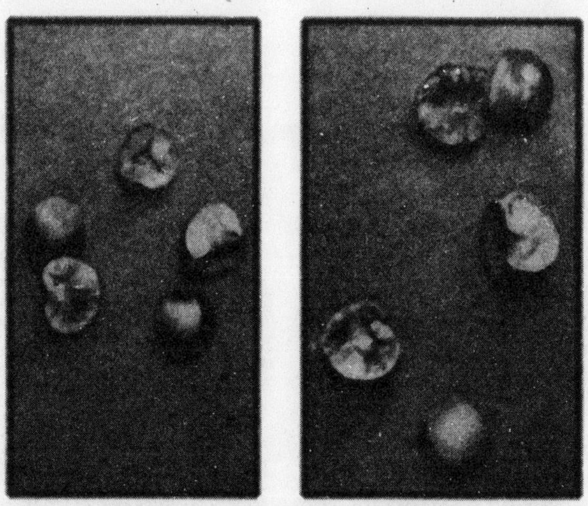

J. J. Ward

MYSTERIOUS MOVING "BEANS"

These photographs are of the fruit of a plant which grows in Mexico. On the left we see the fruit resting on a cool surface; on the right, after heat has been applied, causing the "beans" to move. The mystery of the movement was for long unexplained.

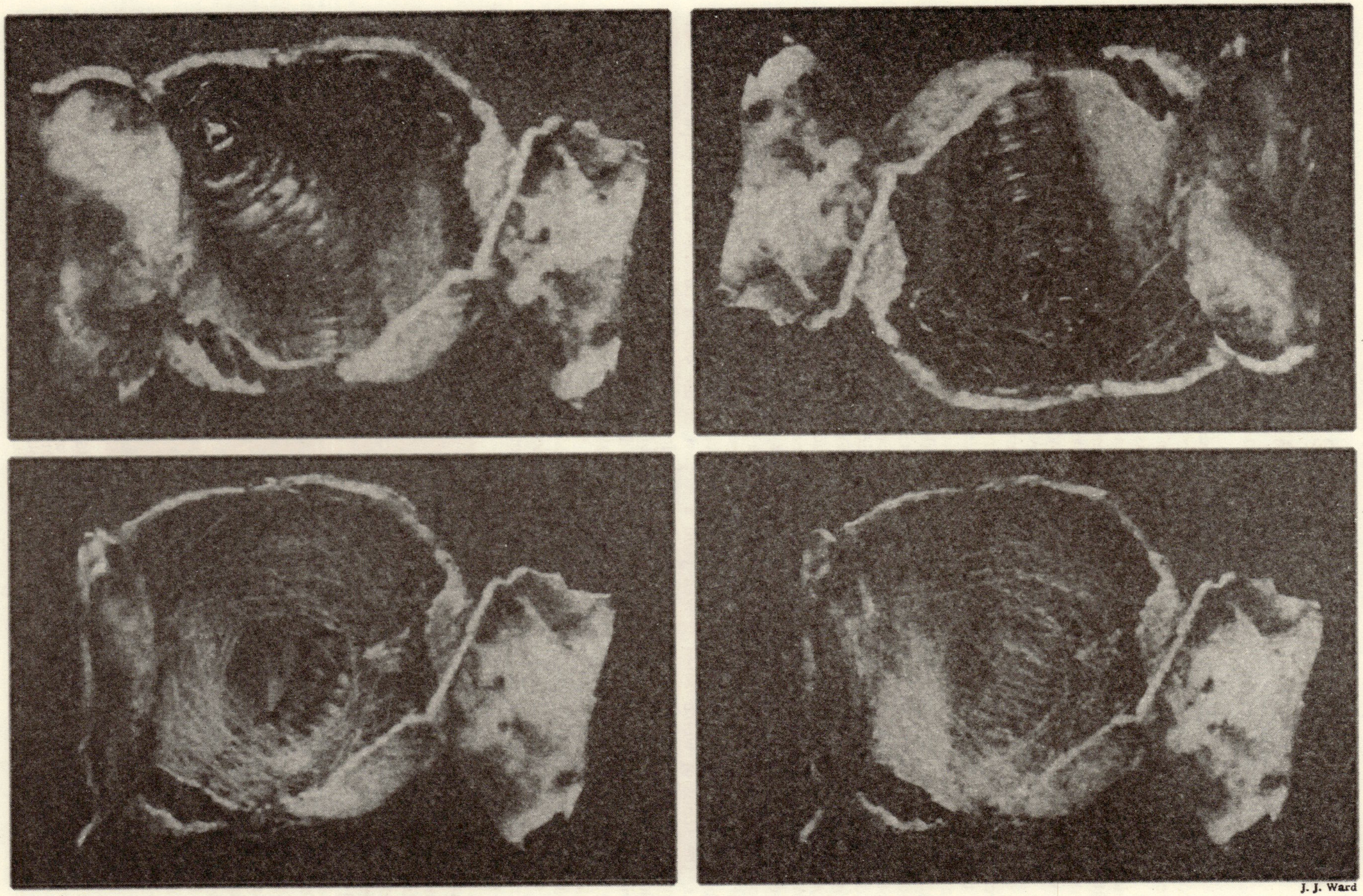

J. J. Ward

WHY THE "BEAN" JUMPS: A PUZZLE OF NATURE EXPLAINED BY THE CAMERA

This series of photographs shows what happened when one of the "jumping beans" was split open, revealing the caterpillar of a moth. In the top left-hand photograph the caterpillar is beginning to repair the damage done to its home by the splitting of the "bean." The "bean" affords the caterpillar shelter from the heat of the sun, and if it falls in a place too exposed, the inmate must move to a sheltered spot. This it does by striking its head against the wall of its abode and using a silk netting as an elastic propellant, thus causing the bean to jerk over. The caterpillar (top right) spins threads across one half of the shell. Next (bottom left) it spins across the other half till, in less than an hour (bottom right), the silk netting is complete.

J. J. Ward

GRUB OF A SAW-FLY FEEDING BUSILY ON A SYCAMORE LEAF

The saw-fly is so called because it possesses an ovipositor—the organ that deposits the eggs—formed like a pair of saws which cut into the tips of leaves. The fly lays its eggs in the point of a lobe, from one to three eggs to each leaf, and the grub hatches out between the upper and lower skins of the leaf. For ten days or so it is hard at work feeding, and is then ready to begin its remarkable disk-cutting operation. The leaf by this time has suffered considerably.

Many unconvincing hypotheses have been advanced by scientific and unscientific people to provide an explanation of these extraordinary movements, such as the fanciful idea that they are due to the expansion of the air within the "bean" when heat is applied; or that they are produced by the alteration in the tension of particles of the fruit coat as it becomes warmed; but experiments readily show that such suggestions are no solution of the problem. Let us therefore investigate the matter more closely with no other evidence than that which the "bean" itself provides, some important details of which have hitherto been overlooked.

On cutting open a fruit-segment containing a larva, the latter (as the photographs clearly show) at once proceeds to repair the damage by means of silken threads, and in about one hour it has woven a loose covering on the exposed side. On the application of warmth the caterpillar when so covered can move its abode just as readily as when it is properly sealed. Obviously expansion of air and alteration of tension in the fruit particles entirely fail as solutions when the larva is covered with an open network of threads. If, however, we apply the stimulus of heat when the caterpillar has spun only a few threads, then we can see what happens inside, and so get its secret revealed.

When the larva feels the objectionable heat it grips firmly with its tail claspers the silken lining of its shell and aims consecutive blows with its head at a given spot on the part above it, apparently with increasing vigour at each blow, until the "bean" jerks along, or rolls over. There is more in this action than at first meets the eye, for if we observe more closely we see that with each thrust when making its aims the larva secretes from a gland beneath its head a viscid thread, against which it throws the weight and pull of its body. Thread after thread is projected until, in connexion with the weaker or stronger pull of the threads to which it is attached at its tail-end, the correct propulsive impetus is obtained to jerk forward, lift, or overturn the seed-capsule. It is really a catapult action, the silk providing the "elastic," the walls of its dwelling the "forked twig," and the caterpillar itself the "stone."

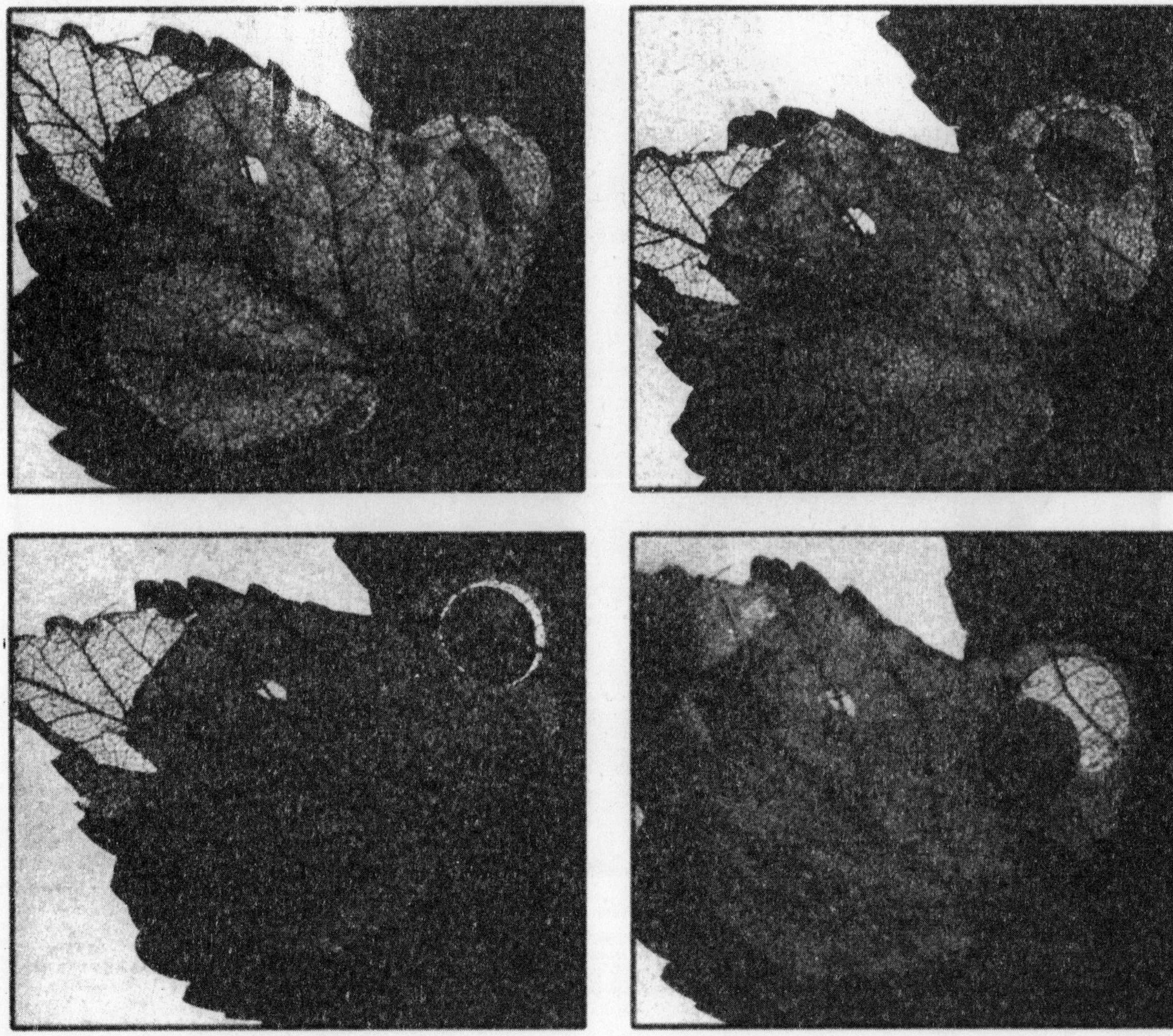

J. J. Ward

"JUMPING DISK" BEING CUT FROM THE LIVING LEAF

When the saw-fly grub has taken in its full supply of food it removes to the far corner of its feeding area and proceeds to bite a circular piece only of the upper skin (top left). It then makes a kind of floor for this leaf disk by emitting a gum-like substance which hardens into an elastic and semi-transparent plate. This lower surface is neatly joined to the leaf disk, and covered inside with network of silk. When all is ready the grub jerks itself about (bottom left) until the disk is torn free (bottom right).

The larva is not, however, hurled helplessly about the interior of its case; indeed, it is so well able to control its threads that it can obtain propulsive power and apply its brakes with astonishing precision. Moreover, if it finds that its movements are not directing it to a cooler spot, by changing its " rudder " attachment and aiming its blows at another part of its case, it can change its course.

Now let us turn to the much less known jumping novelty which the leaves of a sycamore tree will sometimes provide. Here we have a tiny saw-fly (*Phyllotoma aceris*) to deal with, one scarcely half the size of a house-fly, and called " saw-fly " because at its tail-end it is provided with an ovipositor consisting of a pair of saws for cutting incisions in the leaf tips to deposit its eggs. Sometimes only one egg is placed on a leaf, and at other times two or three. When the egg hatches the grub finds itself under cover between the upper and lower cuticles of the leaf; and that is its golden rule in life—that it must never expose itself to the open air. Outside its dangers are innumerable from parasitic foes. The tiny grub proceeds to mine its way between the upper and lower skins of the leaf, eating out the green material for nine or ten days, at the end of which time it is full-fed. The lobe of the leaf in which it has been feeding then bears a bleached and blistered appearance, but the grub still remains between the leaf skins, for it now finds itself up against a difficult problem. It has to descend from the sycamore leaf to the ground for the next stage of its development, and without exposing itself to the open air. This apparently impossible task it immediately proceeds to put into action.

Removing to the most remote corner of its feeding area it pivots, in some mysterious manner, round on what may be termed its own centre, for it completes a circle the diameter of its own length, keeping its mandibles upturned and biting a series of slits in the upper cuticle of the leaf as it moves round. Just how it contrives to turn completely round and retain its centre, is a secret which only the grub itself can reveal. Notwithstanding the difficulties, a neatly perforated circle of considerable accuracy is completed.

The grub then proceeds to turn its attention to the under side of the disk, spending several hours in constructing for it a lower floor, entirely avoiding the under skin of the leaf. This floor is a somewhat remarkable structure, being semi-transparent and formed of a kind of liquid gum which hardens and forms a plate with elastic properties. It is neatly joined to the edges of the perforated disk, the whole then forming a weatherproof shelter in which the grub has to spend some ten or eleven months of its life before it can emerge as a winged fly.

By the time that the grub's "saloon car" is ready for its travels, the air has penetrated beneath the perforations and the disk has a tendency to break away at its edges as it becomes dry, but the centre of the lower floor retains a hold. While so held the grub cannot escape, and, like the caterpillar of the jumping bean, it greatly resents powerful rays of sunlight, which cause it to kick out vigorously inside its disk. Its kicking is quite audible as a clicking noise, and if the tip of the leaf is watched, the disk is seen to respond suddenly to one of the grub's more determined efforts and become detached from the leaf, eventally falling to the ground. There it continues to travel with irregular jerks until a cool and sheltered spot is reached.

The semi-transparent side of the disk allows us to see just what movements take place inside while it is in locomotion. The grub holds firmly by its mandibles to the inner edge and then swings its tail-end from side to side with increasing force, which causes the disk to rock until it jerks along, or it may turn completely over. Here we have quite a contrary behaviour to that of the jumping bean caterpillar, which held by its tail-end and struck out with its head. Since this grub is also able to travel while in a closed chamber, we may again suspect that silken threads play a part in its movements. A careful microscopic examination of the elastic floor entirely confirmed that suspicion, for I found that its nner side was lined with an irregular network of delicate threads. Still more interesting was the discovery that the upper side of the disk—the leaf tissue—was lined only with a layer of the gelatinous substance of which the lower floor was built.

At the tail-end of the grub is a pair of claspers which grip the threads on this flexible floor and snatch them aside as the grub swings its body to and fro. This action then converts the flexible floor into a veritable spring-board. Now we learn why the grub left the lower skin of the leaf intact. It needed a spring-board for jumping purposes, and the leaf tissue did not provide sufficient elasticity.

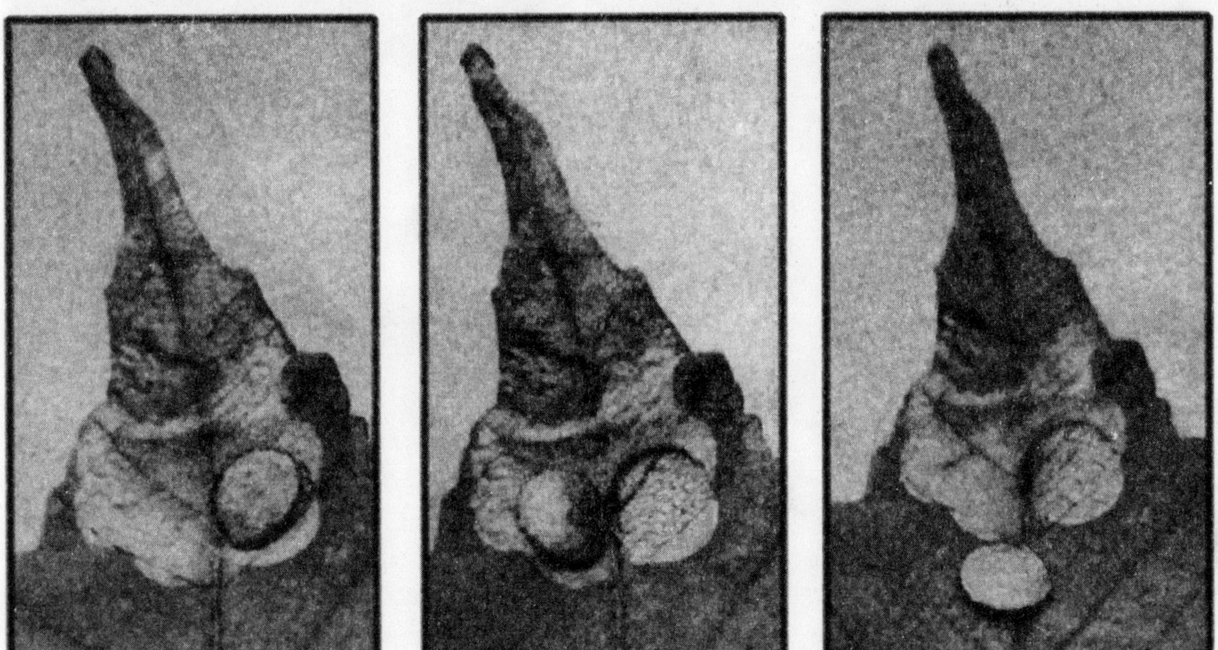

J. J. Ward

DISK DETACHES ITSELF FROM ITS LEAF AND FALLS

The saw-fly grub wants to find a spot on the ground, sheltered and at the right temperature, where it can go through its metamorphosis from grub to fly. When it has made a home for itself, as seen and described in the opposite page, it wriggles until the disk detaches itself and begins to fall (left). It slides down the leaf (centre and right) and eventually falls to the ground. There, by means of the elastic threads inside, the grub swings itself to and fro with enough force to move the disk along till it reaches a suitable place.

W Saville K

W. S. Berridge

GLIDING AND FLYING MAMMALS: PHALANGER AND BAT

Among the numerous kinds of phalanger is the short headed phalanger or flying opossum (bottom) and it, like its kind, makes long gliding leaps from branch to branch or tree to tree. The necessary resistance to the air is provided by a double fold of skin which extends outwards from the body to the limbs. The spreading of the limbs stretches this membrane for gliding. The bat (top) also has a membrane stretched between its limbs but is a true flyer, flapping the wing up and down and not merely gliding with it stiff and still.

Chapter XL

Four-Footed Creatures that Fly

By C. Tate Regan, F.R.S.

Director, Natural History Museum, London

There are perhaps more than a million different kinds of living animals, every one with its own method of finding something to eat and of avoiding being eaten; they have left no source of food untapped and no method of getting it untried, and their devices for deceiving or escaping their enemies are numberless. Flight through the air is an excellent way of baffling a pursuer who cannot fly, and also gives a direct approach to many supplies of food that are otherwise not easily reached.

Flying animals may be broadly divided into those that fly by upward and downward strokes of the wings, carried on by muscular action, such as insects, birds and bats; and those whose flight is merely a prolonged leap, dependent for its extent on the initial impetus and on the size of the wing membranes, such as the various kinds of flying fishes, flying lizards and flying squirrels.

The name Tetrapoda, or four-footed vertebrates, is given by zoologists to the backboned animals other than fishes, which agree in having two pairs of limbs formed on the same fundamental plan, the fore-limb consisting of upper arm, fore-arm, wrist and fingers, and the hind-limb of thigh, shin, ankle, and toes. These animals are primarily terrestrial, with limbs adapted for the support of the body, and for locomotion on land. Some of them, however, have become aquatic, such as the extinct ichthyosaurian reptiles and the whales, and in these the limbs have been transformed into paddles.

Others have developed the power of flight, pterodactyls, birds and bats, and in them the fore-limbs are modified into wings. It is very interesting to compare the skeleton of the wing of a bird with that of a bat, of the paddle of a whale or of the human arm, and to see the underlying similarity of structure in all, the same plan being modified for different purposes in relation to different habits.

Some arboreal snakes of Borneo have the habit of throwing themselves into the air from trees; keeping the body straight they glide obliquely downwards, drawing in the ventral scales so that the under side of the body is concave, and thus increasing the resistance to the air. The little flying lizards (*Draco*), of which more than a score of species are known from tropical Asia, have the skin on each side of the body extended to form a sheet-like membrane, which is supported by the long and slender ribs, and can be folded back against the sides like an umbrella. This structure is quite unique. These animals live in trees and run along the branches in search of insects with their "wings" folded, and then, spreading them out to their fullest extent, glide obliquely down from bough to bough, or from tree to tree. The above are the only living reptiles that can be designated "flying," but millions of years ago there were others. The Mesozoic, or Secondary Period, is sometimes termed the Age of Reptiles, for in those remote times mammals and birds were an insignificant element of the fauna, and reptiles were dominant. Carnivorous and herbivorous reptiles occupied the land, large marine reptiles played the parts now taken by whales and seals, and flying reptiles winged their way through the air.

The pterodactyls, long since extinct, were reptiles in which, as in the bats, an enormous wing membrane extended from the very long fore-limbs to the ankles; the fifth finger was much elongated and supported the wing membrane, but the other four fingers were short and free, and ended in claws. The breastbone had a small keel for the insertion of the wing muscles, and support to the wings was given by the union of the shoulder-blades with the backbone. The head was long, with pointed bird-like beak.

The pterodactyls were a large and varied tribe, some with a long tail and others without one, some no bigger than sparrows and others with a wing span of nearly twenty feet. We know nothing of their origin, but from their structure we may infer their derivation from arboreal gliding ancestors, and we may suppose that, like bats, they could not take off from the ground, but climbed trees by means of their clawed fingers before taking flight. In spite of their bird-like head they are not related to birds; indeed, their modifications for flight are quite different, and much more like those of bats.

The flying mammals, whether they merely glide, or whether they flap wings, are all characterised by the presence of a double fold of skin that extends outward from the sides of the body to the limbs, known as the patagium, or wing-membrane. As will appear below, this has developed independently several times in different groups of mammals.

The phalangers are small arboreal animals of Australia and New Guinea, related to the kangaroos, and, like them, carrying the young in a pouch The species are divided into several groups by structural characters, three such groups being characterised, amongst other things, by the structure of the tail, which in one has a series of long hairs along each side, in another is bushy, and in the third is prehensile, long and tapering, naked below at the tip. Each of these groups includes phalangers both with and without a patagium, so that it seems likely that this structure, and the habit of gliding, has been developed among the phalangers three times independently.

The pigmy flying phalanger is the smallest, a mouse-like animal, with a series of long hairs along each side of the tail. The patagium is a fold of skin extending from the elbow to the side of the body, and thence

W. S. Berridge

NIGHT-FLYING COBEGO OF MALAY

In Malay and the Philippine Islands there occurs an animal called the cobego or kaguan which is even better equipped for gliding than the phalangers, for its wing membranes extend between its fingers and toes. It is nocturnal and herbivorous.

outward again to the knee. These little animals live in trees and, with limbs outspread and patagium stretched, make big leaps from branch to branch, occasionally descending to the ground to run to another tree; they appear to be active during the day. Their flying membrane is hardly large enough to interfere with the free use of their limbs, and they are less specialised in their habits than most of the other flying mammals.

The other flying phalangers are larger, squirrel-like, and have a well-developed patagium that extends from wrist to ankle. With patagium spread they make enormous leaps from tree to tree, gliding obliquely downwards and ascending slightly as they reach their objective; a flight across a river, forty yards wide, starting from a height of thirty feet, has been observed. If alarmed they run to the highest branches and glide to another tree. The large flying membrane renders them clumsy on the ground, and they seldom or never leave the trees. They generally sleep during the day, concealed among the foliage, or in a hollow tree. At night they become active, and go in search of food, running along the branches and leaping from tree to tree. The food differs for the different species, but always is something to be found in the trees: insects, honey, leaves, flowers, or fruits.

The flying squirrels belong to quite another order than the phalangers, that of the Rodents, which includes rabbits, rats, and the squirrels that do not fly. All have a broad patagium, similar to that of the phalangers, between the limbs, and in some extending to the neck and to the tail. In the flying squirrels of North America, eastern Europe, and Asia, the flying membrane is supported in front by a rod of cartilage attached to the wrist, whereas in those of Africa it is supported by a rod of cartilage projecting from the elbow. These African flying squirrels are by no means closely related to the others, and are also distinguished by having a double row of spiny scales on the under side of the basal part of the tail, which assists these animals to climb trees.

Flying squirrels inhabit forests, and sleep during the day, either sitting high up in the trees, or hiding in hollow trunks. At night they go in search of food, fruits, insects, and so on, running along the branches and often making their way from tree to tree by alternate climbs and flights. They launch themselves into the air, and with patagium extended, glide obliquely downwards, ascending somewhat as they reach their destination; flights of fifty yards or more are not uncommon, and the larger squirrels of India may make flights of eighty yards.

The kaguan or cobego (*Galeopithecus*) of the Malay Peninsula and Archipelago is an animal of uncertain relationships, but perhaps allied to the insectivores and bats; it is generally placed in an order by itself. It is about as large as a cat, with long, slender limbs and curved claws, and with a larger patagium than any of the animals previously considered, for the fold of skin at the sides of the body extends not only from limb to limb, and to neck and tail, but between the fingers and toes.

Like most other gliding mammals it is nocturnal in its habits, and in the day-time rests clinging to the trunk of a tree, or hiding among the branches, where its brownish colour helps to conceal it. At night it feeds on fruit and leaves, and has been observed to go up a tree by short runs, and to make an oblique downward flight to a tree seventy yards away. A smaller species, with similar habits, occurs in the Philippine Islands.

BATS, which may be related to the insectivores or shrews, moles, hedgehogs, and so on, have a flying membrane similar in structure to that of the gliding mammals, as it is a thin fold of skin extending outwards from the sides of the body. The reader is referred to the photographs in pages 117 to 127.

The front limbs are very long, with very long and slender fingers; the wing-membrane extends not only from the side of the body and the hind-leg to the arm, but also between the fingers, so that there is a great expanse. The chest is large, with powerful muscles that move the fore-limbs, and with them the wing-membrane; the muscle that depresses the wing is the largest in the body, and the breast-bone is enlarged and bears a keel for its attachment. Bats are thus capable of flight of quite another kind from that of the gliding mammals, as they beat the air with their wings.

BATS are a large and diverse tribe. Nearly all are nocturnal; during the day they rest head downwards, suspended by their feet, and with the wings folded. On the ground they can only shuffle along, but they are able to climb up trees or rocks with the aid of the thumb, which is free and provided with a curved claw.

The largest bats belong to the group known as fruit-bats, some of which have a wing-spread of five feet. The fruit-bats of India, Malaysia and Australia are sometimes termed flying foxes; they have short ears and fox-like faces. They roost on trees during the day, and at sunset fly off to places where trees are in fruit. They fly straight, with slow beats of the wings, and may travel long distances in search of food; in India they have been described as flying one behind the other in large companies. When feeding they generally hang on by one leg and grasp the fruit with the other. At dawn, when they return to their resting places, hundreds may settle on the same tree, and they scramble about upside down, each trying to get the best place. Some African fruit-bats have a large mouth margined by large flabby lips, which probably prevent the escape of the juice of the succulent fruits that they eat.

The smaller bats generally feed on insects, which they catch while flying. As a rule, they fly with more rapid beats of the wings than the fruit-bats, fluttering round trees, and twisting and turning in pursuit of their prey. Most of them have very large ears, and some have "nose-leaves" on the face, flaps of skin fringed with hairs, whereas others are provided with "chin leaves," lappets of skin below the chin; these appendages sometimes give the face a grotesque appearance, well shown in the photograph in page 118. There can be little doubt that these organs enable them to perceive obstacles, and perhaps also to detect insects. An experiment showed that in the dark bats were able to perceive and avoid a number of fine threads stretched across a room, for they flew between them.

During the day some insectivorous bats rest among the branches, others in hollow trees, or in caves or buildings. Not all eat insects, for in South America some skim the water and strike it to catch shrimps and fishes, and the blood-sucking vampires, with sharp-edged teeth, suck the blood of mammals while resting on or hovering over their victims.

The prevalence of nocturnal habits among the gliding mammals and bats is worth attention. The advantage to harmless insectivorous or vegetarian animals of being able to fly from one tree to another without coming to the ground, and so avoiding carnivorous foes, must be considerable; but this involves the development of a patagium, so useful for flight, but somewhat of an encumbrance at other times, as for example when running or climbing are in progress.

The gliding mammals fly obliquely downwards, generally from the top of one tree to near the bottom of another. A climb has to precede another flight, and during this climb they would be exposed to attack. Inclined to be clumsy and slow except when flying, they find it safer to keep quiet during the day and to conduct their operations in search of food at night. The nocturnal habits of bats are doubtless inherited from gliding ancestors, and have been adhered to because it is not worth their

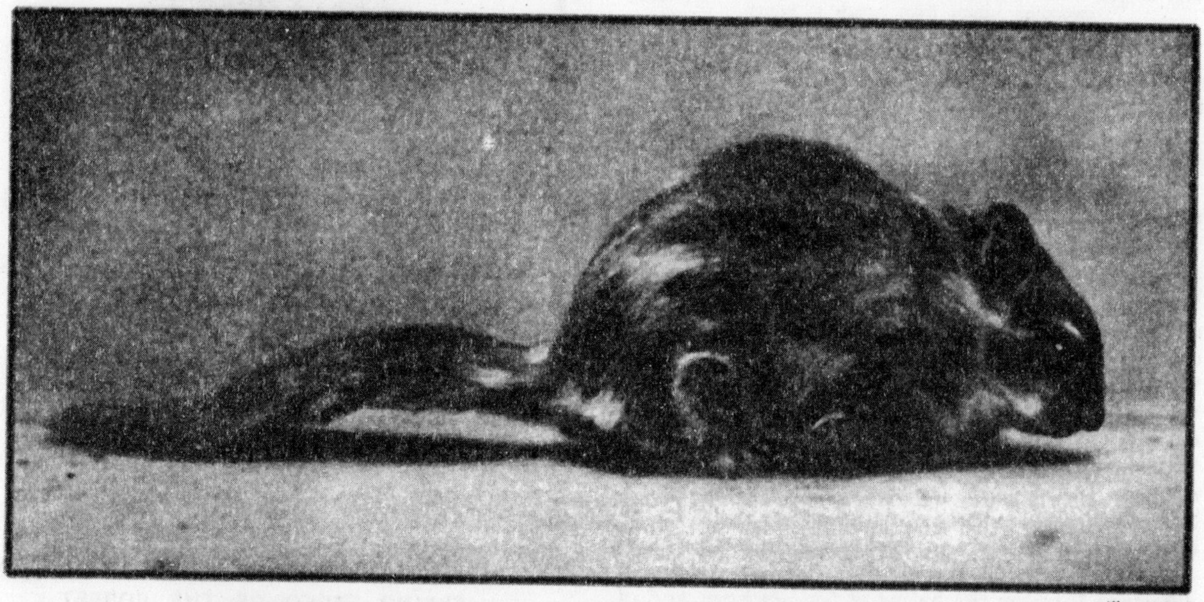

W S Berridge

MEMBER OF THE SQUIRREL FAMILY THAT HAS LEARNED TO FLY

This American flying squirrel makes a long oblique glide from the tops of high trees and can travel fifty yards or more, often altering the trajectory of the flight in an upward direction by virtue of the impetus towards the end of the glide. These creatures seek their food, which consists of insects and fruits, at night, and sleep during the day high up in the trees or else hidden away in some hollow trunk. By developing a wing membrane they have enabled themselves to become independent of the ground

W. S. Berridge

TREE FROG OF BORNEO

Some kinds of frogs living in Java and Borneo have developed the web joining their fingers and toes into broad surfaces with enough wind resistance to enable them to take great swooping jumps from bough to bough.

while to spend the day competing with insectivorous birds, or avoiding the attacks of predaceous ones.

We have seen that a patagium, or wing-membrane, has developed in mammals several times—perhaps three times in the phalangers, twice in the squirrels, and again in *Galeopithecus* and in the bats. None of the gliding mammals can be regarded as ancestral to the bats, but they have a similar wing-membrane connecting the limbs with the side of the body and, like the bats, rest in trees during the day and feed on fruits, leaves, or insects at night, when they perform their flights. They give us an idea of the structure and habits of the animals from which bats must have come, and if some gliding mammal with a large patagium and webbed fingers, like *Galeopithecus*, had tried to prolong its flights by beats of its fore-limbs it would have taken the first step towards becoming a bat; for the principal difference between the habits of *Galeopithecus* and of the fruit-bats is that these take longer flights by flapping their wings. The principal stages that have taken place in the evolution of bats may have been: (1) terrestrial mammals; (2) arboreal mammals that leap from bough to bough and tree to tree, like squirrels; (3) arboreal mammals that take long glides from tree to tree by means of a patagium, nocturnal in habits; (4) arboreal mammals with a patagium, flying by up and down beats of the fore-limbs, also nocturnal.

It is very interesting that millions of years afterwards bats should have developed the power of flight with wings so similar to those of the numerous extinct flying reptiles.

The probable evolutionary history of bats has been outlined above, but the question as to how these things have come about is still in dispute. Which is the more important, cunning or luck? as Samuel

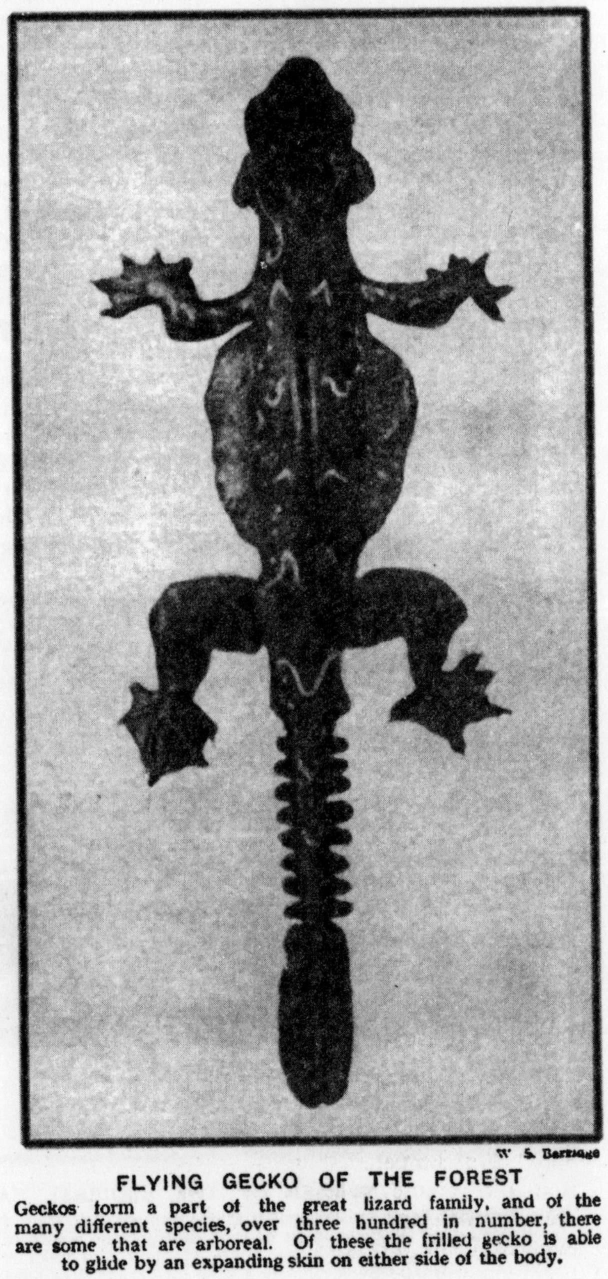

W. S. Berridge

FLYING GECKO OF THE FOREST

Geckos form a part of the great lizard family, and of the many different species, over three hundred in number, there are some that are arboreal. Of these the frilled gecko is able to glide by an expanding skin on either side of the body.

NOCTULE BATS ASLEEP WITH THEIR YOUNG ON A BRANCH

Bats are the most efficient aeronauts of the mammals that fly, for they alone have solved the problem of continued flight and are not dependent on a mere glide like the phalangers. Indeed, the noctule, the largest of the bats found in England and common in the southern counties, is not inferior to any bird in its extraordinary facility in turning and twisting on its course as it flies in pursuit of the insects on which it feeds. The noctule's progeny cling to their mother sometimes till they are nearly as big as herself, as we see in the photograph.

Butler has expressed it. Are the effects of use and effort inherited and accumulated, or does evolution depend on the natural selection of certain small, favourable variations?

Let us take, for example, the pigmy phalanger, in which the patagium is least developed, extending only from elbow to body and out again to the knee. Did this begin as the stretching of the skin between limbs and body of an animal that leaped with limbs outspread, and did this effect continue and increase in further generations of animals with the same habit? Or was additional distance of leap so important that at first those phalangers with any fold of skin between limbs and body, and later those with bigger folds, on the whole survived and left more descendants?

These are the explanations according to the two chief evolutionary theories generally associated with the names of Lamarck and Darwin respectively, but it must be remembered that they are theories only. No competent student of the matter doubts that the remote ancestors of bats were terrestrial animals with normal fore-limbs, nor that they have evolved from these by some such stages as have been already described. What has happened, and why it has happened, is fairly clear; but how it has happened is another question to which we do not yet certainly know the answer.

If we compare flying mammals with birds we have to admit that birds excel; they have dominated the air for a long time, and have not left many places to be occupied by other fliers. The wing of a bird, as of a bat, is a fore-limb; but it is modified to support the light but strong flight feathers, and is not connected by a membrane with the body and hind-limb. This difference is of the greatest importance; it gives the wings greater freedom and a better shape, allows the body to develop the rounded, tapering contour essential for swift flight, and permits the hind-limbs to be used as legs, so that when not flying birds can stand, hop, or run. Moreover, they can take off for a flight direct from the ground, and in this, as in most other respects, are definitely superior to the bats.

The flight of birds by beats of the wings is essentially similar to that of bats, but most birds exceed bats in speed. Some small birds may be seen to follow a short upward flight by an oblique downward glide comparable to that of a flying squirrel; the long horizontal glides of some larger birds appear to be accomplished by taking advantage of air currents.

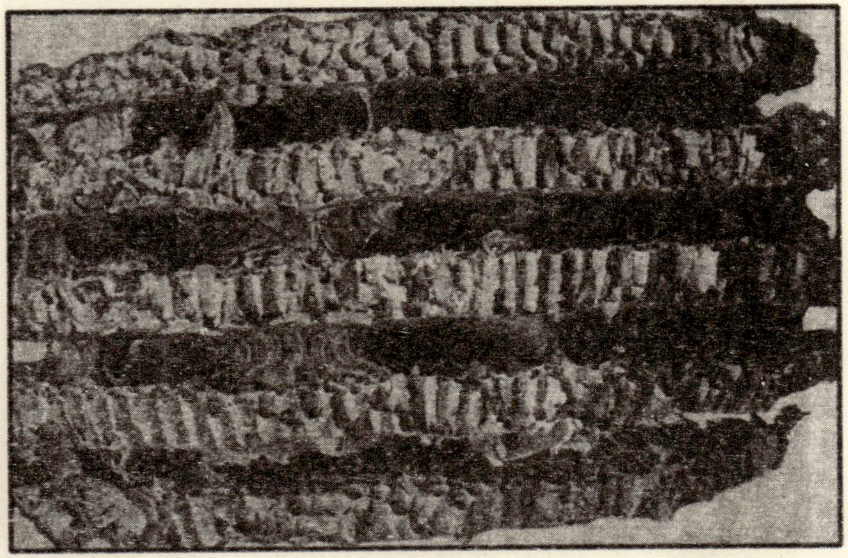

M. H. Crawford

NESTS OF WASPS AND HORNETS AND A PIECE OF WOOD AFTER "WORKING"

Wasps and hornets construct their nests out of a kind of wood-pulp made by scraping the surface off a piece of wood and chewing up the fragments and mingling them with saliva. The pulp so prepared is spread out in layers and then moulded to the required shape. The top left-hand photograph shows a queen wasp at work scraping material for wood-pulp from a fence, while the top right-hand photograph is of a piece of wood after it has been scraped by nest-building wasps. The nest of the tree-wasp (top centre) is made in the same way. The wood-pulp is not altogether waterproof, and nests sometimes get flooded out in a wet summer. The bottom photographs show (left) a hornets' nest, and (right) five pulp combs of a wasps' nest.

Chapter XLI

Carpenters and Joiners and other Workers in Wood

By Henry Neal Milligan

Zoologist of the Horniman Museum

MANY readers will no doubt be surprised to learn that there are animals which are "carpenters and joiners and other workers in wood." But some of man's best inventions were anticipated in nature, and certain instruments of carpentry were employed by animals long before the human era.

Take, for example, the chisel. Probably few people will think of carpentry without thinking of chisels. But what, it might be asked, have animals to do with chisels? We can turn for answer to an animal which nearly everybody has kept as a pet, namely, the rabbit. A rabbit will persistently gnaw the woodwork of its cage, and it does this by means of certain peculiarly-formed teeth. One need do no more than glance into the animal's mouth to see the teeth, for they are those four (two upper and two lower) which are at the very front, but if the reader can examine a skull he will be in a better position to understand the matter. Each of those four teeth is a chisel.

Each tooth is mainly composed (like our own teeth) of dentine, coated outside with enamel, though in the rabbit's teeth the enamel is chiefly on the front surface. Now, the dentine, though hard, is not so hard as the enamel, and wears away with use faster than the latter. Consequently, the working surface of the tooth has always an upstanding front ridge of enamel, backed by a body of dentine; and however much the enamel wears with use the dentine behind it wears faster, the relative proportions of the two materials being thus always preserved. Such is the structure of the four front chisel-like teeth of the rabbit. And such, indeed, is the structure of a man-made steel chisel, for it is composed of a thin and very hard layer of metal supported by another thick but not so hard layer.

With its front chisel-like teeth, then, a rabbit gnaws. This peculiar habit has earned for animals like rabbits the general name of rodents or gnawers. There are many kinds of rodents, including, besides rabbits, such creatures as guinea-pigs, rats, mice, beavers, and squirrels. All rodents find their chisels very useful, for not only can these teeth be used to chip pieces from hard food, but, as in the case of the squirrel, to chisel off the shells of nuts, or to cut through obstacles in the way of burrows and runs. Gnawing is very wearing to teeth, and the chisels of rodents, unlike ordinary teeth, are always growing, the material which is lost at their ends being made good by the addition of new material at their bases. Man has made good chisels, but he has not made one which grows as it wears! But teeth which are always growing may sometimes be troublesome. Suppose, for example, that a rodent does not use its chisels sufficiently, or that they are somewhat misplaced, or that one chisel breaks and leaves its opposite nothing to bite against. In such cases the teeth grow too long, and may not only interfere with feeding but even pierce and injure the head. Healthy rodents instinctively gnaw such substances as wood, thus keeping their teeth in good condition, and it is this instinct which leads captive specimens so persistently to perform the seemingly useless carpentry of cutting away the woodwork of their cages.

The rodents we have mentioned are all carpenters, but one of them, the beaver, is a joiner as well. The beaver feeds on the bark and leaves of

Keystone

BEAVERS AT WORK

This drawing shows how the beaver gets through its work. The trees and branches are cut from upstream and floated down to the proposed site of the dam. There they are cleverly arranged and then plastered with mud and pieces of turf.

BEAVER AND ITS CUNNINGLY CONSTRUCTED "LODGE"

Besides building a dam across a stream, the beaver has also to construct out of it the "lodge" in which it lives and, furthermore, to keep the whole in repair. One entrance to the lodge is from the bank, and there is also an emergency entrance below the surface where the water is deepest. Some lodges, however, are completely surrounded by water. The whole structure is a complex of tree trunks, branches and twigs held together by skilful arrangement, the pressure of the water, and a plastering of mud which the animal makes with its fore-paws.

C. Reid

CARPENTER, JOINER, AND PLASTERER IN ONE: THE BEAVER

On land the beaver is not an active animal. It is much more at home in the water, and deep water is safer than shallow. The beaver, then, likes plenty of depth in his stream, and has learned how to dam up the water for the purpose, and it is the American beaver that is the finest dam builder. A tree is selected for felling, and the animal gnaws a furrow round and round the trunk, and the rasping of its chisel teeth can be heard at quite a considerable distance. When the right number of logs have been cut, the beaver joins them together in a dam.

M. H. Crawford

WOODPECKER AT WORK ON A TREE

Working as quickly as a mechanical drill the great spotted woodpecker's beak is moved by especially developed neck muscles. It taps tree bark for insects and drills out a shaft in the trunk for its nest.

trees and on aquatic plants, and lives preferably in a district well timbered and with a stream flowing through it. Across such a stream the beaver will build its famous dam. It should be mentioned that beavers occur in Europe, Asia, and North America (though sadly reduced in numbers through man's persecution), but it is chiefly the American beaver whose dam-building is so remarkable.

THE dam is composed mainly of trunks and branches of trees, and to obtain these the beaver must in many instances actually fell the trees. Here the powerful chisel-like teeth are employed with good effect. The beaver cuts a furrow round and round the base of a tree, working with such vigour that the rasping sound may be heard a long way off, and sooner or later the tree gives way and falls, usually towards the stream. The tree is dragged and pushed to the water, unless it is large, when it is cut into lengths and brought to the water in sections. The various pieces of wood are thrust together, and finally intermingled in such a way that they make a firm and massive fence across the stream. The beaver now adds the work of a plasterer to that of carpenter and joiner, thrusting such materials as mud and sods well into the interstices of the fence so as to make a wall which is nearly impervious to water. The beaver, it must be explained, plasters with its front feet; the old story that its great flat tail is used trowel-wise, is not true. The stream, stopped by the dam, soon forms a lake. The beaver, always on the alert, discovers and repairs injuries to the dam. Instances have even been described of the animal making a "slip-way" for superfluous water.

A wonderful performance, indeed. But, why the dam? A beaver is not an active creature on land, and it prefers the water, in which it swims and dives with ease. It is much safer in its artificial lake than it would be on land, or in a stream. Moreover, the entrance to the beaver's home is made secure by being concealed under a large mass of water. Again, the beaver needs to make a store of food for the winter, and when such food is an under-water store, as it is in this case, it is convenient to have a safe way to

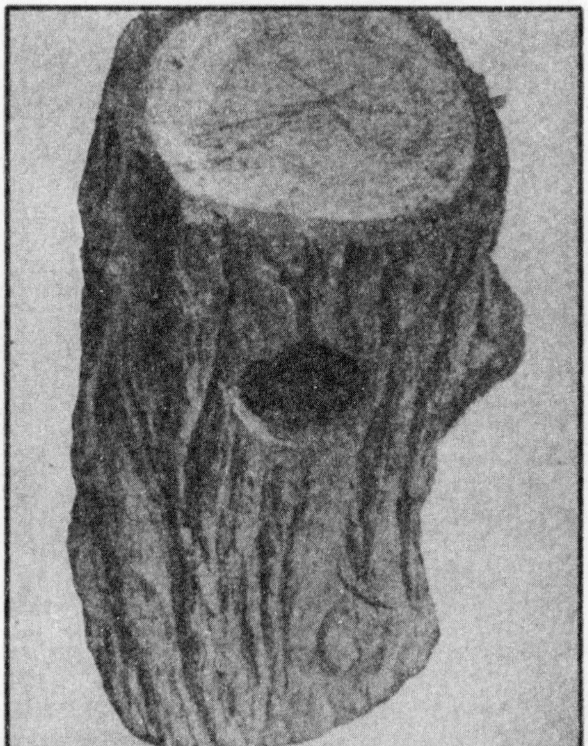

M. H. Crawford

NEST-HOLE DRILLED BY WOODPECKER

This is a piece of a tree trunk that has been very neatly drilled by a woodpecker for nesting purposes. When the tree was cut down this log sawn from it would have made a convenient nesting box for other birds in a garden.

it, particularly when the surface of the water is frozen. The beaver's home, or "lodge," is built, on the bank of the stream, of branches, twigs, and mud, and a burrow leads at one end into the home and at the other to an underwater entrance. Some of them are simple and others fairly complex, and certain examples are wholly above water, resting on "islands" constructed by the beaver with branches.

THERE are many birds which are workers in wood. One which quickly comes to mind is the English green woodpecker. Fairly open woods and large well-timbered parks, particularly those with old trees, are the places beloved of this bird. If we are fortunate, we may see it ascend the trunk of a tree, advancing, often in a spiral course, with short jerky motions, tapping sharply at the bark with its beak as it goes. It wants to dislodge loose bark, and thus secure the insects which are beneath. The suitability of the beak for such a purpose is clear enough, for it is like a pick. It is long, strong, straight, and pointed, and the head which carries it is moved by powerful neck muscles. The hewing powers of the green woodpecker are considerable, but they are outdone by those of the American ivory-billed woodpecker. One of these last-named birds was caught by a naturalist, Alexander Wilson, and it ruined a mahogany table by striking out great pieces with its beak! The beak of the woodpecker is also used for making a nesting-hole in some tree in which decay has rendered the wood easily workable. A horizontal shaft is first picked out, and, leading from that, a vertical shaft. At the bottom of the vertical shaft is the nest.

M. H. Crawford

PICK-LIKE BEAKS OF NUTHATCH AND WOODPECKER

Armed with a strong pick-like beak the nuthatch (bottom) got its name from its method of dealing with hazel nuts. The bird gets the nut into a crevice and then drives at it with its beak until the shell is broken. The lesser spotted woodpecker (top) is another among British birds which are workers in wood.

One may call it the "nest," but truly it is simply the enlarged lower end of the vertical shaft, the fine chippings produced during the work being used as the bed for the eggs and young.

Some birds build nests of wood, and of these the rook is an example. A rook makes its nest along with other rooks in a sort of community or rookery, building as nearly as practicable at the top of a tall tree, several nests, perhaps, almost or quite touching. The nest is made of pieces of tree-wood, some pieces being little more than twigs, whilst others are relatively thick branches. The joinery involved in putting together the pieces of wood is not so simple a matter as might be supposed, for much time is spent in selecting the wood, breaking it up, and interlacing the pieces. The wood is often plastered

but let us now examine a piece of wood into which ship-worms have bored.

This may be of deal, or hard oak, or harder teak, but, whatever the material, ship-worms have cut smooth passages in it and reduced it to a mere shell of wood, with partitions, often not thicker than paper, between the passages of individual animals. Each teredo has lined its passage with shelly matter. It is thought that the passages are rasped out by a rocking motion of the rough shell, and some people have asserted that grating sounds can be heard when ship-worms

King & Son

with mud, and the interior of the nest finished off with turf, leaves, feathers, and so on. It is surprising that a bird can do so much building with its beak.

The creatures already mentioned belong to the higher sorts of animals, but others have ability to work in wood. Indeed, the best workers belong to the lower groups. There are so many of them that a bare list of their names would take up our space, and we can therefore describe only a few representative kinds, including the ship-worm and some insects.

WHO has not heard of the ship-worm? We all call it the ship-" worm," for it is not unlike a worm in appearance, but truly it is an animal of the group Mollusca—the group to which mussels belong. Sometimes, however, it is called the teredo. Now, the ship-worm or teredo is a famous worker in wood. Formerly it was dreaded by those who had to do with wooden ships and piers, and, in some places, it still is dreaded, although since metal has been much used in marine work its operations have not been so formidable. Let us glance at a preserved ship-worm, as we may do in almost any museum. The animal is perhaps eight inches long with a tiny two-valved shell at one end and two fleshy tubes at the other, and the outer surface of the shell is rasp-like.

The teredo seems so much like a helpless worm that those who have read of its ravages may be surprised, and perhaps a little amused, when they first examine it. It seems impossible that such a thing could vex marine engineers and alarm ship-owners,

Wilford

BIRD JOINERY: HERON'S AND CORMORANT'S NESTS

In high trees or sometimes on sea-cliffs or even ruins, the heron build its great nest among a colony of its own kind. The nest (bottom) is flat and broad and consists of twigs and grass on a foundation of branches. The cormorant, unlike many sea-birds, makes a proper nest of twigs and seaweed (top).

A. H Willford

BIRD JOINERS IN THE TREE TOPS: A ROOKERY AND ITS INHABITANTS

This fine photograph shows a busy rookery when the young are growing up and clamouring for food. Some of the parents are attending to their offspring, while others are circling above in the way rooks have. The nests are built up much more carefully than would appear. Great pains and much time are taken over choosing suitable branches and twigs and in breaking these up and putting them together. Often the wood is plastered with mud. The nest has to be strong enough to withstand a high wind.

are working. The animal works fast, and as it reproduces rapidly (the young being free-swimming, and thus able to spread), it may soon do enormous damage to woodwork in the sea.

Holland has suffered severely, for the dyke-piles have been injured, and even threatened with destruction, by ship-worms. It is a bad pest, however, which does nobody good, but it is well to remember that it was the shell-lined passage of the teredo which suggested to Sir Marc Isambard Brunel a means of making the first Thames tunnel. The ship-worm obtains security by burrowing in wood; but it also obtains food, if it be true, as some zoologists believe, that the animal eats fine fragments of wood.

Among the insects mention must be made of the giant sirex, a creature related to the wasps. It is

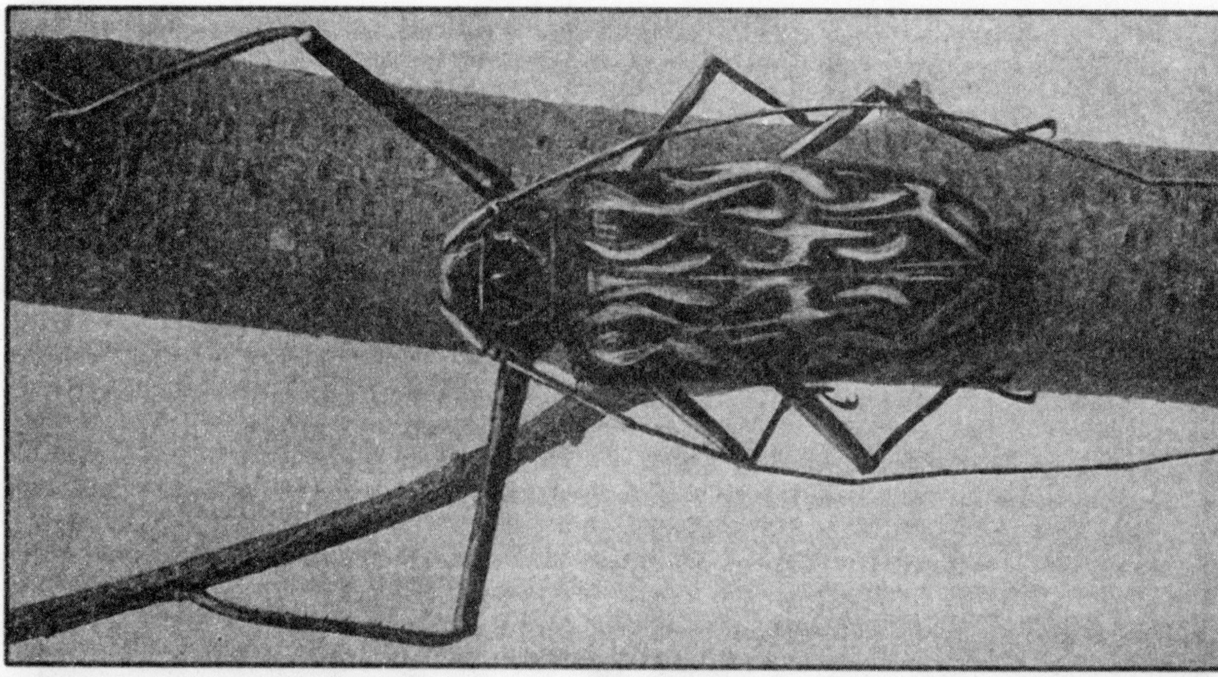

H. Bastin

J. J. Ward

HUGE GOLIATH BEETLE AND THE HARLEQUIN BEETLE LIVING ON TREES

Probably the largest of all the beetle tribe is the goliath beetle (bottom) of Africa, which is almost as large as a man's fist. We see it here with its wings partly expanded from the wing cases. It does considerable damage to wood. Tropical America is the home of the harlequin beetle (top), a very beautiful creature possessing remarkably long front legs and remarkably patterned wing cases. It is a poor flier, but gets about the trees in which it lives and feeds by swinging itself from branch to branch

H Bastin

J. J. Ward

BUSY CARPENTER ANTS AND THE STAG BEETLE

Carpenter ants (bottom) are very careful not to reveal the presence of their nest by leaving sawdust lying about near the entrance to their communal home. The two seen here are engaged in this work of concealment. The one on the left is half emerged from the entrance hole and is handing a fragment of wood to a porter ant for removal. Above is the stag beetle whose grub causes much damage to oak trees. The bottom photograph is by Paul Griswold Howes, Assistant Curator of the Bruce Museum, Greenwich, Conn., U.S.A.

J. T Roberts

J. T Roberts

GOAT-MOTH CATERPILLAR: A GREAT WOOD BORER

The eggs of the goat moth are laid in cracks in wood and the caterpillar, when it hatches out, is a large and powerful grub (top) with the characteristic goat-like smell and a very hard wedge-shaped head and big jaws. It eats long tunnels through the wood and just before it becomes a pupa makes itself a cocoon of wood chips fastened with gum from its mouth (bottom).

nearly as big as a hornet, banded with black and yellow and the female, though not really dangerous, is a terrifying creature, for it bears a conspicuous sting-like appendage at its hind end. It is not common enough to be often seen, but sometimes it issues from the woodwork of new houses, and when it does so not unnaturally causes much alarm, especially if it appears in numbers. The explanation of such visitations is this. The supposed sting is a borer-like egg-layer, and with it the female bores holes in trees (preferably dead or new-felled fir), in which she lays her eggs. From each egg hatches a creature, which, as in all the higher insects, is not a miniature copy of the adult, but is a grub or caterpillar. The grub lives in the wood, and eats it, making long passages in doing so, and wood infested with many grubs may be quite riddled. Before any grub becomes a perfect insect it passes through a quiescent stage, called the pupa. Our sirex grub, just before pupation, approaches the surface of the tree, and, when it has become a sirex, pushes its way out of the hole. Hence the sudden appearance of such insects from wood not seasoned.

The sirex merely bores holes for the eggs, and the grubs eat the wood with their hard jaws. But in certain related insects, called carpenter-bees, it is the mother who cuts channels with her jaws. The fine European violet carpenter-bee is an example. The female cuts out of dead dry wood a short horizontal passage, leading into three or four vertical passages, and in the latter she lays her eggs, dividing the eggs from one another by horizontal partitions made ingeniously of wood chips.

Another insect, belonging not to the wasp-and-bee group but to the moth group, which lays eggs in wood, is the British goat-moth. The moth has no borer, and simply lays her eggs in cracks. The grub is a big, fat, fleshy, repulsive creature, with a hard wedge-like head and great jaws, and with a goatish smell. It eats long wide passages in the wood, and is often called the auger-worm. Just before it becomes a pupa, when it is nearly four inches long, its woodworking instincts take a fresh turn, and it makes a sort of protective covering or "cocoon" out of wood chips, which it fastens together with a gummy substance from its mouth.

There are many other woodworking insects. Amongst the beetles they are numerous. The British stag-beetle is one whose grubs are very destructive to oak trees. Other destructive species are the bark-beetles, one of which, known as the elm bark-beetle or scolytus, may be particularly mentioned. This beetle is about a sixth of an inch long. The female eats into the bark of an elm tree, and then, turning at right angles, eats out a passage between bark and wood, laying about a hundred eggs at fairly regular intervals in this passage. Each grub eats a passage at right

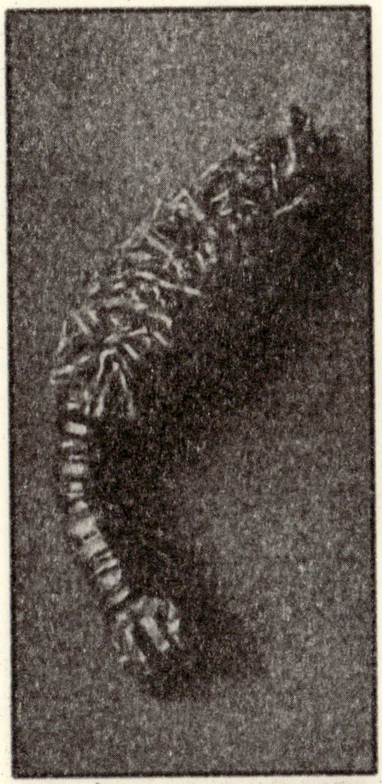

M. H. Crawford

J. J. Ward

GOAT MOTH AS IT DEVELOPS AND ITS EFFECT ON WOOD

How wood can become riddled by the depredations of the goat moth larva may be seen from the two lower photographs. The ash tree shown has suffered in this way so much that its existence is threatened by the next storm. Above are the three stages through which the moth passes. The larva (right) feeding on a tree is busy with its strong sharp teeth. Eventually it makes itself a sheath of wood chips. This "cocoon" (left) was taken from the ground after the moth (centre) had emerged and shows the empty pupa skin projecting.

Oak Apples

Puss-moth cocoons

Root Galls

Nut Weevil and its work

Puss-moth and empty cocoon

INSECT CARPENTERS OF NUT, BARK, ROOT AND GALL

The nut weevil has a very long proboscis and when it has, as a larva, eaten all the contents of a nut bores its way out through the shell. The gall-flies lay their eggs either in wood or roots, and here are the oak apples and root galls, swellings caused by abnormal cell development round the puncture made by the parent insect in depositing the eggs. In the photograph of the root galls, the lower right gall has the larva's exit hole. The other photographs are of the puss-moth, which fashions its cocoon from bark and wood. These photographs are by Mrs. M. H. Crawford.

A caterpillar's home

Orange clear-wing moth just emerged

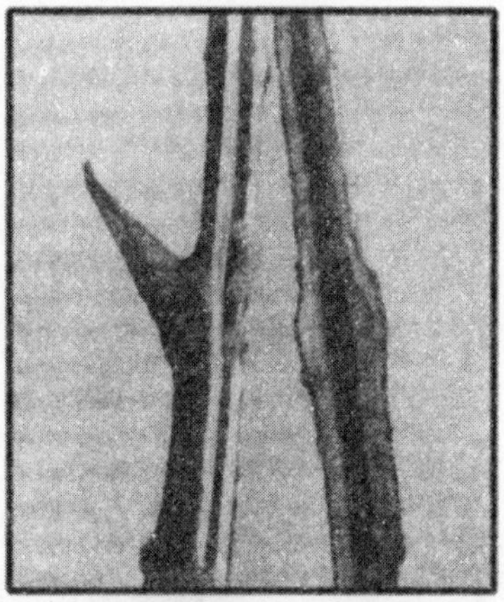

Caterpillar at home

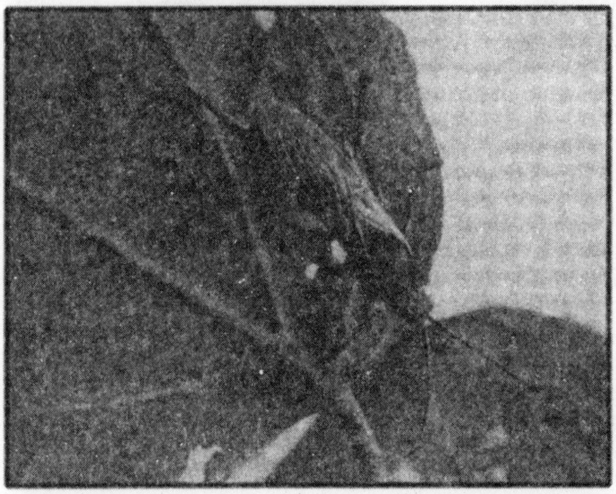

Top view of female sirex

Side view of sirex

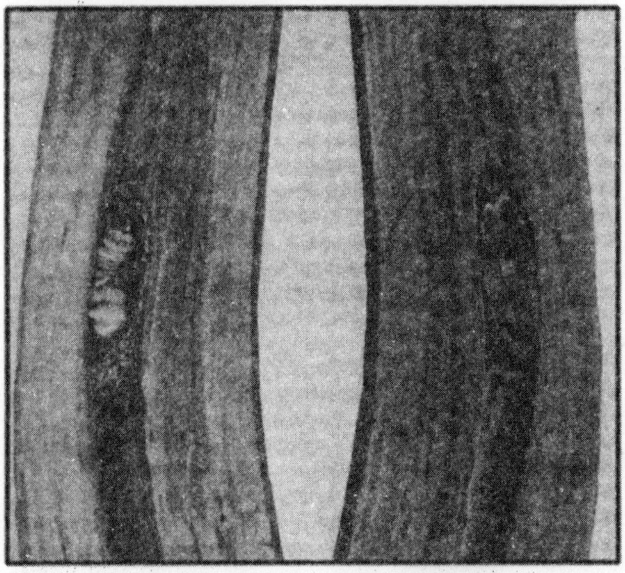

Larva of lunar hornet-moth

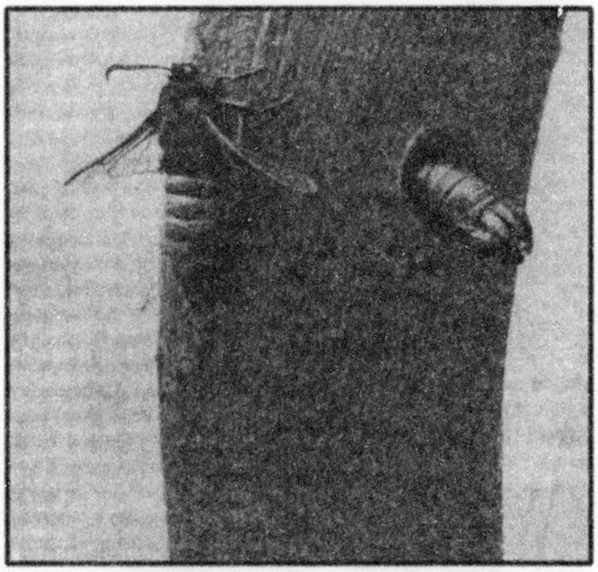

Lunar hornet moth and empty pupa skin

INSECTS WHOSE EGGS PRODUCE WOOD-BORING LARVA

In the bottom photographs we see (right) a lunar hornet-moth (left) just emerged from its pupa skin. In the left-hand photograph is a branch split to show the tunnel bitten out by the larva of the moth. The path is barricaded just below the larva and also at the entrance of the hole. The female sirex (middle photographs) is like a large wasp with a long sting. In reality the " sting " is harmless and is an ovipositor which bores into wood and lays the eggs. The orange clear-wing moth (top) is shown with some of its work. The photographs are by J. J. Ward.

TIMBER CUT FOR MAN, AFTER IT HAS BEEN USED BY SOME OF NATURE'S WOOD-WORKERS

Ravages by the death-watch beetle may cause the collapse of a building. The mating call, caused by the striking of its head against wood and producing a sound like the ticking of a watch, gave the beetle its name. The left-hand photograph shows some irrevocably damaged woodwork from the interior of St. Clements, Eastcheap, one of the old City churches. The centre photograph is of some oak from a breakwater, destroyed by the teredo, a wood-worker of the sea, while on the right is a timber marked by the shot-borer beetle.

angles to the mother's passage, and all the passages together make a curious and characteristic radiating pattern, which may be seen when the bark is lifted from the wood.

Everyone has seen the neat round " worm-holes " in furniture. The animals which make these holes are usually called " worms," but the reader will probably guess that they are really grubs of insects. They are the larvae of furniture-beetles. Much damage may be done by these grubs. The writer was recently shown the remains of a picture-frame so riddled by grubs that it was little more than a husk filled with powdered wood. The great injury done to the old oak beams of the roof of Westminster Hall is fresh in all our minds.

There are several kinds of furniture-beetles in England but one kind is particularly common. It is about a sixth of an inch in length, of rather elongated and compact form, and of a brownish colour. Most people have found examples, living or dead, in houses in which there is infested wood, and those who have watched a living specimen must have noticed its curious habit of " shamming dead." The female lays her eggs in crevices or holes in wood, and the whitish grubs, with their powerful jaws, eat long passages in it about a twelfth of an inch in diameter. Tiny heaps of wood-dust appear under infected furniture. When the time of pupation draws near each grub comes almost to the surface of the wood, where it becomes a pupa, and there remains until, as a perfect beetle, it is ready to bite its way out. The hole through which it emerges is henceforth a " worm-hole." Furniture-beetles creep and fly about, and thus carry infection from wood to wood. The tapping sounds, known to the superstitious as " death-watch," are really sex-calls from one furniture-beetle to another, made by knocking the head against the wood.

Animals which work in wood, then, are of most various kinds. Some of them cut into wood with chisel-like teeth (rodents), or pick-like beaks (woodpeckers), or borer-like egg-layers (giant sirex), or rasp-like shells (shipworms). Some use wood for building homes (beavers) or nests (rooks). To make a hole in a tree is a good way of obtaining safety for eggs and young (woodpeckers), whilst those which both live in wood and eat it (shipworms, insect grubs) are unusually fortunate and safe. Finally, it should be observed that, many and diverse as are the examples which have been mentioned in this chapter, they are few compared with the many which exist.

DESTROYERS OF WOODWORK

The furniture-beetle (right) lays its eggs in crevices of wood. When the grubs hatch they eat their way inwards till as pupae they return to near the surface, eating their way out on hatching. The death-watch beetle (left) greatly damaged the roof of Westminster Hall. Photographs by courtesy of British Museum.

Chapter XLII

Is Evolution Still Going On?

By Professor J. Arthur Thomson

Author of "The Gospel of Evolution"

WHAT is Evolution? In the wide sense it is a process of becoming, in the course of which something new arises. There is no doubt that new stars are still appearing in the sky, and there are nebulae which seem to be making new solar systems far away in space. If some stars die into darkness, other luminaries are being born. For the universe as a whole there does not seem to be any evidence of either its ending or its beginning. Within our intellectual horizon there is a ceaseless flux. Cosmic evolution is going on.

At present, within the chemist's reach, there are ninety-two elements (less four gaps still to be filled); and we know that a kind of chemical evolution goes on. Thus uranium may give rise to ionium, which may give rise to radium. Or uranium may give rise to protactinium, which produces actinium, which produces lead. Or radium by giving off helium may produce lead. The meaning of this is that all the different elements are composed of positive hydrogen-nuclei or protons in the centre of the atom, and negative units of electricity or electrons in zones outside. An average atom is like a sun and its planets. There is a solar core of protons, and outside this there is orbit after orbit of electrons. Even as we write this the picture of the atoms is changing a little, but the large fact is secure that the 88 known elements, qualitatively so very diverse, differ from one another quantitatively, namely, in the number and the position of their protons and electrons. But our point is that chemical evolution is going on, as we see in the succession or pedigree we have mentioned—uranium, protactinium, actinium, lead. It is believed that "lead" is being born in about eight different ways; and since lead does not seem to be transformable into anything else, it may be argued that there is not here much evidence of evolution.

BUT we must get rid of the idea that evolution is synonymous with progress. Evolution is the becoming of something new; and it may be something new "down," as well as something new "up." To use terms less metaphorical than "up" and "down," we may say that evolution works in the direction of increased or decreased complexity. As we have often said, the tapeworm in its inglorious lot in man's intestine is an outcome of evolution as well as the lark at heaven's gate. We say "as well as," but not "as much as," for the simple reason that evolution in the world of life is on the whole "up," that is towards differentiation or complexity of parts, and towards integration or unifying of parts. Moreover, among higher animals there is an undeniable movement towards mental qualities such as alertness, judgement, and aesthetic sensitiveness, and towards moral qualities such as sympathy and synergy—qualities which man at his best has always regarded as best. At the same time, we must remember that this movement is not the only evolution.

To return, for a moment, to chemical evolution; we find abundant evidence that it is still going on, though we must admit that so far as the Earth is concerned, the trend of chemical evolution, outside of the creative chemical laboratories, is all towards simplification, towards a running down of the clocks. The synthetic chemist is a veritable creator of new complexities, some of them life-destroying like explosives, others life-saving like thyroxin against cretinism; but in terrestrial Nature the present-day transformations on the earth apart from living creatures seem to be always from the more complex towards the more simple. It is probable, however, that in the colossal laboratories of the sun and the stars, where atoms are torn to pieces and built up again, elements still unknown, more complex than uranium, may be in process of evolution. In any case it is perfectly safe to say that in so far as that process concerns chemical evolution it is very definitely going on.

ALL the cosmologists are agreed that the earth was once a fiercely hot nebulous mass which had its origin in a nebulous centre now represented by our Sun. If evolution is a change, as Herbert Spencer said, from the homogeneous to the heterogeneous, then the earth has evolved, for it acquired a crust and a core and zones between. It gained a hydrosphere and an atmosphere, and it certainly made progress in the sense that it became fit to be a home of life. Probably the word to use is development or genesis, not evolution; but the fact is certain that the earth passed through a succession of changes, and became more and more interesting as the manifestations of life upon it became more and more abundant.

> They say the solid earth whereon we tread
> In tracks of fluent heat began,
> And grew to seeming random forms,
> The seeming prey of cyclic storms,
> Till at the last arose the man.

This process of complexifying or differentiation was greatly assisted by the hand of life; thus green plants made a breathable air; in early Tertiary times grass began to cover the earth like a garment; the dainty foraminiferal shells accumulated as future chalk cliffs; and coral polyps are still building beautiful islands. Sometimes carelessly, but often beneficently, man has carved at the earth, and still he casts mountains into the sea and turns what was the desert into a fruitful garden.

It is a great intellectual gain to see our present-day earth as only one out of many successive stages on which the drama of life has been

Martin Duncan

WHERE EVOLUTION SEEMS TO HALT

Evolution is not necessarily progressive as that word is usually understood, and in some cases seems to have lapsed altogether for some unknown period. The lamp-shell, for instance, has remained unaltered in its structure since the Cambrian Age.

played for untold millions of years. Tennyson had a fine vision of the evolving earth:

> There rolls the stream where grew the tree,
> O Earth, what changes hast thou seen,
> There where the long street roars hath been
> The stillness of the central sea.
>
> The hills are shadows and they flow
> From form to form and nothing stands,
> They melt like mist, the solid lands
> Like clouds they shape themselves and go.

It makes for clearness to use the term "evolution" with a prefixed adjective, for there are several different kinds of evolution which have little in common save that they are all processes of becoming, in the course of which something new emerges. Thus, as we have illustrated, there is cosmic evolution, chemical evolution, and terrestrial evolution. But our chief interest here is with none of these, nor with social evolution, but with the evolution of living creatures or organisms. How can we define this organic evolution which has led to the plant world and the animal world and ourselves? Organic evolution is a natural process of racial change in a definite direction, whereby new forms of life arise, take root and flourish, alongside of, or in place of, their ancestors, which were in most cases simpler in structure and behaviour. In cases of degeneration and parasitism the ancestors were not simpler, but the reverse. On the whole, however, organic evolution has been an advance. Life has been slowly creeping upwards. As age has succeeded age, there has been an emergence of higher types with increasing freedom and mastery. The evolutionary

James

BARNYARD FOWL AND ITS ORIGIN

Every one of the numerous breeds of domestic fowl, widely different in appearance as some of them now are, is derived from the Indian jungle fowl (top). The cock and hen in the lower photograph are both of a handsome Japanese stock.

Autotype

MIGHTY-MOUTHED HIPPOPOTAMUS FROM THE RIVERS OF TIME

Evolution, the process of becoming, seems to have paused for an indefinite period in the case of the hippopotamus. Geologists have found, from fossil remains of the Pliocene epoch, that there was then a hippopotamus indistinguishable, save for its greater size, from the beast as we know it to-day. It was widely spread over Europe and, in England, wandered as far north as Yorkshire.

James Keystone

EXTRAORDINARY VARIETY EVOLVED BY MAN FROM THE STOCK OF THE WOLF

The ancestors of the common wolf and of every one of our modern breeds of dog—from mastiff to pomeranian—were the same animals. It is thought that the original tendency to such wide variation in one stock was brought about by cross-breeding in wolves of different species with perhaps an occasional admixture of jackal blood. But the original taming and handling of the wild dog remains a prehistoric mystery. Above are (top left) the Siberian wolf; (top right) Alsatian; (bottom left) Bulldog; and (bottom right) Highland terrier.

process is not necessarily progressive, but on the whole it is an advance that is revealed by the history written in the fossil-bearing rocks. If a fish does not show progress when compared with a worm, if a bird does not show progress when compared with a newt, then we must invent some other word to take the place of "progress," which admittedly had its first reference to human history.

Some organisms have certainly remained the same for ages. There are not a few conservative types which are known as ancient fossils and yet are living to-day without appreciable change in the course of millions of years. As examples may be mentioned the lamp-shell (*Lingula*) since the Cambrian Ages; the pearly nautilus, since the Cretaceous; the mud-fish, Ceratodus, since the Triassic. The New Zealand lizard Hatteria, with a pineal eye on the top of its head, is a living animal of great antiquity, the sole survivor of an otherwise extinct class of reptiles. There are many other animals which differ but little from their extinct fossil ancestors, and Darwin called them "living fossils." Perhaps there is nothing very surprising in the fact that evolution sometimes stands still, for if a creature has attained to a harmonious constitution and to a balanced adjustment to a more or less permanent condition of life, there is no reason why it should change if its environment remains the same. If novelties cropped up now and again they would be nipped in the bud. We may say, then, that in many living creatures evolution has stopped for the time being.

On the other hand, when we settle down to study living species carefully, weighing and measuring one character after another, we find that there is often great variability. Among our common birds and mammals the members of a species seem to the ordinary eye practically identical, but this is not the actual state of affairs. Many of them exhibit continual fluctuations, a little more of this and a little less of that; and these slight variations form part of the raw material of evolution. Every now and then there is something striking, like a white blackbird; but probably more important are the small variations that only the experts notice. Lotsy speaks of a collection of two

Is Evolution Still Going On?

hundred specimens of buzzard (*Buteo buteo*) in the Leiden Museum, "hardly two of which are alike." The individuality of the male ruffs is famous, each an artistic unity by himself, but all the females or reeves seem to be identical.

COLOUR ALTERATIONS EVOLVED IN RABBITS

In the course of artificial breeding, where rabbits are concerned, it often happens that some of the colour factors are lost to the inheritance and such forms occur as we see above. At the bottom is a tortoise lop-eared rabbit, and (top) black and white Dutch rabbit. These types are examples of what man has helped to evolve in the animal world.

The variability of living creatures is particularly conspicuous in certain unaccountable cases, where there occurs what has been called "an epidemic of variations." This is well illustrated at present by the fruit-fly, Drosophila, which has given off numerous true-breeding mutations in the course of a few years. The Dutch botanist De Vries was led to recognize the frequency of mutations or brusque sports in Nature by a study of a stock of Lamarck's evening primrose (*Oenothera lamarckiana*), which he found as an escape in a potato-field near Amsterdam. It was "sporting" in an extraordinary way. Almost all its organs were varying, as if swayed by a restless internal tide. From this stock De Vries obtained, in a short time, half a dozen or more distinct varieties or elementary species, breeding true generation after generation. The evening primrose showed species in the making, and there are many other instances. Variability is a great fact of life. As Alfred Russel Wallace said: "Even Darwin did not realize how much and how universally wild species vary." The fountain of change is welling forth abundantly.

It may be said, however, that variability is all very well, but is it leading to anything? Are there any new species appearing on the earth or in the sea? Part of the answer is that many true-breeding varieties seem to be at present taking grip, like the dark-coloured sugar-birds (*Cœreba* or *Certhiola*) in certain West Indian islands, or like several dark varieties of moths in Britain.

The reason why we do not see more of these novelties is that we are so short-lived. A mutation or brusque variation may arise all of a sudden, but it may take centuries for the new strain to become a stable variety or species. The process of evolution in Nature is usually very slow. It may have taken a million years to fashion a feather, and organic evolution as a whole has probably been going on for more than five hundred million years. Yet some people expect to find the scarabee beetles of to-day different from those in the ancient tombs of Egypt. The mills of evolution grind very slowly. If the span of our life was only a few minutes we might be willing to give evidence that the small hand of a clock remains stationary.

It is sometimes said that there is no evidence of one species turning into another. In answer to this anti-evolutionist pronouncement several sets of facts must be noted. In the first place, there are fossil series, for example, of water-snails, where A and Z are very different, yet the intermediates, preserved in the strata, form a continuous gradation, just like the stages in the growth or development of an individual. In the second place, while it is part of the definition of a species that it is discontinuous—itself and no other—there are often very striking intermediate forms that link one species to its nearest relative. In the third place, the objection suggests an entirely wrong view of evolution, for it cannot be supposed that one species turns into another as if under a magician's wand. This is the error hinted at in the old word "transformism." What has usually happened is probably like this: variations arise which spread from their birthplace; as they spread they may continue varying in the same direction; they may be isolated from the originative stock by some topographical change, such as the making of a peninsula into an island; in isolation there is a tendency to inbreeding which gives stability to the new stock; intercrossing with the originative stock becomes rare, and by and by it may become impossible. The new variety—a new species in the making—does not necessarily supplant the originative species: but environmental changes may occur which are fatal to the first species, yet favourable to the second; and so the evolution goes on. An old species does not change into a new one; a new species arises as an offshoot from an old one; and various forms of isolation help greatly.

It is part of a biological education to go to flower shows and dog shows and all sorts of similar shows. For one sees how many true-breeding races man has established in a relatively short time, and one also sees that novelties are still emerging—new roses, new chrysanthemums, new fowls and new dogs, many of them novelties to be proud of. All the races of domesticated pigeons have been derived from the wild rock dove (*Columba livia*); all the fowls from the Indian jungle fowl (*Gallus bankiva*); all the pigs from two species of wild boar; all the dogs from wolves, probably of several species and perhaps occasionally helped by crossing with jackals. How the original taming and domestication came about we can only guess, for in most cases it is a prehistoric secret; but we know what man has continued to do. He starts from a variable animal, perhaps unusually variable because (as in dogs) the pedigree may be multiple. Variations crop up which seem to the breeder desirable; he pairs similar variants together and thus starts a strain. He continues doing three things: (1) eliminating undesirables, (2) bringing similar forms together as pairs, and (3) preventing intercrossing with other strains. A strain, confirmed by inbreeding, that is, pairing near relatives, grows into a breed; and gradually, with care, a breed becomes a reliable race, in which like usually begets like, such as collie dogs, polled-angus cattle, white leghorn fowls, marquis wheat, shirley poppies. It is not that man is a creator, for he can only operate with the variations that occur; he is rather like an artist who is supplied with fine materials which he arranges in new patterns.

DOMESTIC PIG AND ITS WILD ANCESTOR

From two species of wild boar all the different kinds of domestic pigs have been evolved by years of careful breeding. The fact that animal generations, for the most part, greatly exceed man's in their rate of occurrence has enabled him to control, to a great extent, the type he wished to survive. The domestic pig will survive and change just so long as man has need of it.

With the further aid of Mendel's clue—a fundamental law of inheritance—the breeder is now able to work even more rapidly and certainly than before, grafting one good quality after another on to a promising stock. Thus he can produce a wheat race with heavy ears, early ripening, fine flour and strong straw, to which good qualities he can add immunity to the disease called "rust." Or he can secure a race of poultry laying over two hundred eggs in a year, or a race of cows that will produce not only more milk in less time, but milk with more butter and less water. It cannot be pretended that man's sifting and breeding methods are always attended with perfect success. Hens are on the whole stupid birds, compared with the lively experimental chicks; and no one can say that ordinary sheep fulfil the promise of the adventurous lambs. But that is partly because an over-sheltered life tends to individual degeneration of wits; partly because man has selected his fowls for egg-laying qualities and palatability of flesh, not for their wits; his sheep for mutton and fleece, not for brains; and partly because he has in the course of generations consistently eliminated those hens and sheep that showed any tendency to be original and adventurous. Some of the breeds of dog that man has created seem to us undesirable and semi-pathological products, which Nature would do away with within a week. They are sometimes delicate, dull-witted, even deformed, non-viable types, which man cherishes because they please his or his customers' perverted taste. But these dysgenic products we are glad to forget when we see the large number of really fine and noble dogs. On the whole, we can say that dog breeding has been eugenic.

What has happened during the domestication of animals and the cultivation of plants is closely parallel to what has occurred in Wild Nature in the evolution of new species. Variations that crop up are sifted and separated. Changing and entailing, sifting and segregating, these are the evolutionary factors in both cases. But the part that is played by the breeder is played in Wild Nature by the various forms of the struggle for existence, helped by isolation. The reason why man can work so quickly as compared with Nature, is that he can artificially secure that similar forms pair together, and can artificially prevent cross-breeding. He can also extend his shield over small beginnings. There is no doubt that man has been a very successful evolver, and there was great force in Darwin's question: If Man has done so much in a short time, what may Nature not have done in a very long time?

Some serious students of evolution find a difficulty in the fact that man's achievements in plant and animal breeding do not always last. In some cases, but only in some, there is a harking back to the original wild type. The reason for this is interesting, and may be illustrated in connexion with the fur of rabbits.

When one looks at a wild rabbit one sees a beautiful complexity, and there are eight hereditary "factors" or "genes" that combine to produce this. In the course of artificial breeding it often happens that some of the colour-factors drop out of the inheritance—a common occurrence that cannot be explained in this chapter. If all the pigment-factors drop out in egg-cell and in sperm-cell before fertilisation occurs, then the individual young rabbit is bound to be an albino; and it may be used to start a pure-breeding white race. But if the dropping out is partial, there may be, not a pigmentless, but a yellowish, or bluish, or black or otherwise coloured offspring rabbit. If some of the cards are lost in shuffling a pack there are likely to be some very poor "hands"!

Now if the rabbits of a well-established colour-variety pair with others like themselves they breed true indefinitely; but if no care is taken, and if the pairing is promiscuous, there must be sooner or later a restoration of the original complexity of the wild rabbit; and this is called a reversion. Yet in this case it is plain that the original wild rabbit had, as regards colour, a richer inheritance than any of the domesticated varieties we have mentioned.

Disappointments with well-established breeds are often due to undesired pairing with dissimilar forms, or, in other words, to imperfect "isolation." Disappointments with new races of garden flowers may be due to cross-pollination (very difficult to avoid); or to the origin of the new strain from bud-variations which are much less reliable than seed-variations; or because the new "breed" is put on the market before it has become a stable "race."

It is certain that man has enriched the world with his races of domesticated animals and cultivated plants. In many cases he has been able to pool the good qualities of several wild species. There is no reason why this kind of amelioration should not continue for ages yet to come. But there is another kind of change which has involved losses as well as gains: man has greatly altered the numerical proportions of the plants and animals in many countries, and he has exterminated many forms of life altogether. He has naturalised many useful plants and animals in countries to which they were strangers; but, on the other hand, he has had his share in deteriorating the fauna and flora of many lands.

The number of different kinds of wild animals in Scotland has not decreased since Neolithic man settled there some eight to ten thousand years ago, but there has been a deterioration of quality. Rabbits and sparrows, earthworms and caterpillars, rats and cockroaches, crickets and bugs, are among the additions, but are a poor exchange for the reindeer and the elk, the wolf and the bear, the lynx and the beaver, the bustard and the crane, for these are among the losses. The same is true of many another country: the standard of the fauna tends to fall.

For various reasons, some of them not man's fault, many fine creatures have disappeared for ever from the Earth, creatures like the quagga, the Irish deer, and the great auk; but what man must be blamed for is the careless disturbing of the balance of Nature by short-sighted introductions, such as rabbits in Australia and sparrows in America.

Chapter XLIII

The "Wolves of the Sea"

By Herbert G. Ponting, F.R.P.S.

Author of "The Great White South"

During many years of travel in search of the picturesque—travel which has taken me three times round the world, and to within a few hundred miles of both Poles—it is, perhaps, scarcely surprising that interesting experiences should have come my way sufficient to fill a dozen books, and that I should have had more than one narrow escape from unconventional ways of shuffling off this mortal coil. In adventure one should not, of course, take anything too seriously, but I have always held that it is the duty of every bona fide traveller who has a real story to tell to get it into print, for it may be of interest, and even value, to his fellow creatures. Hence this account of an incident that befel me which is probably unparalleled in the annals of adventure, for I believe there is no record of a similar experience having happened to any other explorer.

Let me preface my story by stating that once—while I was a correspondent with the First Japanese Army, during the war with Russia—when I was swimming from a ship which was anchored about two miles from the shore in Fusan Bay, Korea, I was menaced by a shark, and I owed my escape to the facts that I have from boyhood been at home in the water, that I was at the time in the heyday of my strength, and that I did not lose my nerve.

But even a shark, as an antagonist in a bout in the water, is not to be compared for cunning and ferocity with some ocean fiends with which I was destined to make acquaintance a few years later, when in the Antarctic with Captain Scott, of immortal memory, during his last expedition.

That whales are mammals most people know, but there are many erroneous ideas current about these great creatures, one of them being that they never attack man unless themselves attacked by man. The family Cetacea, to which all whales belong, is a large one and comprises ocean mammalia ranging from the smallest porpoises and dolphins to the leviathans of the seas.

The blue whale is not only the biggest creature, so far as is known, that lives to-day, but it is probably the largest creature which has ever existed. Specimens have been killed which considerably exceed one hundred feet in length. It is one of the rorquals, or fish-eating whales, which feed by cruising open-mouthed into shoals of small fish. The right, or Greenland whale (so highly prized by the whaling men of the last century for its baleen, or whalebone), which is rapidly becoming extinct because of the ruthless manner in which it has been hunted for its valuable products, though smaller than the blue whale. is yet a colossal creature, seventy or eighty feet in length. Its food consists of enormous quantities of minute crustacea, called Euphausia (small shrimps), with which it fills its cavernous mouth, then swells its immense tongue until all water is ejected through the ragged fringe of horny baleen plates which depend from its upper jaw, and swallows down its little pipe of a throat the remaining catch.

The sperm whale which, like the right whale, is in danger of becoming extinct, and for the same reason, for it is the most valuable of all whales because of the high quality of its oil, is believed to be the largest toothed creature that has ever lived in the world. Instead of baleen plates in the *upper* jaw, as in the case of the right whale and the rorquals, the lower jaw of the sperm whale is furnished with huge teeth, more like those of a hippopotamus than of any other animal, and it preys upon the colossal octopods, or squids, which exist hundreds of fathoms deep in the sea: monster molluscs which almost equal in bulk the great cetaceans which they feed.

Enormous masses of squid flesh, a cubic yard or more in size, have been found in the stomachs of sperm whales, proving that the tentacles of those ocean horrors are sixty or seventy feet from tip to tip. Incidentally, it was doubtless a sperm whale which figured so prominently in the story of Jonah's adventure during his voyage from Nineveh to Tarshish, in the time of Jeroboam, for a man might easily pass down the tunnel-like throat of a full-grown sperm whale with ample room to spare. Sperm whales frequent African coasts to this day, and three thousand years ago they may have been plentiful in the Mediterranean.

At the other end of the Cetacea family are the beautiful dolphins, which not infrequently play about the bows of ships in temperate seas. Midway between these extremes is the killer-whale, or orca, which has been well named by mariners "the wolf of the seas"—a ferocious carnivore, twenty or thirty feet in length, which preys upon seals and other warm-blooded creatures. Killer-whales also prey upon various species of their own order, even on whales much larger than themselves, which they hunt in packs, as wolves hunt the larger ruminants. When the object of attack is a full-grown rorqual, perhaps half-a-dozen times the bulk of a killer-whale, the orcas show, indeed, the cunning of wolves, for they band together and assail their prey with carefully-designed concerted action.

Two of the assassins, one on each side, seize the lower jaw of the great beast they intend to destroy, while others leap out of the sea and lash the quarry with their flukes or huge tail fins as they fall upon its back. This torturing and battering is continued until the unhappy victim becomes so weak and exhausted by the repeated blows that it

Herbert G. Ponting, F.R.P.S., Copyright

DANGEROUS KILLER WHALES: THE FIERCE WOLVES OF THE SEA

This is probably the only photograph ever taken of these great sea mammals at such close quarters—and for a very good reason. The photographer who gets as near as this to these savage and very cunning whales is risking his life. We see them coming up to blow, and the spiracle or nostril can be seen plainly in the one towards the right of the illustration. From this the breath is exhaled with the force of a blast from an air compressor, descending in a cloud of vapour. "Wolves of the sea" is an apt name for the killer whales, for they hunt in packs and destroy their prey, which is often far larger than themselves, by sheer weight of numbers, displaying a cunning and ferocity equal to that of wolves.

ON THE EDGE OF DEATH: THE AUTHOR'S ADVENTURE WITH KILLER-WHALES

While accompanying the Antarctic expedition of Captain Scott the author of this chapter saw, when the ship had been moored off Ross Island where winter quarters were to be established, eight killer whales come to the surface near by. He snatched his camera and ran to the edge of the ice. But the whales burst through the three-foot thickness of ice, leaving the photographer standing on an unstable fragment By a seeming miracle the piece on which he stood drifted within reach of the main floe just in time, as this drawing shows.

can no longer support the weight of its massive jaw. The great mandible drops, and the victorious ghouls then enter the mouth of the helpless beast and devour its tongue. Deprived of a vital organ, the dying leviathan becomes a mere derelict—and easy prey for the shoals of fish which then proceed to consume the huge carcase piecemeal.

As our expedition ship, the *Terra Nova*, approached the Great Ice Barrier—which is the largest known ice sheet in the world, and estimated to be 160,000 square miles in area, or approximately the size of France—many killer-whales rose and "spouted," as, presumably, they browsed upon the multitude of penguins that sported in the sea. The next day, soon after we moored the ship to the ice-foot off Ross Island, where we decided to build our winter quarters, I was about to start across the ice for the land with my photographic sledge, when eight killer-whales appeared near the ship, blowing loudly as they headed for a promontory of the ice, under which they eventually dived.

Hastily estimating where they would probably reappear, I snatched up my reflex camera to try to get a "shot" at them, and ran to the edge of the ice, adjusting the camera for the exposure as I did so. Just as I reached the edge, almost breathless from my rapid spurt, to my consternation the ice was suddenly heaved up under my feet and broken into fragments all about me, and the eight killer-whales, lined up fin to fin, burst from under it and blew. The head of one was within two yards of me.

I saw its spiracle open, and at such close quarters the sudden exhalation from its great lungs was like the release of a blast from an air compressor. The roar of the eight simultaneous blows was deafening in my ears, and I was enveloped in the warm vapour of the nearest "spout," which had a strong and distinctly fishy smell.

For a moment I was completely bewildered as I staggered on the raft of ice on which I was isolated, but providentially the shock sent me backwards instead of precipitating me into the sea, in which case my Antarctic experiences would have ended some-

James

KILLER-WHALE THAT HUNTS THE SEAS IN PACKS

Even such whales as the rorquals, some of which may be over eighty feet long, are not immune from the ruthless killer whale, which is only from twenty to thirty feet long. The secret of its success is that it hunts in packs. Two killers will open the attack on the rorqual, one on either side, and seize its lower jaw. The rest leap out of the sea and fall on the rorqual's back, lashing with their tails until the great beast is tired out and its jaw drops. Then the killers enter its mouth and bite out the tongue. Above is a museum specimen.

what prematurely. As the whales rose from under the ice there was "a loud booming sound," to use the expression of Captain Scott, who was a witness of the incident, as they struck and broke the ice, which was about a yard thick, with their backs. The instant they had cleared it, with rapid swings of their flukes they made such a commotion in the water that the floe on which I stood was rocked so violently that it was all I could do to keep from being thrown into the sea.

Then the eight whales turned about and deliberately attacked me. The ship was not a hundred yards away, and Captain Scott and all my shipmates were watching, transfixed with horror, for, as they told me afterwards, they expected every moment to see me fall into the open jaws of one of the eight furies that were now pushing their heads out of the sea in the endeavour to get me. I heard frantic shouts of: "Jump, man, jump! Be quick! Look out! Run, for God's sake!"

BUT I could not run, as the ice was broken up for forty yards around me. I was hard pressed to keep my feet as, hampered with a large reflex camera, which I would not have lost for anything, I made my way from piece to piece of the broken ice, with the whales close at my heels, snorting and making a horrible noise as they turned over the floes behind me. I recollect distinctly wondering if I should reach safety or would the whales get me; and how very unpleasant the first bite would feel, but that it would not matter much about the second. The broken floes were drifting in the current, and as I reached the one nearest the firm ice, I thought my number was up, for the leap was so wide that had I attempted to jump it I should inevitably have gone into the water. More frenzied shouts from the ship. "Jump, man, jump quick!" But jump I absolutely dare not.

Then a miracle happened. Either the commotion made by the whales, or else the current caused the ice floe on which I stood to drift nearer the firm ice, and I leaped to safety, not, however, a moment too soon, for, looking back as I fled I saw a huge black and tawny head rise out of the sea at the very spot where I had leapt, and it rested on the ice-edge, looking with little glistening eyes to see what had become of me. The great jaws opened wide, and I saw the terrible teeth I had so narrowly escaped. One after another the sinister heads shot up through the cracks to a height of seven or eight feet, all showing fearful teeth. But I was safe, and I ran until I was out of all further danger. Captain Scott met me. He was deathly pale as he grasped my hand and said: "Thank God, you are safe! That was the nearest squeak I ever saw!"

In his account of this incident in his journal, Captain Scott wrote: "Of course, we have known all along that killer-whales continually skirt the edge of the ice floes and that they would undoubtedly snap up anyone who was unfortunate enough to fall into the water; but the fact that they could display such deliberate cunning, and that they were able to break ice of such thickness, and that they could act in unison, was a revelation to us."

The picture which illustrates this adventure is not, of course, a photograph. It has been drawn from my own desciption of the incident, from that of Captain Scott, from my photographs of the surrounding landmarks, and from personal study of the models of killer-whales in the Natural History Museum at South Kensington, London.